THE NEW CAREER MAKERS

THE NEW CAREER MAKERS

Revised and Expanded

JOHN SIBBALD

 HarperBusiness
A Division of HarperCollins*Publishers*

HarperCollins books may be purchased for educational, business, or sales promotional use. For information, please write: Special Markets Department, HarperCollins Publishers, Inc., 10 East 53rd Street, New York, NY 10022.

FIRST EDITION

Designed by C. Linda Dingler

Library of Congress Cataloging-in-Publication Data

Sibbald, John (John R.)
   The new career makers / John Sibbald. — 1st ed.
     p. cm.
   "Revised and expanded."
   Rev. and enl. ed. of: The career makers. c1992
   ISBN 0-88730-686-1
   1. Executives—United States—Recruiting—Directories. 2. Executives—North America—Recruiting—Directories. I. Sibbald, John (John R.). Career makers. II. Title.
HD38.25.U6S53 1994
658.4'07111'02573—dc20   94-28771

95 96 97 98 99 ❖/RRD 10 9 8 7 6 5 4 3 2 1

Performance is what happened.
Potential is what might.
Both are worth knowing,
But only one for a price.

—John Sibbald

CONTENTS

ACKNOWLEDGMENTS

This book should be dedicated to the survivors of the last recession and the restructuring of North America's employers of all types. Foremost among these are the many thousands of white-collar professionals who along the way lost jobs and sometimes hope, but persevered nevertheless. Right alongside these clingers to the life rafts of renewed opportunities paddled many an executive recruiter. They saw clients go under, merge, purge, and virtually cease all hiring. Too many job seekers and recruiters alike lost their will, their grip, and gave up.

There is some new light on the horizon, but it is a terribly slow sunrise. Opportunities are returning, but the mid-1990s are a far cry from the heady times of the 1980s. Our world of employment has already undergone profound change, and we have just witnessed its first tentative steps. There will be changes to the world of work the likes of which this hemisphere has never seen before.

The heroines and heroes of this edition will have to contend with these changes, as they have with those that have come before. The 250 who are honored in these pages have already had to contend with a variety of surveys and communications from my office. They've done so with grace and dispatch—for the most part, that is. (We did maintain a "dirty dozen" list of those who were particularly laggardly in getting back to us. All eventually did.)

If we had our "dirty dozen" list, my ever-patient executive editors at Harper Business, Virginia Smith and Frank Mount, and their able assistants, had a considerably shorter list but no less vexing villain: John Sibbald. If I can yet convert the furrows of anxiety in their brows into the crow's-feet of forgiving smiles, I will feel that a considerable miracle has been worked. My own special thanks goes to the venerable "Conscience of the Consultants," Jim Kennedy, for his personal interest and his unequaled industry knowledge. His publication, *An Analysis of Executive Search in North America, 1993,* was of particular benefit for its statistical content.

My greatest gratitude goes to two members of my own staff, Kathryn Costick and Joanne Melone. In effect, they performed a search in four months' time for not one but 250 placements. They followed up on questionnaires, faxes that supposedly were never received, telephone calls that were slow to be returned, photos that were lost in the mail, and more requests for special dispensation than have reached the Pope or the Clinton White House. They calculated rankings and pumped their souls out, profile after profile on the computers. All with a smile. Next to me, they are the happiest that this task once again is over.

INTRODUCTION

This is the third edition of *The Career Makers*. The first edition roiled the placid waters of the headhunter world like nothing else in print. How audacious! screamed its critics. Who would ever think of soliciting the workplace to find out who the best recruiters truly are? And then rank them against each other? Outrageous! After all, shouldn't we all believe what the press and the largest search firms' public relations arms tell us? Or the several newsletters devoted to executive recruiting? How dare one go so far as to actually solicit what our clients and competitors really think of us! That's market research, and it shouldn't apply to us.

The second edition of *The Career Makers* came out in 1992, barely two years after its highly controversial progenitor. What one recruiting industry observer had first ridiculed as nothing but a "beauty contest" in selecting the most effective recruiters was now heralded by him as "raw meat for all recruiters and clients" to sink their teeth into. If it had become raw meat to North America's recruiters, a volume they would pore over to see who made the book and where they ranked in their specialties, *The Career Makers* had become a staple in the libraries of employers and outplacement firms. But vastly more important was the fact that this one-of-a-kind guide to reaching the top executive recruiters in the United States, Canada, and Mexico had become a trusted vehicle for helping many thousands of job seekers find new employment in very hard times. *And that fundamentally was what it was written for in the first place.*

The New Career Makers you are reading, like its two predecessors, has been completely revised and expanded (250 recruiters are now profiled, compared to 150 in the last edition). Formats have been changed, and the quality of the profile pages increased. The latter improvement may or may not enhance the facial features of the recruiters pictured, but there is only so much that good photography and premier paper stock can do for these veterans of numerous shoot-outs, candidate declinations, and client rebukes. Pretty faces and full heads of hair don't last long in the headhunting business, as this writer bears witness.

The last few years have also shown that there's something else that may not last long in today's business climes: Chief Executive Officers. Relegated to the pitiable fate of golden parachutes, more outside directorships, fewer chauffeured limousine rides, and much more flogging of the air at golf courses from Pine Valley to Seminole were such titans of the corporate throne as James Robinson of American Express, Kay Whitmore of Eastman Kodak, Paul Lego of Westinghouse, Theodore Cooper of Upjohn, Howard Wentz of Tambrands, Michael Miles of Philip Morris, and, most prominently, John Akers of IBM.

In its highly publicized worldwide search in early 1992 for a new Chief Executive Officer, IBM managed to shake the very foundations upon which executive search has plodded along essentially unchanged for seventy years now. In one savvy and bold move orchestrated by James E. Burke, an outside director and chairman of its search committee, IBM:

1. Enticed—for a handsome fee, of course—two of America's most celebrated recruiters, Gerry Roche of Heidrick & Struggles and Tom Neff of SpencerStuart, *from competing firms no less, to work in tandem on a major search.*
2. Excised very adroitly the complication of "client blocks" on the part of either major firm *by creating the opportunity for one firm to approach candidates the other firm had previously placed.* (Louis Gerstner, IBM's eventual hire as CEO, had just a few years before been placed by Mr. Neff of SpencerStuart at RJR Nabisco.)
3. Enlisted the world's press in publicizing the progress of the search, *virtually step by step, as it proceeded.*
4. Exposed publicly *the actual names of executives who were reportedly on their so-called short list of finalists.*

More than any executive search in American history, the IBM search laid bare many of the shibboleths of executive recruiting.

This search, which caught the world's attention, took the cloak completely off the hush-hush world of executive search and showcased for the first time its significance, relevance, professionalism, and value.

Prominent as the IBM search was, this has been only one small gust in the termination tempest. What has been well publicized among the *Fortune* 500 companies has been going on even more rampantly in smaller companies and organizations of all types. Never in American history have more Chief Executive Officers been forcibly ejected into their parachutes. The Association of Executive Search Consultants (AESC), to which about 100 of North America's 1,100 or so retained search firms belong, reported that its members alone conducted a record-high 2,623 CEO searches in the year September 1992 to September 1993—a figure that, notwithstanding recruiters' propensity to exaggerate, is still fairly staggering.

In Pericles' time, there was a "Golden Age of Greece." With more corporate heads rolling today than met the guillotine during the French Revolution, is this then the "Golden Age of Headhunting"? Don't believe it for a minute.

The unprecedented publicity accorded these senior firings and the attendant jockeying for position by recruiting firms to win the searches to replace them have obscured what has really been going on in the world of headhunting. The truth of the matter is, not much. During the last three or four years, almost one-fifth of all retainer-type executive search firms have folded. The largest firms have pruned their less productive recruiters, and hundreds of entrepreneurial souls have retired their shingles, tucked in their tails, and sought refuge back in the mother womb of the largest firms.

Middle management positions, long the bread and butter of the headhunters, have become the vanished species of the employment world. Senior officer positions have often been consolidated, with one person doing the work that two or three others used to do. The staff fat in organizations of all sizes and types has gone the way of Tommy Lasorda's girth. The time-honored concept called span of control, which decreed that one manager could effectively oversee no more than seven or so subordinates, is as repudiated now in organizational literature as Tonya Harding is in figure skating. On top of all this is the plain cold fact that it's hard as hell to hire when you really have to fire.

The New Career Makers updates the "Academy Companies" chapter that was a major and very popular new feature in the second edition. It steps out boldly and perhaps provocatively again with a new chapter devoted entirely to the most hunted heads in America, or those that will be: the select new leaders who will one day soon be filling the CEO jobs in North America's companies, universities, hospitals, and nonprofit organizations of all types. We call them the "Heirs Apparent."

The addition of this new chapter is a logical and very timely response to one of the questions raised time and again by the business press as the IBM and similar *Fortune* 500 company CEO searches unfolded: Where does one look for executives who can successfully run such organizations? This is a challenge to every top recruiter and company embarked on such a mission. It's a subject of regular speculation in trade journals and within companies themselves. Who will step up to tomorrow's brass ring? For the first time anywhere, *The New Career Makers* has taken a peek into the most closely guarded secrets of North America's top headhunters. We've asked each of them to nominate their own choices of future Chief Executive Officers of our major employers of all types.

The book remains, however, what it was intended to be from its inception:

- A handy reference for professionals in every line of work who either need a job now or aspire to a better one.
- An equally handy guide for employers of all types who spend countless hours and dollars trying to find the right professionals to employ.

The heroes and heroines of the book are executive recruiters, those shadowy figures whose telephone calls can start the adrenaline flowing in anyone who toils in the workplace. But as virtually everyone knows, most recruiters shun the limelight. *The New Career Makers* thrusts the very best of them into a most unaccustomed—and perhaps to some, uncomfortable—position of personal visibility.

Being of low visibility has been the traditional posture for executive recruiters, who also answer to a wide range of other titles: search consultants, searchers, and headhunters—a name they used to detest but increasingly accept. But whatever they are called, they all stand for the same thing. For the job seeker lucky enough to be known by them, these are the true Good Samaritans of the job market. They can grease the skids to the perfect job for you now.

But, alas, they are an elusive group and terribly whimsical. When they want you, you may not want them; and when you need them most, they are nowhere to be found.

Even in hard times, when job openings are few, executive recruiters are the keepers of the key to many of North America's best opportunities in every field of endeavor. Because of the significance of the top management positions they fill, the business press often labels them as "kingmakers." Yet you will find recruiters filling, by many thousands more, positions in what is left of lower management ranks. That's why the title for this book, *The New Career Makers,* seems so apt—because in the final analysis that's really what recruiters do. Very few of us will emerge in top management, but in one form or another we all have careers.

In the minds of most of us, executive recruiters do their work in the corporate jungle. And most of it *is* done there. They're the people we spot in the airline clubs, notepad in hand, furtively interviewing some anxious-looking chap with his twenty-year pin from Exxon stuck in his lapel. Yet there is a large and growing number of recruiters who have an eye especially calibrated only for university presidents, hospital administrators, school superintendents, physicians, lawyers, association executives, city managers, government officials, and many other non-business-sector types. In fact, the pleasant gentleman in the bow tie sitting next to you in your church pew, whom you've never seen before, just might be sizing up your rector for a pulpit somewhere else.

Although executive recruiters may be directly engaged with only about one-fourth of all managerial and executive hiring done today, the positions they are asked to fill represent a disproportionate number of the highest-paying and most prestigious jobs in the United States and abroad. Thus, for an executive in any line of work or the manager who aspires to the executive level, and for every young professional on the way up, it is prudent to know one or more executive recruiters, *especially those recruiters who specialize in searches in one's particular line of work.*

The latter point is worth special emphasis. Although the business press may highlight the Chief Executive Officer searches like that for IBM, top management searches represent only the tip of the executive recruiting iceberg. The 90 percent that are below the headlines are where the bulk of the search work goes on in the executive employment marketplace. It is this vastly larger part of the job market that makes it *imperative* for job-seeking professionals to identify and cultivate those specific individual recruiters who concentrate their recruiting activities in fields of mutual interest. *The New Career Makers* is the only guide that can help you do that.

Up to now, we've been speaking about the value of knowing a search consultant from the employee's or job seeker's perspective. It is every bit as important for employers to know individual recruiters—the right recruiter for the specific need they're out to fill. Sometimes the choice is easy because the organization has used the recruiter for a similar successful search in the past. But what if that search did not go well? Or what if the job to be filled is a new one or in a field where the recruiter customarily used has no prior experience? Although many of the most accomplished head-hunters profess to be generalists able to recruit for any position in any field, the truth is that virtually all of them have certain functional areas, industries, or professions in which they are considerably more proficient and up-to-date. An employer who ignores this modern fact of executive recruiting is, in effect, entrusting a general medical practitioner to perform brain surgery.

So where does the savvy employer turn to locate the best individual executive recruiter in North America to help fill the highly specialized and supercritical job that can make or break the entire organization? For starters, the employer can make some phone calls to friends. (But is it safe to let others know about how crucial this need is or to reveal that the employer is planning to replace the incumbent in the job?) Fortunately, there are two particularly good reference guides to executive search firms. One is the old standby put out so dutifully and accurately by Jim Kennedy: *The Directory of Executive Recruiters* (Kennedy & Kennedy, Templeton Road, Fitzwilliam, NH 03447) contains listings of almost all executive search firms, and it also cross-indexes the firms by areas of particular expertise and geographic location. The second one is *Executive Recruiters of North America* (Hunt-Scanlon Publishing Co., Two Pickwick Plaza, Greenwich, CT 06830), which provides information on approximately one-fourth of all retainer recruiters and their areas of specialization.

Useful as these guides are, however, they provide no way *to pinpoint those few individual recruiters best equipped to handle the employer's all-important search.* Thus, the process of finding the most effective recruiter to help the employer fill a specific need comes down to the time-consuming and risky process of calling each of the search firms listed under the directory heading of particular interest and trusting those called to be candid about their expertise in recruiting in a particular field. I do not intend to impugn the integrity of any executive search firm, but I have found that the margin of distortion in firms' statements of apparent qualifications or preeminence can range from complete truth to downright fiction.

Complicating the situation further for both the professional seeking a new opportunity and the employer scouring the universe for an employee who walks on water is this cruel fact: There are recruiters and there are recruiters. This is not a book about those who hunt heads for a bounty. Recruiters who work on a contingency basis are paid when and if they are successful in bagging the right body for the right job opening. Such recruiters serve a worthwhile purpose in satisfying many organizations' recruitment needs, but they are most effective in filling lower-level jobs.

Those headhunters who are not contingency recruiters are called *retained recruiters* and belong to retainer-type executive search firms. The most ethical of these firms do not do any search work on a contingency basis—even in the grip of the recession we hope we're now finally out of. Retainer firms pride themselves on standards of ethical conduct and performance that they believe reflect well on the caliber of clients they serve and the candidates they place. They get paid whether they're successful in the search or not, with the first one-third of their ultimate fee usually coming as their retainer at the time they start the search. They are paid only by employers, never an individual.

The New Career Makers: America's Top 250 Executive Recruiters is a book about a very select few of the eight thousand (some say double that) men and women employed with retainer-type executive search firms. This is not a book about the search firms themselves, because in my twenty-four years in the search business, both as a partner in the large consulting organization of Booz, Allen & Hamilton and in the firm I now run, I've never known a recruiting organization to make a placement. Individual recruiters, not recruiting firms, make placements.

The book is divided into three parts for ease in use. Part I, "Working with the Top Executive Recruiters," contains three chapters. The first of these describes how the Top 250 recruiters were selected, some of the characteristics they share, and what they look for in candidates. Chapter 2 is intended primarily for job seekers and those who contemplate changing employers or careers at some time in the future. Employing organizations of all types will find Chapter 3 helpful to them in pointing out how to work most effectively with executive recruiters.

In Part II, the most accomplished 2 to 3 percent of all of North America's executive recruiters are individually profiled (perhaps a better term is "exposed"). For once, the headhunters have had the tables turned on them. The phantoms of the employment world have stepped out of their closets for the first time—and even shown their faces. Part II also contains the important chapter entitled "Areas of Recruiter Specialization." This chapter ranks the recruiters who qualified for this book in the order of their expertise as seen through the eyes of clients and fellow recruiters alike.

Part III contains two chapters that tell the world where the best future leaders are and then names them. Chapter 6 identifies and ranks "academy companies" of the United States, by both industry and function. Chapter 7 is the utterly audacious chapter that actually identifies and names North America's future organizational CEOs.

There are also some things this book is not intended to be. An employer will not find information here on how to negotiate a compensation package or conduct the ultimate interview. Likewise, an individual will not discover how to compose the perfect resume or launch the most successful job search in history. Bookshelves are sagging with these types of guides now. Astute users of this book—whether they are job seekers or employers—will find that their days of shotgunning the marketplace in search of the right recruiters to help them have ended. Now, too, executive recruiters themselves have two market-derived guides for their own use:

- Where the best-stocked fishin' holes in America are in which to cast for candidates,
- And the first fish finder that actually spots and names exactly the right big fish to go after. (Of course, they still have to hook and land 'em.)

The New Career Makers: North America's Top 250 Executive Recruiters gives its readers—be they job seekers, employers, or headhunters—the chance to bring some true precision to what has long been one of mankind's most frustrating and inefficient practices, the process of seeking employment.

PART I

WORKING WITH THE TOP EXECUTIVE RECRUITERS

1

THE TOP 250 RECRUITERS: THEIR SELECTION AND CHARACTERISTICS

For individuals to be selected as among the 250 best search consultants in North America is an exceptionally high honor. It means that they stand in the top 2 to 3 percent of all of their recruiting peers. This recognition is especially noteworthy in a personal services business seemingly unable to establish for itself any type of individual certification of competency. That in itself is a giant black eye for the calling. Until such time as executive recruiters establish an appropriate mechanism for certification, the business can never legitimately claim to be a profession.

Many of the celebrated names in the recruiting business have come and gone. These men founded and led some of the premier search firms and represented the epitome of executive recruiting skills with thousands of significant placements. They include people like Spencer Stuart, Thorndike Deland, Sid Boyden, John Struggles, George Haley, Bob Gette, Robert Lamalie, Ward Howell, Lester Korn, Max Ulrich, and Russell Reynolds; the list could include a dozen or so more. Never to have their distinctive skills and leadership commemorated by any form of individual certification—especially in a business where recruiters themselves so highly value pedigrees and credentials in others—is a gross disservice to these pioneers and visionaries. It is one more example of the search industry's provincialism and petty jealousies.

Executive recruiters' skills are on display to only three groups:

the clients they serve, their peers in the business, and the candidates with whom they deal. This third group was rejected as a survey category because of the transitory nature of candidate contacts with recruiters, their consequent lack of perspective or objectivity, and the logistical difficulties of locating them to solicit their responses. Thus, the focus of the selection process has been on surveying clients and peers of recruiters, both competitors and those employed in the same search firms. The career makers featured in this book have been identified by what the marketplace thinks of them and not by the arbitrary and subjective judgments of the media and a few self-styled industry experts.

Because the book was intended from its inception to be of value to the widest possible range of professionals—not just those in business—questionnaires were sent to the Chief Executive Officers, their equivalents, or the top human resources executives of America's

- 1,000 largest public corporations from the *Fortune* 500 list of industrial and service companies,
- 500 largest privately held companies from *Forbes* magazine and the *MacMillan Directory of Leading Private Companies,*
- 75 prominent venture capital firms,
- 200 leading public and private colleges and universities,
- 150 largest professional societies and trade associations,
- 150 largest hospitals and health care providers,
- 95 major hospitality organizations, including hotel and restaurant chains, private clubs, and resorts,
- 10 governmental and quasi-governmental agencies known to have used search firms.

These senior officers were asked, "In your opinion, who are the most effective *individual recruiters* (by name and firm) who have served your organization in the last several years?" The respondents were asked to list no more than five recruiters, not necessarily in order of preference. The list of recruiter nominees was further refined by this question: "If you were personally responsible—*to such an extent that your own job was on the line*—for recruiting the next Chief Executive Officer of your organization, to which *individual recruiter* would you entrust that search?"

To balance the employer or client side of the picture, a similar inquiry was made to key contacts or managing principals of 520 retainer executive search firms based in the United States, Canada, and Mexico. For firms with more than one office or key contact, the mailing was made to the principal headquarters listed. One question asked of these recruiters was: "In your opinion, who are the most effective *individual recruiters* within your *entire organization* (including those in other offices), working with North American–based clients, who actually handle client searches directly—not those who act as managers or overseers of more junior consultants who actually do the majority of the work?"

As with the clients, the heads of the search firms were requested to limit their nominees to no more than six from their own organizations. Again, in order to establish the most capable individual of those they listed, the addressees were asked, "If the entire reputation and future of your firm rested on the success of one exceptionally significant search, to which of those you nominated would you entrust that search?" The last question asked of the recruiter group was to provide the names of up to six of the most effective headhunters from executive search firms *other than their own.* Survey forms came back from 436 of the 520 search firms queried, an outstanding response rate of approximately 85 percent.

The combined survey responses from both client organizations and executive search firms resulted in a total of 931 individual executive recruiters who received at least one nomination for excellence. All of those individuals were then invited to submit the names and addresses of six client executives they had recently served. This dimension to the nomination process ensures equal consideration for those recruiters who work at levels below Chief Executive Officer, with small companies and subsidiaries, in Canada and Mexico, or in such seldom-surveyed fields as venture capital. A letter with nominating questionnaire was sent to each client listed by that recruiter—*but without any indication of the recruiter who had submitted their name.* (A fair number of the recruiters would have been dismayed to discover that the clients they thought would nominate them did not.) Adding this new feature to the client nomination part of the survey resulted in an overall client response of 39 percent, a statistically significant response rate.

The Weighting System Used to Select and Rank Nominees

The value of nominations for a recruiter varies depending upon their sources. Recognition of a recruiter by a competitive search firm is considered to be particularly valuable. Accordingly, a nomination from a competitive search firm is worth three points. The value of a nomination from one's own firm is rewarded with two points, although to be judged as the very best recruiter in one's own firm is worth an additional point. Nominations from clients are worth two points each, with an additional two points being awarded if the client considered the recruiter to be the very best of those listed.

Some may quibble with this weighting formula and the point allocations, or even with the selection of executives with client organizations to whom the original questionnaires were sent. Nevertheless, we can find no other system that is as fair and objective for recruiters with both large and small search firms and for those who specialize or work at levels lower than top management.

The profiles of the Top 250 are arranged in the book alphabetically, just as in the previous editions. In the chapter entitled "Areas of Recruiter Specialization," only the top 10 recruiters in each category are ranked on a frequency-of-mention basis. All others who ranked among the top 30 in that category are listed in alphabetical order. There is one important exception. In the highly significant functional area of General Management, the top 25 recruiters are ranked, with the following 75 most highly rated headhunters listed alphabetically.

To create the areas of recruiter specialization, each of the Top 250 recruiters was asked to select up to ten *functional* areas of recruiting competence and up to ten *organizational* specialties. Choices were listed in descending order of the recruiter's own preference and experience.

A weighting formula is also applied in arriving at the actual rankings of recruiters within each of the functional and organizational categories. Although a few may differ with me, it is my conviction that no recruiter can be equally competent in every choice of functional or organizational expertise. Thus, a sequential reduction of 10 percent of the recruiter's total nomination points was made for each selection below a first choice. As an example, recruiters who accumulated an overall point total of 85 received full value for their first choice in both the functional and organizational preferences. But their point totals—and thus their place in the rankings—for their fifth choices would be 51, a reduction of 40 percent of their point total. Their tenth-place choices, if they selected that many, would give them a point total of 10 percent of their overall total, or 8.5 points.

Search consultants who work almost exclusively in specific fields such as health care, hospitality, and legal are ranked only in the organizational categories in which they concentrate. Their choices of functional competencies, however, are treated in the same way as the choices of those who do not specialize. With this in mind, the user of this book should consult the rankings of both functional preferences *and* organizational specialization in selecting recruiters to contact. Failure to cross-reference, for example, by either an employer or individual seeking a general manager's position in industry could result in the mutually wasteful consideration of a recruiter who is experienced only in health care searches—simply because the health care recruiter ranked relatively high in the functional area of General Management yet does no recruiting at all in industry.

Characteristics of the Top 250

Geographically, North America's top headhunters hail from all over the United States—and sixteen now call Canada and Mexico home. Most have found their professional bases in major cities. As one might expect, the New York metropolitan area is the home office for the greatest number, seventy-two, with Chicago living up to its reputation as second city. California has forty-four of the best, but the rest of the West, the Mountain and Plains states, and the Middle Atlantic region have sparse representation. Texas has nearly as many top recruiters as the entire Southeast.

Of the 150 who qualified and were profiled in the second edition of *The Career Makers,* 134 are repeaters in this edition. Of those who ranked in the Top 10 in that previous edition in the highly significant functional area of General Management, 9 made this especially select group again.

The Top 250 are also well seasoned. There are none of the young hotshots Wall Street and the investment community brag about—or at least used to. The average age of North America's most accomplished recruiters is an AARP-qualifying fifty-five. The youngest is thirty-eight, as of this writing, and the oldest is eighty-four. Perhaps even more impressive is that the group averages nearly twenty-three years each of executive recruiting experience. It clearly takes many years to build up the relationships, credibility, and reputation to make it into the top 2 to 3 percent. Once there, though, few step down at sixty-five. With apologies to Douglas MacArthur, it might be said that old headhunters never die; they just dial away.

This third edition shows that an increasing number of women are doing the dialing. Their number among the top recruiters has risen sharply from nine in the first edition to thirteen in the second to twenty-eight in this third edition.

The Top 250 are perhaps most distinctively different from their colleagues in other personal services vocations such as medicine, teaching, law, public accounting, banking, the ministry, and the like in that none of them probably ever visualized a career for themselves in executive recruiting before they got into it. If serendipity was how they found their way into the career they are now so good at, not one that I have talked with would ever think of leaving it.

As noted in earlier editions of *The Career Makers,* the survey reveals that with the exception of a few search consultants who concentrate their work in a single area of specialization, *no one of the Top 250 who recruits essentially in industry enjoys anything close to preeminence in the minds of those who engage recruiters in client organizations.*

Yet there are, of course, those who stand out even among the crème de la crème. The Gerry and Tom show continues without an intermission. Gerry Roche of Heidrick & Struggles has retained his position as North America's most accomplished recruiter of top management—a position he has occupied now for all three editions. Tom Neff of SpencerStuart has fended off all challengers for second place, also for all three versions of this book. Yet it is worth noting that both of these surefire inductees into a future Headhunters Hall of Fame (Tombstone, Arizona, would make a most apt spot for the Hall, especially adjacent to the OK Corral) achieve their high standings with a relatively small percentage of client nominations. What propelled them and most others in the Top 10 in the General Management category were the abundant nominations they received from competitors. The chart that follows provides a clear picture of this.

North America's Top 10 General Management Recruiters

Ranking in Total Points 1994	1992		% of total points from competitors	% of total points from clients
1	1	**Gerard Roche**, Heidrick & Struggles, New York	72.5	27.5
2	2	**Thomas Neff**, Spencer-Stuart, New York	77.7	22.3
3	4	**Leon Farley**, Leon A. Farley Assoc., San Francisco	75.2	23.5
4	3	**Frederick Wackerle**, McFeely Wackerle Shulman, Chicago	76.7	21.3
5	6	**William Gould**, Gould & McCoy, New York	54.3	43.2
6	5	**Robert Dingman**, Robert W. Dingman Co., Los Angeles	84.7	15.3
7	9	**Roger Kenny**, Kenny, Kindler, Hunt & Howe, New York	77.4	19.9
8	10	**John Johnson**, Lamalie Amrop Int'l., Cleveland	57.7	39.4
9	16	**Pendleton James**, Pendleton James & Assoc., New York	76.5	19.5
10	7	**Windle Priem**, Korn/Ferry Int'l., New York	74.8	20.7

In sharp contrast to this are 127 recruiters who had lower over-all point totals than those in the Top 10 but who received at least twice as many nominations from clients as from competitors. One recruiter, who has a particular specialty, was selected by twenty-three different client organizations and was judged the very best in that entire area of recruiting specialization by seventeen of these employers.

Although growth continues for large firms—many with their own international arms or affiliations—executive recruiting is still a business of individuals. Recruiters may band together in large, medium-sized, and small firms, but what counts most is how well they perform as individuals. Both clients and the recruiters them-selves strongly agree on this point. Almost 99 percent of all client organizations surveyed said that it was the individual recruiter, not the recruiter's firm, that made the difference in whom they selected to serve them. And 97 percent of the recruiters agreed. This response underscores the need for growing specialization on the part of individual recruiters, if not firms themselves. Most exec-utive search firms are already acknowledging this development.

The survey data contain several important messages for North America's executive recruiters. The client survey pointed up that 71 percent of employer organizations prefer a fixed-fee pricing arrangement to the industry's traditional percentage-fee struc-ture. There are also two highly welcome pieces of good news in the survey data: 69 percent of all employers reported that they were anticipating executive-recruiter use to be about the same as in the past, and 20 percent said they would be using recruiters even more in the near future. Only 11 percent of the reporting client organizations said they would be using recruiters less than before.

Perhaps the best news of all for North America's retained recruiters is the report card that employers made out evaluating the quality of search work the recruiters did for their organiza-tions. Over 46 percent felt that the work done for them by these top recruiters was "consistently high." Another 44 percent graded those recruiters included in this book as doing work that was "gen-erally good" for them. Executive recruiting has come a very long way when nine out of ten clients respond that they are being well served. Our hats are off to these 250 talented women and men who have achieved something quite remarkable in quality of performance. One has to wonder if the top 250 professionals in any other personal services business in modern society would rate nearly as high in terms of customer satisfaction.

Academy Companies: The Other Career Makers

Just as the top executive recruiters are career makers for working professionals worldwide, so, too, are companies—the ones with the right stuff, that is. With very few exceptions, every industry and every organizational function has a small cadre of employers that over the years have developed a particular knack or expertise in developing talented performers. These companies have earned reputations of being the top boot camps for aspiring professionals in everything from aerospace to packaged goods marketing. They have a leg up on even the best graduate business schools. No case studies here, no ivory tower theorists—this is the real world. These are what we call the academy companies.

Books have been published in the past about the best companies to work for, those that offer the best employee benefits, working conditions, promotion policies, location, and other nice-to-have goodies. Academy companies, on the other hand, are usually not *nice* companies to work for. They have a mission, and working for them is more like serving in the Marine Corps than just keeping your nose clean and retiring with security from a public utility. They heap on responsibility early, and when they find someone who can handle it, they just keep pouring it on.

The New Career Makers is the first and only publication in which America's academy companies are systematically identified and ranked according to their organizational and functional areas of management development prowess. To accomplish this task, what better panel of experts exists than the subjects of this book? Decade after decade, headhunters have made their livings and created the $4-billion-a-year business they preside over by probing the right corporate corridors and consuming all the press and gossip they can about talent.

Thus, for every experienced professional who aspires to a better job and for every recent graduate who has the brass ring in his or her view, it pays big dividends to gain employment with an academy company. *Academy companies multiply your visibility to the out-*

side world and its opportunities even as they create and sharpen your occupational skills. Academy companies are where competitive companies turn when they are out to recruit their own new superstars. Academy companies are where every astute headhunter starts a search. And as a logical consequence of these factors, academy companies usually pay a better-than-competitive dollar to retain their high achievers.

Work hard to work for an academy company—the earlier in your career, the better. But it's essential that you choose the right academy company for your particular field of interest. If your chosen field is corporate finance, bring good things to life with GE. If it's the transportation industry that you're interested in, fly as fast as you can to American Airlines. But be alert. If you're interested in health care marketing, Merck stands as number one among all drug *industry* employers but can't hold a Bunsen burner to Baxter International when it comes to the *functional* area of health care marketing. To maximize your opportunities to develop your management skills and to reap your ultimate rewards, you have to be employed with the right functional *or* industry leader.

For the list and rankings of the academy companies found in Chapter 6, every executive recruiter who was nominated for this book was asked to select four areas of his or her own recruiting specialization. Two of the areas were to be functional specialties and the other two industry or organizational competencies. The recruiters were then requested to select and rank the three employers in each area that in their experience had been the most fertile organizations for finding talent in that particular specialty. The total points and rankings that appear in Chapter 6 were derived from 418 recruiter responses, with three points awarded for a first-place nomination, two for a second, and one for a third.

The "Heirs Apparent": North America's Top 250 Future Chief Executive Officers

Each edition of *The Career Makers* has added at least one new perspective to the ever-evolving world of careers. This edition is no different, and in doing so it may, like its predecessors, stir some tiny tempests of controversy.

As the much-publicized IBM search brought home to those

who watched it unfold, not only is there great job insecurity in the offices of America's Chief Executive Officers, there appears to be few who are capable of filling them—whether from within the organization or from the outside. In following the IBM search and several of the other major corporate searches undertaken during approximately the same time period, the press kept raising the question: Where will the new CEOs come from?

It is a valid question for sure. The obvious choices at the top have been pretty well picked over. And some of the oft-mentioned superstars on everyone's list, like John Sculley, formerly of PepsiCo and Apple Computer, are not as lustrous as they once were. Then there are many who no longer have the zeal or fortitude they used to have in reaching for the brass ring.

Fortunately, in an era when homegrown talent is increasingly suspect, a large pool of high-potential high achievers are poised to step up to the challenge and opportunity—if not with their present employer, then with others. We call these the "heirs apparent." Selected from a universe of many thousands by North America's most accomplished executive recruiters, this book identifies the 250 who received the largest number of nominations from these top recruiters. The Top 250 are organized into five broad organizational categories: manufacturing, service, communications, health care, and not-for-profit organizations. Chapter 7 talks about how they were selected and lists alphabetically each of these extraordinary up-and-comers who are destined, at least in the minds of the best executive recruiters, to rise to the top of North America's profit and nonprofit organizations.

Are executive recruiters the best judges of who these future Chief Executive Officers are? Who would be better qualified? The headhunters have a vested interest in seeing them advance and will play major roles in their paths to the top. The involvement of executive recruiters in CEO searches, always a frequent one, will become even more prevalent and necessary in the future. With the flattening of organizations, the elimination of layers of middle management, and fewer major leadership positions available in organizations of all types, *the ability to discern true potential for success in an individual will become paramount in executive assessment.* Presumably, this is the special skill executive recruiters are uniquely endowed with. If North America's top executive recruiters are not able to step up to this challenge, and rely instead upon the traditional ways of judging future performance solely on the basis of past performance, they will be abdicating their proper role and not fulfilling their critical mission in identifying the right new leaders for our times and our future.

As we contemplate those 250 men and women who stand out in this first-ever predictive survey of executive leadership, may we trust that those who nominated them have done so with this vital new perspective.

Will the recruiters like where they stand in this edition of *The New Career Makers*? Probably about as much as they liked where they stood—or did not stand—in the first two editions. From my years as an executive recruiter, I am comforted by the awareness that even those colleagues of mine whose feelings are wounded in one way or another are still blessed with egos sufficient to sustain them until the next edition of this audacious volume, should there ever be one.

And how will the academy companies like being singled out and ranked? About the same as in 1992, quite probably. We didn't hear a single complaint from any of them that year because they knew full well that they were in fact the best developers of talented professionals in their field. Like the rest of the headhunters in this book—and for every professional who yearns to get approached by one—we pray that these particularly fecund companies never get around to disconnecting their telephones.

Speaking of disconnecting telephones, the 250 heirs apparent named in this book may have to do just that. What a dreadful fate awaits them. Imagine having to fend off all of those calls from panting headhunters and prospective employers. Who could be bothered with those multimillion-dollar pay packages, great chunks of stock, club memberships, and all of the other unseemly perquisites that accrue nowadays to CEOs? And clout and prestige—who in his or her right mind wants the clout and prestige of a CEO?

Leave it to *The New Career Makers* to stir up so much grief. Again, just like its predecessors.

2

GAINING THE HELP OF THE RIGHT RECRUITERS

The New Career Makers is a reference for only one specific group of individuals—those who earn, or want to earn, in excess of $60,000 on salary. This happens to be the lower limit of the hunting grounds of North America's retained recruiters, the women and men this book is all about. In your job search, anywhere from one in five to one in three of your new opportunities will involve an executive recruiter. If you are looking for a position at the $125,000 level and above, you can increase that to something like one in two. At some very senior levels, and for certain jobs where committees are the selection bodies, a top recruiter will be a party in almost every situation. Accordingly, *you cannot afford to take on a proper job search without tapping into the unique resource that executive recruiters comprise.*

Initiating a Relationship with the Right Recruiters

Except for those fortunate few who are approached regularly by the *right* headhunters, most of us have to initiate the relationships we establish with recruiters—and that is what it is, a relationship. To think that any recruiter is going to jump through hoops for you just because you believe that your resume paints the picture of an exceptional talent is naive. Not only do search consultants get many resumes every day "over the transom," but most of these resumes are never seen by the recruiters they're addressed to. Search firms, except for the smallest, have research departments, and these unsolicited resumes are first screened by researchers. Only if a background appears to meet the specific needs of a current search is the resume passed along to the recruiter handling that search. Without getting your resume to precisely the right recruiters, the chances of your unsolicited resume's fitting an ongoing search, even in one of the largest search firms, is probably less than one in a hundred. The odds are worse in smaller firms.

Some recruiters never consider an unsolicited resume. They always generate their own candidates, or so they say. Consider this type of headhunter to be about as smart as the prospector panning for gold who throws away the nugget that gets wedged between his toes because he didn't find it in the bottom of his pan. Don't be discouraged by such claims. The recruiters good enough to be listed in this book are savvy enough to accept any favor, including those that come unexpectedly over the transom.

Even directing your resume to the right recruiters is no guarantee of success in initiating that all-important relationship. There are some ways to dramatically improve your chances, however. It comes down to basic marketing. If you think of yourself as a new product—a very good new product that you're launching—then your resume represents that new product. Your resume reflects what your product is made of, what it has been able to do in the past, and what its potential is for the future.

But an appealing new product by itself is not enough in today's job market. Your consumer—in this case, a headhunter—must want to pick your new product off a shelf that's already glutted with both old and other new products. What your new product needs is what we call a "handle"—an attractor that positions your new product (consider it packaging) and causes your consumer to reach out and select it from all the others on the shelf. The handle we're talking about is best presented in the cover letter that accompanies your resume. The cover letter should not take up more than three to five paragraphs and should never exceed a page in length. But most important is what the cover letter says and to whom.

Virtually all resumes that reach our top recruiters are accompanied by cover letters. Yet not one cover letter in a hundred contains an effective handle. This deficiency is even more pronounced with the standardized cover letters (to say nothing about resumes) pouring out of guidebooks on how to write "the perfect" resume and spilling from the boilerplate files of the less reputable out-placement firms. *Finding the handle that makes your resume stand out to the right executive recruiters is the single most important goal you have in winning that crucial first interview.*

This book gives you more opportunities for coming up with handles that sell than have ever been available before. You should start your search for these handles by first identifying the recruiters who will be the targets of your new-product marketing effort. Let's say that your background and future interests happen to be in the high-tech, electronics, and office machinery industries. A quick turn to Chapter 5, "Areas of Recruiter Specialization," and the sub-heading "Organizational or Industry Specialization" will give you a list of those individual search consultants most heavily involved in these industries.

Your interests then should be further refined to include your *functional* areas of competence. Let's say that they are in general management and industrial marketing. Under the other subhead-ing in Chapter 5, "Functional Specialization," you can find recruiters with significant recruiting experience and clients in these two func-tional areas. Look for the overlap of those who have proficiency in both the *organization and industry* areas of interest and the *func-tional* areas you prefer. It should make no difference to you whether the recruiters you select are in the top ten or twenty, or ranked alphabetically. The list of recruiters you generate from this cross-referencing will become your own personal target list of exec-utive recruiters.

The recruiters listed in your organization and industry selec-tion should always take precedence over those listed under your functional specialty. The optimum choices are those recruiters you find listed in both the organization list *and* the functional list. The higher they stand on both lists, the higher on your target list they should rank. As you would expect, the more specialized and eso-teric your interests, the fewer the number of headhunters who will appear on your target list. Opening up your criteria somewhat will give you a larger number of headhunters to contact. For example, the merchandising manager interested in making a radical career switch into television broadcasting should include both recruiters with strengths in the functional area of advertising/promotion and those with organization and industry specialties of communica-tions and radio/television broadcasting.

Armed now with your target list of names of recruiters, it's time to get personal. Chapter 4 contains the profiles in alphabetical order of North America's 250 top recruiters. As will be shown, there are many opportunities to find handles for those with profiles. Incidentally, do not concern yourself too much with where the recruiters in this book are based. Virtually all serve clients throughout North America, and, in many instances, they serve international clients as well.

Study the profiles of the recruiters from the Top 250 who make your list. In addition to the obvious handle you already have—that they recruit in your areas of functional and organizational interest—these profiles will suggest additional handles on which you can capitalize. Your goal is to find as many common threads of interest, contacts, or coattails as you can.

The possibilities are limited only by one's resourcefulness and luck. I remember when one of America's largest search firms would interview almost anybody who graduated from Yale. (And not coincidentally, many of the firm's original staff hailed from that esteemed Ivy League institution.) Another senior recruiter was an avid supporter of Ducks Unlimited. He was never blind (pardon the pun) to meeting with those who shared his waterfowl hunting interest. The old school tie has great appeal for many recruiters. If you can establish a link to anything and communicate that effectively, your chances of meeting that headhunter face-to-face soar.

Each of the top recruiters has been asked to describe *in their own words* what they look for in a candidate. The adroit professional who picks up on what a recruiter says about candidates who have "the right stuff" and draws a convincing parallel, or offers a sharp rebuttal, may well be rewarded with some form of dialogue with that recruiter. Headhunters, even busy ones, are natural philosophers and generalizers. They enjoy stimulating communication.

There is one other major area of opportunity for finding a handle in each profile: the recruiter's employment history. Perhaps you were toiling in the textile stretch department of Jockey International at the same time your target recruiter was over in marketing warming up Jim Palmer for his classic underwear ads. Reference to a former employer held in common works even better when you were higher up in the organization than the recruiter—unless, of course, you were part of the reason the recruiter left, in which case it may be more astute for you to skip to the next individual on your target list. (Search consultants have long memories for setbacks.)

By this time you have the picture: The way to get the initial attention of top recruiters is to employ a handle that plays to their background, recruiting specialties, and special interests. You don't need many handles with each recruiter on your target list. One will do nicely, more if you have them, but don't force them on the headhunters you wish to contact. The handle or handles you come up with belong in your cover letter. Getting past a headhunter's secretary via the telephone is about as easy as reaching the IRS with a question at tax return time.

Some job seekers may not be able to identify any handles at all for certain search consultants on their target list. Among them may be the ones highest on their list. What then? Well, you're reasonably fortunate because you know precisely which recruiters you need to establish relationships with—the ones in your fields of particular interest. These same recruiters also have interest in getting to know you because you have experience in the fields in which they do much of their work. Their research department or secretaries will have instructions to forward such resumes to them with or without handles.

Or you can be audacious and solicit the help of a gadfly or two. Every industry and every profession seems to have a few of them. They can be both a curse and salvation for an executive recruiter. A gadfly is that unusual person who seems to know everything going on in a given industry or occupation and what's happening to the key players in it. Gadflies get their name because they are endowed with a special antenna for picking up scuttlebutt and then passing it along with about as much discretion as your local barber or hairdresser.

Executive recruiters enjoy a love/hate relationship with gadflies: On the one hand they appreciate the industry information and names that gadflies volunteer so readily; but on the other, gadflies have no qualms about breaking a confidence—which, for many searches, can spell disaster. Enlisting the aid of a gadfly can help you make a connection with a recruiter. Gadflies know the recruiters who work in their fields, and whether the recruiters like it or not, they to some extent depend on referrals from these individuals. So take a gadfly to lunch—at least once. It can work wonders for you in opening recruiters' doors.

Gadflies usually work in organizations other than your own. Yet there may well be individuals within your own organization—supervisors, peers, or subordinates—who are in a position to help you make contact with those on your target list. Then there are all the fellow alumni of your old employer. They may be scattered to the winds, but some will know the recruiters on your target list. A few may even have been placed by the very recruiters you also need to meet.

What to Do When the Headhunter Calls

Whether you used resumes with smart cover letters or the intercessions of contacts, sooner or later your efforts will be rewarded with a call or letter from some of those on your target list. When this happens, you can consider yourself to be on the brink of being in the recruiter's system. You want that more than anything. Most often the first communication from the headhunters you're trying to cultivate will come in the form of a telephone call. How you handle the contact determines your chances of becoming a prospect, and perhaps later a candidate, to that recruiter.

The best recruiters do not make idle telephone calls. When one calls you, you can be sure that the recruiter is doing one or more of these three things: (1) sounding you out as a possible candidate, (2) determining whether you might be a source—in other words, whether you can suggest a candidate or two for one of the searches the recruiter is handling, or (3) repaying a favor to a client, former client, prospective client, a prior placement, a fellow recruiter, a current candidate, or a gadfly. Regardless of the recruiter's motives for calling you, do something on your end of the line to cause that recruiter to have good reason to either arrange a personal visit or make a mental note to keep in touch with you. In brief, don't squander the opportunity to make yourself memorable to that headhunter.

Let's take the optimal situation. One of North America's top recruiters is calling you. She's phoned you after reading your resume, which had been referred to her by the firm's research department. You had written her after discovering that she specialized in your line of work. Your recruiter passes along some other background on the opportunity, and it all sounds interesting to you. You know you want a personal interview, but you also know that you do not want to sound overly eager.

Be savvy but not coy. You don't have to go through the normal ritual of determining whether the headhunter calling you is reputable. She's got to be, or she wouldn't be one of those profiled in this book. In fact, she's one of the top 2 percent in the business. After her first description of the job to you, she will have some reasonably probing questions to ask you over the telephone. She needs to be as sure as she can be that she doesn't waste her time or her client's dollars on a very costly face-to-face interview.

Be prepared to respond to questions that attempt to fix the current scope of your responsibilities and the structure and nature of your current or past employer. If you've listened well when the recruiter first described her need to you, you'll pick up on some of the key background and personal experience factors the recruiter must find in your background in order to qualify you as a viable candidate. Headhunters are working from what they call a specification, or candidate profile—an outline that highlights the must-have and desirable-to-have features in a prospect's background.

Further along in the conversation, your recruiter is going to inquire about your willingness to relocate, whether children and a working spouse are involved, and at least some idea of what your compensation requirements are going to be. Make no mistake about it—your recruiter is still just sizing you up against the job specifications. She'll also ask you such delicate-to-deal-with questions as why you're looking for a new position and, if you're currently out of work, the names of your most recent superior and others who know your work and circumstances. Obviously, it's wise that the reason you give for being between jobs—or "on the beach," as the recruiters put it—jibes with what your boss says. And you can be quite sure that your recruiter is going to run a reference check on you with your last superior before having you visit for a personal interview.

As noted in the Introduction, this is not a book about interviewing techniques. Hundreds of paperbacks on this subject fill the "careers" section of your local bookstores. Unfortunately, most have been written for entry-level job seekers or hourly paid workers. The best book that I know of on interviewing techniques and most other aspects of job changing for middle managers and above is a hardcover volume by John Lucht. The author knows what he's talking about because he's also one of the top recruiters profiled in these pages. His book is entitled *Rites of Passage at $100,000+* (Viceroy Press). He also now publishes a handy companion, *Executive Job-Changing Workbook* (Viceroy Press), which provides the most comprehensive set of forms and guidelines ever produced to help one organize and self-administer a job search.

I hope you win your interview, and I wish you good luck with it. There is one tip I might offer: If your interview happens to be with one of the top recruiters profiled here, it would be smart for you to review the recruiter's profile before you make your visit. That way you might avoid the rather awkward moment that I experienced a few years ago with a job seeker who wanted to leave me with a nice personal touch. The interview happened to be in the fall, during football season, and he smiled broadly at me as he was exiting my office. Then he suddenly thrust out a big hand and chanted, "GO BIG RED!" I was momentarily stunned. Then it dawned on me. I had graduated many years ago from the University of Nevada. He had apparently misread my school somewhere as the University of Nebraska. Oh well; it was a nice try. Both schools do start with "Ne."

Cultivating a Long-Term Relationship with Recruiters

As anyone who has ever been the recipient of a pink slip could tell you, the best time to start looking for a job is before you have to. So perhaps you're one of the very fortunate who still has a job, but you're not happy or fulfilled in it. Or maybe you're still hanging on as a middle manager in some organization that has not quite flattened its organizational structure enough yet to compress you into escape velocity. But you can see it coming, and you want to prepare for the worst.

It's never too soon to start building that all-important relationship with North America's top headhunters. Once again, you must start with the identification of the right executive recruiters—those whose recruiting interests coincide with your own employment interests. It's a matter of creating your personal target list of recruiters to cultivate, as outlined earlier in this chapter. Then comes the ongoing process of becoming known to the right recruiters and helping them create a file on you that causes them to call you on every search they do that is in your field of interest and aspirations.

The first step, of course, is getting your well-crafted resume into the hands of the right recruiters. Your cover letter with a compelling handle helps you accomplish this critical step. Maybe the first callback from a headhunter will be right on target. But chances are better that it will be about a job in which you neither would fit nor be interested. Let's say your call is from a recruiter who is looking for the new general manager of the Detroit Athletic Club. You happen to be managing one of America's top country clubs. You know how difficult it is today to run a successful city club. You also have the wisdom to realize that with the dues deductibility issue and the major shift in member lifestyles, city clubs of all types are having significant difficulties. And then, of course, there is the issue of working in downtown Detroit. Besides, you like to get in an occasional round of golf, which you can do on Mondays at your current club. Do you just say, "No, Mr. Recruiter, I'm not interested," and hang up? No; instead, you put your mind in gear to help that headhunter with a suggestion.

A light bulb goes on in the recesses of your memory, revealing seldom-used but hopefully useful facts, and out comes a response like this: "I'm sorry I'm not quite right for your search, but I do have a suggestion of a possible candidate for you. Mortimer Clubhead and I went to school together at Michigan State, one of the top hotel and restaurant schools in the country. He is also a CIA graduate. Incidentally, that's the Culinary Institute of America, not the less reputable outfit you might be thinking of. He's been at the Cosmopolitan Club in New York for the last twelve years. He runs one of the best city clubs in the country. He grew up in Michigan, and I know he would like very much to get back there. Would you like to know more about him?" Of course your recruiter friend would.

Or maybe your response is along these lines: "Try as I might, I don't have a single individual to suggest to you as a candidate, but I can give you the names of a couple of terrific sources. They manage top athletic clubs themselves, so they aren't recruitable, but they know everybody who ever ran a gourmet dining club or bounced a hard rubber ball off the wall of a squash court." In addition, you might know of the various club management journals and the association to which virtually all club managers belong. Whatever you do, leave that recruiter whom you have worked so hard to cultivate with food for thought—and a nice warm feeling that you are a very worthwhile contact. Your name and phone number will go into the recruiter's workbook as a good source, someone for him to call again.

Then, as fate would have it, a week later you bump into Sally Donovan, the manager of your own city's athletic club. She had heard about the search at the Detroit Athletic Club and told you that she might have some personal interest but didn't know who to contact. You promptly follow up with your recruiter friend by phone with Sally's home telephone number and some complimentary comments of your own about her. By this time most of the Top 250 recruiters in this book will very likely have started a file on you even if you have not yet become a candidate for any of their searches.

Now it's a matter of gently but regularly stuffing the file folder with your name on it in that headhunter's office. You're in no immediate hurry to make a change, but you do want to know when an exceptional opportunity opens up. Your recruiter will not only add items to your file but will also store key elements from your background in a computer. This data will be available for years to come not only to that recruiter but to all other search consultants in his firm and those in branch offices.

Don't be concerned if no acknowledgments come from your recruiter. Keep adding to his file on you. Some always-helpful items are news releases or publications that talk about your activities or clippings from a trade journal that has an article referring to you or a new program you've launched. If you happen to be with a government agency, school system, college or university, hospital, hotel, or association, the same logic holds. Take advantage of articles and stories that talk about you and what you are responsible for. Please do not send complete curricula that you've worked on for your high school, a copy of the Federal Budget for the United States of America with a paper clip on the page that refers to your department in a footnote, or the membership directory for the University Club—copies of each of which I received in the past.

Annual reports can be good or bad. Unless you are president, chairman, or the vice-president of communications responsible for its production, do not send the full report. Select a summary page from the financials or those pages from the president's letter or from the report somewhere that refer to you and your department. Annual reports pollute headhunter's offices and take up valuable space in the circular files and recycling bins already overflowing with the monsoons of ill-directed resumes raining down upon North America's recruiters.

Periodically, it's wise to update your resume and be sure you get it in the hands of every executive recruiter you've been able to build a relationship with. Try attaching a short note to it that says something along these lines: "Just thought you'd like to add this most recent resume of mine to your file. My current compensation is a base of $75,000 with a bonus paid last February of $15,000. I remain keenly interested in a general manager position in a top country club in the desert."

Now what's this we hear? You've won election to your local school board. Or you've been selected for the board of the Club Managers Association of America. That is major news for your file, so send it in. Membership, but especially leadership, in your association is one of the most important credentials you can add to your attributes in furthering your relationship with those on your target list. One of the most well-worn directories in any recruiter's office is the *Encyclopedia of Associations.* Few searches neglect contacting the leadership of trade associations or professional societies. The fact that your peers think enough of you to elect you to a leadership role in your field of work is one of the very strongest credentials any professional can have. Broadcast it.

In the final analysis, what every smart professional is really after is *visibility* with those recruiters on your target list. Very few of us become renowned in our own field. We can dream about writing an article or a book or making a scientific discovery of great merit that catches everyone's attention. But most of what goes into our file with our headhunter friends will be a steady accumulation of little things that eventually add up to a significant record of achievement. Never forget that visibility can also be acquired by what Daniel Patrick Moynihan once called "creeping gradualism." It may not be as exciting as achieving instant fame, but it often proves far more enduring.

As one might expect, some things will go into your file that you have not provided or even knew that your recruiter contact had. The headhunter you're out to win over will have made a note and put it in your file if you were abusive, devious, or pushy with his secretary. Or maybe he noticed that you wore short socks to your interview with him or that you bathed in so much cologne that he got a headache from it and couldn't work the rest of the day. Like many firms, my own has a form on which we evaluate every person we meet on such subjective factors as presence, energy level, listening ability, language facility, and many other personal factors. This too goes into your file, although you will never see it. So will copies of the reference reports the recruiter does on you, including verification of your college degree—the single biggest item of candidate fabrication today, and yet one of the easiest things for employers to check.

Perhaps you "forgot" in your resume to add a former employer you had for less than a year; a recruiter from your target list may discover this and add the information to your file. Or you might have made a "simple error" in calculation and overstated your earnings by 30 to 40 percent. When the recruiter uncovers that tidbit, another entry goes into your file. A cardinal rule for every headhunter is *no surprises for a client.* Your headhunter's entire reputation as a top professional rests on thoroughness. The best sniff out every fabrication. You can count on that from every one of the Top 250 in this book.

It is hard for me to confess this, but even these top search consultants have an endemic weakness. They are not very forgiving when a job seeker takes advantage of them. It is difficult for headhunters to build a relationship with a client and then win a search from that client. Recruiters do not take it kindly when a job seeker lets them down in a way that jeopardizes the relationship between consultant and client—or, worst of all, ends it.

Two of the most common embarrassments that recruiters suffer through are (1) when a candidate's spouse or family will not move after the breadwinner has proceeded all the way to the altar and received an offer, and (2) when a candidate has received an offer from a new employer and then used that to extract a counteroffer from the old employer. Although black balls tend to take up too much file space, Avery Label makes a nice flat black dot that applies very neatly to an individual's file folder. Only the most foolish would risk that censure with any of the Top 250. Many a professional who has taken advantage of a recruiter has discovered that even elephants don't survive as long as the memory of a head-hunter wronged.

Fortunately, nothing like this is going to happen to you. You are out to develop the most positive possible relationship with the headhunters in your future. You know that every placement of these top recruiters at one time was nothing more than a name on the recruiter's long list of initial possibilities on that search. Somehow they prevailed over all the others. Each had a file started on them in that recruiter's office, probably years before they were placed. They very likely had files in other recruiters' offices too. Some had been placed by headhunter after headhunter throughout their rise to the top.

Many of America's top executives in every field of work have never really had to look for a job, even though they've had a number of different employers. The opportunities always came to them. In an increasing number of instances, the bearers of glad tidings were the headhunters they had met and cultivated along the way. Wouldn't it be nice to have the feeling that even while you have your head down working away at your current grindstone, someone out there is constantly sensitive to you and your aspirations? Your recruiter friends would be minding your career for you.

Even after you've succeeded in taking a new position with the help of a recruiter, don't just close the door on a relationship that took a long time to build and to pay off. A good recruiter will stay in touch with you, but that recruiter is more interested in hearing from you periodically. A time may even come when you can reward your friend by passing along a search yourself. Just because you've been placed doesn't mean that your file goes into storage. Although no reputable recruiter is ever going to recruit you away from the client organization where you were placed, the world of employment takes strange turns. Who knows when you may need your hard-earned friend again? Make that *friends*—you will want to keep in touch with all of those on your target list.

Cultivating the right headhunters can be the wisest investment you'll ever make—one that pays dividends for a working lifetime and costs you nothing more than postage and an occasional phone call.

3

AN EMPLOYER'S GUIDE TO WORKING WITH THE TOP RECRUITERS

No astute employers should ever have to submit to the outlandish fees of an executive search firm as long as they feel confident about their responses to such basic questions as these:

- Are we free to approach candidates using our organization's name?
- Do we mind if our competitors learn quickly of our need for this new manager or executive?
- Will it cause us any internal morale problems with our staff when they learn, as they will, that we are recruiting from the outside?
- Do we have an in-house research staff that maintains many thousands of files on high-talent individuals and what's happening with their employers on an up-to-date basis?
- Are we able to network with several dozen or more "sources"—especially knowledgeable individuals who know the best performers in their respective fields of work and each of whom is strongly inclined to assist us with suggestions of candidates *because they owe us a favor?*
- Will our in-house recruiter possess the national and/or international perspective to advise us on trends in compensation, incentives, contracts, benefits, and other executive employment factors? Will our in-house recruiter also have the credibility to influence us properly in these matters?

- Does our recruiter possess the personal skills, experience, maturity, self-confidence, knowledge, and stature to gain easy access to the level of executive we are seeking? Is our in-house recruiter capable enough to conduct a probing hour-and-a-half or more, face-to-face screening interview with candidates who may be several layers higher than he or she in another organization and earning multiples of his or her salary?
- Are we confident that our recruiter is as adept in assessing *potential* in a candidate as *performance* from a candidate?
- Will our recruiter be able to devote at least 20 percent (preferably more) of his or her time to this search?
- Is our recruiter prepared to make numerous telephone calls from home after hours, to work Saturdays, Sundays, and holidays, and to travel extensively to see candidates during the course of this search?
- Can our recruiter make the tough "go" and "no-go" judgments on every candidate, especially those that fall into the gray areas where significant questions exist about their ultimate recruitability, sincerity of interest, and actual accomplishments?
- Is our recruiter astute enough to get beyond the candidate's "approved" references and obtain other essential references—legally?
- Does our recruiter have the negotiating skills and technical knowledge to close the deal and structure an overall hiring package that can be highly complex and sensitive?
- If we are doing this search to replace an incumbent in the job, will it be difficult or embarrassing for us if word leaks back into the organization that we are seeking a replacement?
- Will our recruiter make good to us in some way, or guarantee, his or her placement if we find within the first year or two that the placement is not up to the job?
- Does our recruiter have the ingenuity and resourcefulness to go beyond the traditional fields and most likely places of employment to find the type of candidate we are seeking?
- Could our recruiter generate and sustain clients on the outside because of his or her overall recruiting skills and personal track record of consistently outstanding placements?

- If we are a committee, are we as a group able to be fully objective in not responding to pressure from members of our own organization to pursue their favorites? Are we confident that we know how to explore properly the full universe of candidates—not just those who come to us with their resumes?

So now, Ms. or Mr. Employer, after thinking of all of these issues, are you comfortable in *not* using an executive recruiter? Especially when 9 out of 10 of the 847 employers who participated in the creation of this book rated the work of these top recruiters as "generally good" to "consistently high"? And considered their "outlandish" fees to be worth it!

Whatever the reason an employer initiates contact with a headhunter, the single most important decision is the choice of the right recruiter to engage. Large search firms claim to provide expertise and resources to an employer that are unmatchable by smaller firms, and the small firms counter by emphasizing the personalized services they can offer and their access to a wider range of organizations that they are free to probe for candidates. Both clients and recruiters agree, however, that the success of a search rests essentially with the skills and motivation of the individual recruiter handling the assignment.

Ironically, however, the most revealing piece of information derived from the comprehensive survey of client organizations and 436 executive search firms that forms the backbone of this project is that, notwithstanding the prominence in the business press of a few New York–based headhunters, *no single executive recruiter is preeminent in the minds of corporate clients.* As noted in Chapter 1, many recruiters well down on the list of rankings actually received more nominations from client organizations than those standing in the Top 25. Is it any wonder that employers of all types are frequently confused about who to call when a need arises in their organizations?

Or for themselves. It is a cruel fact of our world of employment that all jobs today are subject to someone else's call. Today's employer is tomorrow's job seeker. It is especially prudent for employers to know that they may well need help someday from North America's best headhunters in a more intimate way—personally.

Selecting the Recruiters to Get to Know

If you could persuade a headhunter to be completely open with you, and if you asked this individual to tell you exactly which functions and types of industries or organizations he or she felt most competent and up-to-speed in, you would get the candid, marketplace-tested, first-of-its-kind information you will discover later in this book. Unfortunately, at least for employers, organizations often approach recruiters with a question like this: "Fred, old buddy, we're going to be looking for a new Senior Vice President of Technology for our health services division. Have you ever done a search like that?"

Fred, as eager as any other recruiter to book a search at a salary level well over $100,000 and not being totally dishonest—after all, he did a search ten years ago for a Director of Laboratories for a pharmaceutical firm—responds with, "Well, yes, I have." Without further probing from the employer, one more search consultant who lacks the know-how and feel for the marketplace has just been hired by an employer to perform a search that he is not nearly as well equipped to carry out as others would be.

Can you blame the recruiter? Probably not. Ask a similar question of professionals in other fields of competitive endeavor and you're likely to receive just as suspect an answer. Too many employers, whether they are in business or whether they are other types of organizations, are naive when it comes to selecting the right search consultants to serve them. They make three basic mistakes. The first of these is trusting good ol' Fred, who has recruited faithfully for them for years, to do all of their search work, regardless of the functional area or business involved. The second occurs when an employer attempts to screen several recruiters for their competencies and makes the mistake of inquiring about their experience with no great diligence. The third mistake takes place when an employer calls a friend or contact who knows little regarding the exact need and inquires about which recruiter the friend has used in the past.

All three of these mistakes cost employers dearly. Not only should you as an employer wonder about the comprehensiveness of the universe for candidates ostensibly explored by a less qualified recruiter, but you must also be concerned with the overall caliber of your placement—if, in fact, you achieve one. In addition, the reality is that *a major part of the fee you paid that recruiter went to educate him or her about your industry or the function in which the search was conducted.*

Those same dollars spent with the right executive recruiter go toward a precisely directed, decidedly more discriminating, and less time-consuming search. This usually leads to a considerably more successful ultimate placement. Until now, however, employers had few ways to identify the best-qualified recruiters to help them with each specific search. And major employers who hire many executives and other professionals every year often find themselves in a recruiting rut. They turn again and again to the same individual or individuals simply because they don't know better-qualified alternatives. Just as these organizations bring in fresh talent from the outside, they should periodically engage *well-qualified recruiters who are new to them.*

So you might ask, "How do I know whether I've been using the right recruiter to help me?" You've raised the right question. It's time to take advantage of the information in Chapter 5, "Areas of Recruiter Specialization." Just as professionals looking for a new job were encouraged to do in the preceding chapter, you should turn to the section entitled "Organizational and Industry Specialization." If you have a recruitment need in the academic, association, health care, hospitality, or consulting areas, your recruiter choices are usually confined to those specialties alone. The same holds true for many industry areas of specialization. On the other hand, a number of industry classifications might warrant your inclusion of several different categories for recruiter consideration. For example, if your main business is in food products, the recruiters able to help you could also be listed in several other consumer product areas or possibly even under the "holding-company" category. For the same reason, an employer whose principal business is in nonelectrical machinery may find it advantageous to consider recruiters listed under the fabricated metal products and electromechanical equipment categories.

In doing this initial sorting out of recruiters, you are beginning to create your own target list of the right recruiters for you to become familiar with and possibly to use in the future. You are likely to come up with a rather lengthy list of recruiters from this first screening, so it will be important to fine-tune your list further. You can do this by referring next to the section entitled "Functional Areas of Specialization," which lists those recruiters who report expertise in specific functional areas.

Some functions, like finance, planning, public relations, and human resources, can appear to be transferable to virtually any kind of industry or organization. Even so, there are subtle or not-so-subtle differences in the types of industries or organizations in which they operate. Whether you acknowledge this or not, your goal is to create a target list of recruiters whose names appear in your areas of choice in both the industry or organizational rankings *and* those for functional specialization.

When you have reduced your target list to a half-dozen or so finalists, you're ready to make your first direct contacts with the recruiters themselves. Note that I say "recruiters themselves"—not their firms. Keep in mind that, in using the information in this book, you are now able to do your own search, in effect, for the best individual recruiters to serve you and your organization. You have the right names and telephone numbers to use. Under no circumstances do you want to get passed along to some junior recruiter who is a less-experienced member of the same search firm. And unless your need is for an executive at the highest level of your organization, that's exactly what is likely to happen.

Accordingly, when you make your initial telephone calls to the finalists on your target list, ask who will actually handle your search. A number of other questions are equally important; all of these qualifying or screening questions should be asked of the recruiters on your list themselves—not an associate, the administrative partner, the new business department, or even the recruiter's executive secretary. If you can't talk directly to the recruiter you're interested in doing business with, scratch that individual from the list of those to consider.

Let's turn now to those key qualifying questions that you should ask over the telephone. It is appropriate for you to identify yourself and your organization to the recruiter, *but don't tip your hand yet about the specific need you have in mind.* After identifying yourself, your flow of screening questions might go like this:

1. **In what industries and types of organizations do you personally do most of your work?** How closely does this jibe with what your research from this book shows?

2. **Are there functional areas in which you feel especially competent and current?** Does this parallel your research findings?

3. **How do you determine whether you personally handle the work or delegate it to another individual?** This is a very important question, so listen carefully to the recruiter's response. Is the determination based on salary level, organization level, current search load, or what? Would your search qualify for the recruiter's personal handling or not?

4. **Who does the research on the search, and is the researcher involved directly with the client?** Optimally, the recruiter will handle personally the most important research. A recruiter who is fed all candidate information from a researcher is seldom as up-to-speed on a given industry as one who personally conducts research. One of the fringe benefits of a good search assignment is the industry scuttlebutt passed along by a recruiter. This type of supertimely market research can often be of competitive value to you.

5. **Who makes the initial contact with a possible candidate— you, a junior recruiter, or a researcher?** This is another very important question. Would you trust a junior recruiter, maybe someone who has never met you or sensed your organization's culture, to initiate that critical first contact on your behalf? Can a junior recruiter represent your opportunity properly and at the same time maintain the confidentiality of your search? How well have you responded when junior recruiters or researchers called you?

6. **When do you start reference checking, who conducts the references, and what kind of references do you ultimately provide a client?** Are references checked before or after a client's first visit with the candidate? Does the recruiter or a less-involved individual conduct them? Are references submitted in narrative form attributable to those individuals offering specific comments, or simply summarized?

7. **Approximately how long after you start the search will I, as the client, begin to meet candidates face-to-face?** Is it the recruiter's practice to offer up a few "trial balloon" candidates within a few weeks of starting or to reserve candidate presentations until most of the research is completed?

8. **How do you price your work?** Is it a percentage of starting

base salary only or a percentage of first-year total compensation? Will the recruiter work on a fixed-fee basis? What happens if you call off the search a few weeks into it? How are out-of-pocket expenses handled?

9. **What kind of guarantee do you offer if a placement leaves or doesn't work out?** Most will re-place at no additional professional fee, charging out-of-pocket expenses only, if the placement does not last a year.

10. **What is your client block policy—that is, how long will you abstain from approaching any person in our organization after your last search with us?** Most will refrain for two years, and a few longer than that, but it is also important to determine whether all of your divisions, subsidiaries, and plants are off-limits—including those located outside your own country.

These ten questions should give you enough information about your recruiter to help you decide whether you want to reveal more and possibly set up a direct visit or politely close out the conversation and save both of you a considerable amount of time and later grief.

Let's say, however, that the recruiter's answers seem satisfactory to you. Only then is it appropriate to be more specific about your staffing need. You should start by giving the recruiter a capsule description of the search you envision. It is essential that you tell the recruiter the title and scope of the job, whom the position reports to, how soon you need it filled, and whether it is newly created or a replacement (and if the latter, why). The recruiter also should be told a bit about the expectations for the position and whether the search is a confidential one. After providing this background, you are ready to ask the recruiter a few final questions:

1. **Would you be personally interested in handling this search on the basis of what I've told you?** A good straightforward question deserves a similar response. If it is "no" or something like "I'd be pleased to oversee the work of one of our best associates," close the conversation with a comment to the effect that you will call the recruiter again sometime, and place a quick call to the next one on your target list.

2. **Have you done a comparable or near-comparable search to**

this one? How recently? Again, listen carefully to the recruiter's answer. Does it sound credible? Has the work been done within the last year or so, or is it older than that?

3. **May I ask you who your client was on that search? Are there some others for whom you've done similar searches?** Many of the top recruiters will be able to give you specific names of clients they have served. Others, however, may work for firms with more circumspect policies regarding the confidentiality of client information. Some client information is understandably off-limits, but not all client information should be. *Don't ever let a recruiter or recruiting firm hide behind a veil of total confidentiality.* Why engage a recruiter who must be counted on to reference-check candidates but who is unwilling to provide you with references on his or her own past performance?

4. **What companies or organizations that might be good places to find candidates for my job will be off-limits to you because of your firm's previous work with them?** This is one of the most important but infrequently asked questions of recruiters. Be especially sensitive to "Academy Companies" [see Chapter 6] that are off-limits to the recruiter. If two or three of the most likely target firms are blocked to this recruiter, you may be better off working with another one from your target list who is less restricted.

5. **With your sense of the job market for the kind of person I'm looking for, what do you think will be the principal challenges in completing this search? How long do you estimate it will take to find our placement? And what do you think it will take in compensation to attract the right person?** Weigh the recruiter's response in light of your own hunches; and on the compensation issue, realize that enticing a high achiever is almost always going to involve a premium over your current internal salary structure.

6. **Again, with your knowledge of the marketplace for this individual, what do you estimate your out-of-pocket expenses will run?** Look for specificity—regardless of its magnitude. It can be an actual dollar range like $5,000 to $6,000 or a percentage of the professional fee. But watch out for an estimate like 15 to 20 percent of the professional fee on any search where the base salary is over $150,000—unless you

also always fly first-class, stay in $400-a-night hotel rooms, and dine at five-star restaurants.

If you still have an interested and interesting recruiter on the line after posing these questions, this valuable resource should be asked to submit a formal proposal (complete with names of client references). He or she is worth inviting to your offices for a face-to-face visit. You should also invite one or two competitors. Recruiters do not jump up and down with glee over "shoot-outs," as they call them, where they have to compete head-to-head with others. But they're getting increasingly accustomed to them. As employers become more sophisticated in their use of search consultants, and especially as they become smarter in selecting the best-qualified recruiter for a precise need—not just good ol' Fred every time—shoot-outs will become the norm and will ultimately benefit employers and headhunters alike. Even good ol' Fred will eventually settle into his proper market niche.

Your selection process has now wound down to its last stage. It's time to bring in your finalists and get specific with them. Each of them should receive the same overview and interview. Their visits ideally will occur on the same day or in close proximity. This is especially necessary when a search committee is involved or when a group of individuals will be included in the selection process. You want impressions to be fresh in everyone's mind.

Allow about two hours for each recruiter, and have your agenda worked out in advance. If a brief plant tour or some other quick orientation is necessary, do that first. Then proceed to fill in the recruiter on all pertinent information to provide an accurate picture of your need. Above all, be honest. If others from your organization will be closely involved with the search or the product of that search, be sure to include them in these final screening sessions.

Your purpose is to select not only the recruiter most qualified from a technical aspect but also the individual with whom you and your group are personally most comfortable. Much of your assessment of the recruiter's skills and knowledge of your industry or activity was obtained in your initial telephone call. Now you're judging the intangible factors—the recruiter's sense of your culture, compatibility with you and the others involved, communication skills, intellect, sense of humor, and presence. In short, you're selecting a member of your team. There must be no hidden agendas or surprises for the recruiter down the line. Neither can there be a human resources executive or personnel manager who feels threatened by the recruiter's work. Once you make your selection, you and your recruiter are in this project together. Although he or she may be the quarterback on this particular drive, you remain the captain of the team—and for the full season.

Following the recruiters' visits, and after polling those who sat in, you should be able to make the decision about your first choice. Assuming that the preferred recruiter's references have also been favorable, it is time for the advisory call to pass along the good news. The runners-up also deserve the courtesy of a phone call to advise them of your decision and to thank them for taking the time to meet with you. You may retain them one day, too.

Getting These Top Recruiters to Perform Their Best for You

Congratulations. You've done a fine job in picking the right quarterback for your search from the ten thousand others who very likely would not have scored as well. Does this mean that you can just sit back and watch that recruiter do his or her thing? No way. The best results in any search come when both employer and recruiter interact together through the entire process—and beyond. I have referred previously to the need to function as a team, and that is exactly what it takes to obtain a successful search outcome.

Sounds easy, doesn't it? After all, recognizing the importance of your search and what you are paying for it, why wouldn't you want to work as a team? Yet one of the harshest surprises every headhunter sooner or later discovers is that all searches are not truly on the level. In some instances the client actually wants to see the search come up empty-handed or the candidate, once hired, fail miserably in the job.

Fortunately, such counterplays are not the norm in searches, but they are far more frequent than most would imagine. Especially common is the situation in which the client feels threatened by the caliber of the candidates being presented and seeks every possible avenue to disqualify each of them. All recruiters have had their share of these types of clients.

Your search has no hidden agendas, however, so we can get on with cultivating the kind of positive relationship you need with the top recruiter serving you. At the core of this relationship must be *trust*. It must run both ways, between the employer *and* the recruiter. As an employer you must think of your recruiter as though he or she sits on your board of directors. So once you have made the selection of the right recruiter to serve you, it's time to get back together and open up with every bit of pertinent information. This includes sharing with your recruiter your organization's financial situation, the real problems and opportunities you see now and those that are on the horizon, the people relationships and issues that the new hire will have to contend with—in brief, where all the bodies lie in your organization. Especially important at times like these is trusting your recruiter with information as sensitive as the fact that your company may be on the block to be sold, merged, or restructured, or is otherwise susceptible to anything like these disruptive events so common today.

Your recruiter must assimilate all of this and incorporate what is relevant in a *candidate specification*—the vital document that sets forth the ideal personal and professional qualifications the candidate must possess in order to succeed in the job. Much of this outline will highlight personal traits and professional skills, but it must also convey in words the culture of your organization and the nuances of the actual work environment. A well-crafted candidate specification is a type of template; only the right candidates pass through it easily.

It is normally the employer's place to provide the *position description,* although on occasion the recruiter is asked to prepare this. The position description, equally as important as the candidate specification, details the basic functions of the job, reporting and supervisory responsibilities, coordinative relationships, and major duties and responsibilities in the position. The recruiter uses both the position description and the candidate specification in developing candidates for the job. It is important that both be well written and that you agree with what is said in both.

Armed with these materials, and with copies of your annual report and other organizational literature, your recruiter is equipped to sally forth in search of the needle in the haystack. But you want to know one more thing from your search consultant. What is the *work plan?* Although the sequence of the search may have been outlined in your recruiter's proposal letter, do you know more specifically which organizations by name will be probed? Are the right academy companies included? Are there some individuals or organizations on the recruiter's list that would prove awkward or embarrassing to you should they be approached? Do you think that the recruiter is soliciting candidates with the most appropriate titles and from the most appropriate level in their current organizations? Do you know about some organizations that might be good places to look for candidates but do not appear on the recruiter's list? Do you know some individuals who would be helpful *sources*—people who may not be candidates themselves but might offer good suggestions of others? And are there some associations your recruiter should know about, conventions coming up, or trade journals that will prove helpful?

You're in this together. As the search goes forward, you may hear of someone who might be a candidate or another good source. Let your recruiter know about that. For a search to go well there cannot be "your" candidates and "the recruiter's" candidates. They are all your team's candidates.

It is the recruiter's job to use all the resources and ingenuity that can be mustered to generate an array of candidates who fit your job specifications to various degrees, some better than others. It is also the recruiter's responsibility to perform the work ethically. One of the very unfortunate by-products of the pressure on researchers to obtain candidate names or organization information is sometimes gross deception. In several recent incidents, researchers with search firms or with outside research suppliers have been caught using such surreptitious devices as to say they are performing research for an academic project or seeking names for *Who's Who* directories.

It is also the recruiter's responsibility to maintain the confidentiality of a confidential search and an appropriate degree of confidentiality even when a search is not a confidential one. No organization benefits from having its management needs broadcast to the world at large—except in those very rare instances when public awareness can help generate a candidate who might otherwise be nearly impossible to find. For example, searches for commissioners of major sports groups and heads of government agencies are often aided by wide public knowledge of the need.

As the employer, you are responsible for ensuring that the search proceeds on schedule and with regular feedback from you to the recruiter. If you haven't seen your first candidate within five or six weeks from the start of the search, something is awry. Either your recruiter is spending too much time on other assignments or having trouble getting a handle on your industry or area of activity. It's time to reconvene for a heart-to-heart talk. Maybe the marketplace is telling both you and the recruiter that your specifications or compensation package are unrealistic.

Your role includes seeing that the recruiter you selected is still personally deeply involved with the search. Many search firms employ gifted "rainmakers." These are individuals who are especially accomplished at selling the assignment—they frequently are the ones who brag about "selling over a million dollars a year" in searches—but who are equally skilled at avoiding the trenches where the gruntwork on a good search really takes place. Rainmakers usually surround themselves with go-fers, the bag people who do their work for them. Don't forget, *that's not what you contracted for when you selected one of the top recruiters.*

Throughout the search your recruiter has been doing various types of reference checking. Initially it is the kind of quick-and-dirty call or two to references the recruiter knows personally. The recruiter just wants to be sure there are no major flaws or flags with the candidate. The fine-tuned, in-depth references are reserved for your actual finalists, usually not more than one or two. Here's another place where your top recruiter earns his or her pay—and be sure that it is your recruiter doing your reference checking, not just some underling.

Reference checks may not constitute the most critical element in the outcome of a search, but they are everything in predicting the ultimate performance of the candidate once in the job. Quality reference checking is the single most important ingredient in a search well done. Many a candidate, especially one who has had considerable prior interviewing experience, can fool an employer or the most seasoned recruiter in an interview regardless of its length or apparent thoroughness. I repeat, *references are everything.*

Regrettably, they are getting much more difficult to check. The privacy-of-information acts and other regulatory restraints make reference checking difficult, and too many employers and recruiters alike shy away from any but the most cursory and superficial ones. Do not allow your recruiter to avoid doing in-depth references. Good thorough reference checking can still be accomplished. It just takes the right knowledge, skills, contacts, and the instincts of Peter Falk's Columbo. Speaking personally, I've always felt that thorough reference checking is as much in a candidate's best interest as it is in the employer's. Who in his right mind would ever want to be placed in a job where a limitation in his background that could be uncovered through good reference checking would cause him to fail?

The skills of your top recruiter also come into play when it's time to put together the hiring package with your preferred candidate. It is a bad mistake for employers to get directly involved with a candidate in negotiating a compensation package. Your role as the employer is to give your recruiter the parameters to work with but then trust that the deal can be worked out between candidate and recruiter. You, however, should be the one who extends the ultimate formal offer, not your recruiter.

We work in a time of more job uncertainty and career chaos than in any period since the Great Depression. Megamergers, LBOs, downsizing, spin-offs, takeovers, and other employment discombobulations have wreaked havoc on hundreds of thousands of working professionals. Now, many of these talented but displaced individuals find themselves looking for jobs on their own or with the help of outplacement firms. In the recent past, most employers would turn their noses up at those "in the job market." And they were, to a certain extent, correct in that feeling. This attitude should no longer exist on the part of any hiring organization. Consequently, your recruiter should be encouraged as never before to consider those high achievers who send their resumes over the transom as objectively as any other candidates whom the search identifies. There is almost as much likelihood of finding your perfect placement among the write-ins at the recruiter's office as there is in turning every stone out there in the field of the still employed.

Working together for the past three months, give or take a few, your team has succeeded in finding and hiring the right individual for your very significant need. Does this mean that you and your recruiter part company until the next search that appears right for him or her? It should not. Even as the new hire comes aboard and settles into your organization, little tips might better be communicated to the placement by your search consultant than by you personally. Call them informal pieces of constructive criticism to correct small habits or traits that might become larger problems worth formal mention later on. Your recruiter is also going to want to speak with you every few months about how the new hire is performing. Like doctors, headhunters have egos, and they need to know not only that the operation was a success but that the patient is thriving.

PART II

NORTH AMERICA'S TOP
EXECUTIVE RECRUITERS

4

PROFILES OF THE TOP 250 EXECUTIVE RECRUITERS

JOHN R. AKIN
President
J.R. Akin & Company
183 Sherman Street
Fairfield, CT 06430
Telephone: (203) 259-0007

J.R. Akin & Company

HONOREE: 1992, 1994

Date of birth: January 25, 1937

EDUCATION:
    Boston College
        B.S.B.A., finance, 1959
    Northeastern University/NYU
        M.B.A., 1970

MILITARY:
    First Lieutenant, United States Army Signal Corps, 1960 to 1962

SPECIAL INTERESTS AND HOBBIES:
    Boating, fishing, bird-watching, running

EMPLOYMENT HISTORY:
    1983 to present: J.R. Akin & Company
    1979 to 1982: Partner, Antell Wright & Nagell
    1978 to 1979: Vice President, Human Resources, Burndy Corporation
    1959 to 1978: Various positions to Director, Human Resources, GTE

WHAT I LOOK FOR IN GENERAL IN A CANDIDATE:

In the selection of executive talent, the interview focus is on accomplishments. What was done and what was the impact on the company's profit-and-loss statement? In addition, emphasis is placed on activities and accomplishments that are indicative of superior intelligence, ambition, people skills such as team building and effective selection and retention, and adaptive skills and flexibility.

Retained executive search is basically a simple business. It is a function of listening carefully and asking dozens of appropriate questions of the client organization (all of the key executives participating in the selection process) and, in particular, the hiring manager.

The next step is a thoughtful development of a description of both the position and duties and the personal traits and characteristics of the successful candidate. The draft is submitted for intensive review by the client. Following approval of the description, a well-disciplined search follows. There is no substitute for hard work, sharp focus, and exercise of discipline and excellence in selection criteria at this point.

The rest of the search process follows, including active participation in the offer process on the part of the search consultant and frequent contact with the placed executive after he or she starts the new position. We at J.R. Akin & Company feel that one of the most important ingredients in this process is the continuity of having one consultant doing the soliciting, telephone interviewing, and personal interviewing.

GEOGRAPHIC SCOPE OF RECRUITING ACTIVITIES:
    Serve clients nationwide, European common market, and Far East, specifi-
        cally Taiwan and Hong Kong

TOTAL YEARS OF RETAINER-TYPE RECRUITING EXPERIENCE:
    15 years

DONALD T. ALLERTON
Partner
Allerton Heneghan & O'Neill
70 W. Madison Avenue, Suite 2015
Chicago, IL 60602
Telephone: (312) 263-1075

HONOREE: 1990, 1992, 1994

Date of birth: January 4, 1940

Allerton Heneghan & O'Neill

EDUCATION:
Farleigh Dickinson University
    B.S., business administration, 1965

SPECIAL INTERESTS AND HOBBIES:
IACPR board member

EMPLOYMENT HISTORY:
1978 to present: Allerton Heneghan & O'Neill
1975 to 1978: Vice President and General Manager–Midwest, Staub Warmbold
1972 to 1975: Director, Corporate Employment, G.D. Searle & Company
1969 to 1972: Celanese Corporation
1965 to 1969: Warner-Lambert Company

WHAT I LOOK FOR IN GENERAL IN A CANDIDATE:

Experience has taught me that executives with certain core qualities tend to be the most successful over time. These qualities include:

Innate intelligence and common sense.
Effective communication skills to articulate a sense of purpose and goals.
Proven leadership skills to inspire people to achieve a vision.
Unquestioned personal integrity and honesty.
Broad business perspective to learn from others and take advantage of global opportunities.
Sense of humor, because taking yourself too seriously stifles creativity and takes the fun out of working.

The position and client determine what I specifically look for in a candidate. Each assignment requires recruiting a person with a unique blend of accomplishments, experience, and expertise. However, a successful match demands compatible chemistry. Candidate and client must experience a sense of positive chemistry, or all the candidate's other positive attributes will place a distant second.

GEOGRAPHIC SCOPE OF RECRUITING ACTIVITIES:
Serve clients nationwide and in Canada, Europe, and Latin America

TOTAL YEARS OF RETAINER-TYPE RECRUITING EXPERIENCE:
19 years

JACQUES P. ANDRE
Partner
Paul Ray Berndtson, Inc.
101 Park Avenue
New York, NY 10178
Telephone: (212) 370-1316

HONOREE: 1990, 1994

Date of birth: August 29, 1937

Paul Ray Berndtson, Inc.

EDUCATION:
University of Miami
B.B.A., personnel management, 1959

MILITARY:
Captain, United States Army Reserve, 1959 to 1967

SPECIAL INTERESTS AND HOBBIES:
Golf, scuba diving, gardening, travel

EMPLOYMENT HISTORY:
1975 to present: Paul Ray Berndtson, Inc.
1965 to 1975: Manager, Executive Search, Ernst & Young
1964 to 1965: Senior Employment Specialist, P. Ballantine & Sons
1960 to 1964: Assistant Personnel Director, Sealtest Foods

WHAT I LOOK FOR IN GENERAL IN A CANDIDATE:

Our objective is to form a judgment whether a candidate will be successful within a client's environment. To accomplish this, we assess the person's education and experience as well as the fit with the client's culture. We need to understand the person's interests, reasons for making career decisions, accomplishments, likes and dislikes, and self-insights. Initial impression is a factor, but there must be substance behind that. Some candidate specifications are requirements; some are preferences. We need to keep the candidate specifications in mind but not lose sight of the primary issues: Will the person be successful in the position, in the client's culture, and prosper over the longer term?

GEOGRAPHIC SCOPE OF RECRUITING ACTIVITIES:
Clients nationwide and internationally

TOTAL YEARS OF RETAINER-TYPE RECRUITING EXPERIENCE:
29 years

JERRY H. BAKER
Partner
Schuyler, Frye & Baker, Inc.
1100 Abernathy Road, N.E., Suite 1825
Atlanta, GA 30328
Telephone: (404) 804-1996

Date of birth: August 16, 1946

Bern-Art Studios

EDUCATION:
    Wake Forest University
        B.A., 1968
    Harvard University
        M. Div., 1971

SPECIAL INTERESTS AND HOBBIES:
    Theological education, radio broadcasting and history of rock 'n' roll

EMPLOYMENT HISTORY:
    1991 to present: Schuyler, Frye & Baker, Inc.
    1983 to 1991: Partner, Lamalie Associates, Inc.
    1979 to 1983: President, U.S. Operations, MSL International
    1976 to 1979: Vice President, Billington, Fox & Ellis, Inc.
    1974 to 1976: Corporate Recruiter, Miller Brewing Co.
    1974: Assistant Corporate Personnel Manager, American Thread Co.
    1971 to 1973: Minister, The Congregational Church

WHAT I LOOK FOR IN GENERAL IN A CANDIDATE:

An individual impresses me positively when there is clear evidence of a "balanced life." One whose perspective is "my work is my whole life" is much too narrowly focused. An individual should have a level of self-confidence that allows one to take risks—a pioneer willing to chart new territory is interesting to me. One should recognize the impact that other persons have had in one's career—and be enthusiastic about sharing credit. One should have superior intellectual capacity and equally superior common sense. A sense of humor is always essential to success—a smile and some laughter in an interview are required. One must be cognizant of weaknesses and failures—and have learned enough about both to benefit from these perceived negatives. And one should be able to discuss objectively and intelligently the factors which the individual considers to be the most prominent in having led to success.

GEOGRAPHIC SCOPE OF RECRUITING ACTIVITIES:
    Serve clients nationwide

TOTAL YEARS OF RETAINER-TYPE RECRUITING EXPERIENCE:
    18 years

GARY R. BARTON
Partner
Barton Raben, Inc.
Three Riverway, Suite 910
Houston, TX 77056
Telephone: (713) 961-9111

Date of birth: May 31, 1939

EDUCATION:
> Miami University
>> B.S., mathematics, 1960
> Wharton School of Business
>> M.B.A. (Sarnoff Scholar), 1972

Woodallen Photography

SPECIAL INTERESTS AND HOBBIES:
> Member of board of directors of Karitas Foundation; The Wharton Club; Northwest Academy; Boys and Girls Country of Houston, Inc.; and the YMCA

EMPLOYMENT HISTORY:
> 1979 to present: Barton Raben, Inc.
> 1976 to 1979: Director, Occidental Petroleum
> 1965 to 1976: Manager, R.C.A./Hertz Corporation
> 1961 to 1965: Project Leader, General Electric
> 1960 to 1961: Management Trainee, MONY

WHAT I LOOK FOR IN GENERAL IN A CANDIDATE:

Successful executives possess similar traits regardless of the industry or function. The qualities I value are leadership, knowledge, and creativity. Leadership is demonstrated by taking full responsibility for successes and failures and assimilating what you have learned from either outcome. It is also the ability to meld diverse talents into productive, proactive teams with common goals. Knowledge is best described as a hunger or passion for the business and always seeking methods of improving the business. Creativity is the ability to look at existing challenges in a new light or from a nontraditional perspective and positively impact the business through the resulting vision.

To complement these characteristics, I look for a proven track record of achievement, measured risk taking, and a strategic perspective. In today's increasingly competitive business climate of global challenges, a successful executive must be able to quickly assess situations, weigh the variables, and make decisions with confidence. The executive who has these qualities, or is striving to attain them, will be successful.

GEOGRAPHIC SCOPE OF RECRUITING ACTIVITIES:
> Serve clients nationwide and in Europe, Africa, Middle East, Canada, Mexico, South America, and former Soviet republics

TOTAL YEARS OF RETAINER-TYPE RECRUITING EXPERIENCE:
> 14 years

BRUCE M. BASTOKY
President
January Management Group, Inc.
513 E. Rich Street, Suite 302
Columbus, OH 43215
Telephone: (614) 462-2703

Date of birth: June 15, 1953

January Management Group, Inc.

SPECIAL INTERESTS AND HOBBIES:
Amateur astronomy, playing soccer, physical fitness

EMPLOYMENT HISTORY:
1989 to present: January Management Group, Inc.
1986 to 1989: Vice President Human Resources, Cardinal Industries
1978 to 1986: Personnel Director, The Lawson Company
1974 to 1978: Employee Relations Manager, The May Company

WHAT I LOOK FOR IN GENERAL IN A CANDIDATE:

I am particularly interested in those candidates who have achieved a high level of professional success *without having sacrificed* their families, their individual development, or their personal happiness.

Candidates who work excessive hours (especially later in careers; we're all workaholics, or should be, when beginning our careers), seldom see their families, fail to take care of themselves physically, and have developed few if any interests outside the workplace generally fail to own any useful and "real-world" insight or perspectives into their customers, shareholders, and employees. I feel it's as important for executives to read *Newsweek* as *The Wall Street Journal.*

I prefer candidates with a broad understanding of the world, their role in it, and how events shape them and their business environment. In my opinion, these executives perform best for my clients.

GEOGRAPHIC SCOPE OF RECRUITING ACTIVITIES:
Serve clients nationwide and the Western Hemisphere and Europe

TOTAL YEARS OF RETAINER-TYPE RECRUITING EXPERIENCE:
5 years

O. WILLIAM BATTALIA
Chairman
Battalia Winston International, Inc.
300 Park Avenue
New York, NY 10022
Telephone: (212) 308-8080

HONOREE: 1992, 1994

Date of birth: December 18, 1928

Battalia Winston International, Inc.

EDUCATION:
Cathedral College
B.A., social science, 1951
Columbia University Graduate School of Business
M.B.A., 1956

MILITARY:
Corporal, United States Army Security Agency, 1951 to 1953

SPECIAL INTERESTS AND HOBBIES:
Swimming, jogging, tennis, skiing, theater, reading, music

EMPLOYMENT HISTORY:
1963 to present: Battalia Winston International, Inc.
1959 to 1963: Director, Personnel, ITT Information Systems Division
1956 to 1959: Employment Supervisor, Unisys, Sperry Division

WHAT I LOOK FOR IN GENERAL IN A CANDIDATE:

I look for a candidate who fits the specification, not loosely but tightly. I try to find the person who has the right number of years in the right function in the right industry.

Beyond that, I look for intelligence, motivation, management, style, integrity, creativity, promotability, people skills, judgment, and mind-set.

Over and above these "hard" and "soft" criteria is the need to match an individual to an environment—both the company as a whole and the group with which the person will interface on a daily basis.

GEOGRAPHIC SCOPE OF RECRUITING ACTIVITIES:
Serve clients nationwide and through EURAM offices in Canada, Denmark, France, Germany, Sweden, and the United Kingdom

TOTAL YEARS OF RETAINER-TYPE RECRUITING EXPERIENCE:
30 years

MARTIN H. BAUMAN
President
Martin H. Bauman Associates, Inc.
375 Park Avenue, Suite 2002
New York, NY 10152
Telephone: (212) 752-6580

HONOREE: 1990, 1992, 1994

Date of birth: December 26, 1929

Duncan Wagner

EDUCATION:
New York University
    B.S., personnel management, 1956
New York University Graduate School of Business
    M.B.A., management, 1961

MILITARY:
Corporal, United States Army Signal Corps, 1951 to 1953

SPECIAL INTERESTS AND HOBBIES:
Outdoors, swimming

EMPLOYMENT HISTORY:
1968 to present: Martin H. Bauman Associates, Inc.
1965 to 1968: Assistant Personnel Director, United Merchants & Manufacturers
1961 to 1965: Vice President, Personnel, Branch Motor Express
Five years prior experience in personnel, training, and development in retailing and manufacturing

WHAT I LOOK FOR IN GENERAL IN A CANDIDATE:

For our clients, who tend to be very entrepreneurial and satisfied by nothing less than "the cream of the crop," we specifically tailor each search to match their unique needs and cultures. Certain traits, however, distinguish a very good candidate from a truly exceptional one. Very high IQ, sound judgment, conceptual ability, decisiveness, and bottom-line orientation. How do we measure these traits in a candidate? We utilize a peerless all-day management assessment process that give us greater insight into each individual's brilliance and personal skill set. One of our clients summed it up by saying, "Our candidate selection is distinguished not just by the science he uses, but by the art."

GEOGRAPHIC SCOPE OF RECRUITING ACTIVITIES:
Serve clients nationwide and Europe, China, Hong Kong, Canada, Scandinavia, Philippines, Latin America, Australia, Middle East, India, Eastern Europe

TOTAL YEARS OF RETAINER-TYPE RECRUITING EXPERIENCE:
23+ years

ROBERT E. BEAUDINE
President and Chief Operating Officer
Eastman & Beaudine, Inc.
1370 One Galleria Tower
13355 Noel Road, LB-31
Dallas, TX 75240
Telephone: (214) 661-5520

Date of birth: March 6, 1955

Eastman & Beaudine, Inc.

EDUCATION:
   Southern Methodist University
      B.B.A., 1977

SPECIAL INTERESTS AND HOBBIES:
   Golf, tennis, skiing, civic and charitable activities; member of advisory board
      of directors for SMU Graduate School of Business

EMPLOYMENT HISTORY:
   1981 to present: Eastman & Beaudine, Inc.
   1977 to 1981: Marketing (Brand Management)–Los Angeles, Sales–Dallas,
      Carnation Company

WHAT I LOOK FOR IN GENERAL IN A CANDIDATE:

   A candidate for any executive position must have the experience background
that meets my client's requirements. In a search, I am also looking for plus-values
in the candidates. These include additional skills beyond the position specification
and above-average accomplishments and growth in responsibilities and authority.

   The personal qualities of the individual are equally important. Factors such as
presence, ability to communicate effectively, intelligence, leadership, strategic
thinking ability, a sense of humor, and self-confidence are important. I also look
for individuals with high levels of integrity. Being a team player with a management style that includes the ability to delegate responsibilities and to develop subordinates is also an important evaluation factor.

   Finally, I try to be sure that the position provides a significant opportunity for
the candidate, provides potential for further growth, and is positive in terms of his
or her family.

GEOGRAPHIC SCOPE OF RECRUITING ACTIVITIES:
   Serve clients nationwide and internationally

TOTAL YEARS OF RETAINER-TYPE RECRUITING EXPERIENCE:
   13 years

JEFFREY G. BELL
Managing Director
Norman Broadbent International, Inc.
200 Park Avenue
New York, NY 10166
Telephone: (212) 953-6990

HONOREE: 1992, 1994

Date of birth: August 28, 1945

Norman Broadbent International, Inc.

EDUCATION:
Wesleyan University
B.A., history, 1968
The Wharton School, University of Pennsylvania,
M.B.A., finance, 1973

MILITARY:
Captain, United States Marine Corps, 1969 to 1972

SPECIAL INTERESTS AND HOBBIES:
Toy-soldier collecting

EMPLOYMENT HISTORY:
1987 to present: Norman Broadbent International, Inc.
1983 to 1987: President, Morgan Research Inc.
1976 to 1983: Vice President, Russell Reynolds Associates, Inc.
1975 to 1976: Associate/Corporate Finance, Blyth Eastman Dillon & Co., Inc.
1973 to 1975: Administrative Officer, Brown Brothers Harriman & Co.

WHAT I LOOK FOR IN GENERAL IN A CANDIDATE:

I always look for a combination of technical expertise and personal attributes that translate into a track record of accomplishment over time. The more junior the requirement, the more I weight the technical skill sets required in the position specification. For senior positions, I look for "leadership by example," that is, the ability to set standards, motivate colleagues, and discharge one's responsibilities in a highly professional manner. While origination ability, technical competence, creativity, effective interpersonal skills, and a strong work ethic are highly desirable attributes, a demonstrated commitment to sound business ethics combined with personal integrity are critical and will always determine whether or not I introduce a prospect to a client.

GEOGRAPHIC SCOPE OF RECRUITING ACTIVITIES:
Serve clients nationwide and in the United Kingdom, Europe, and Latin
America

TOTAL YEARS OF RETAINER-TYPE RECRUITING EXPERIENCE:
18 years

JOY REED BELT, Ph.D.
President
Joy Reed Belt & Associates, Inc.
P.O. Box 18446
Oklahoma City, OK 73154
Telephone: (405) 842-6336

Date of birth: September 28, 1939

Joy Reed Belt & Associates, Inc.

EDUCATION:
University of Arkansas
M.Ed., 1968
University of Oklahoma
Ph.D., 1977

SPECIAL INTERESTS AND HOBBIES:
Arts, antiques, orchid cultivation, civic organizations

EMPLOYMENT HISTORY:
1979 to present: Joy Reed Belt & Associates, Inc.
1977 to 1979: University of Oklahoma
1974 to 1976: Oklahoma Indian Affairs Commission and Oklahoma Art
Humanities Council

WHAT I LOOK FOR IN GENERAL IN A CANDIDATE:

A company is only as good as its people. Therefore, my quest is to identify and recommend the best when I am evaluating candidates for our clients. I look for professional experience, competence, and potential as well as personal factors when I evaluate candidates. I believe I have the ability to assess the personality and management styles essential for good chemistry between candidate and company.

GEOGRAPHIC SCOPE OF RECRUITING ACTIVITIES:
Serve clients nationwide and internationally

TOTAL YEARS OF RETAINER-TYPE RECRUITING EXPERIENCE:
14 years

JOHN R. BERRY II
Co-Managing Partner
Nordeman Grimm, Inc.
150 N. Michigan Avenue, Suite 3610
Chicago, IL 60601
Telephone: (312) 332-0088

Date of birth: May 9, 1939

Nordeman Grimm, Inc.

EDUCATION:
University of Colorado
B.A., 1961

SPECIAL INTERESTS AND HOBBIES:
Family, travel, curling, church and community volunteer work, crossword
puzzles

EMPLOYMENT HISTORY:
1992 to present: Nordeman Grimm, Inc.
1990 to 1992: Partner, The Hiedrick Partners, Inc.
1982 to 1990: President and CEO, The Wabaningo Corporation
1977 to 1982: President and CEO, Travel and Tourism Group of Companies,
   Holland America Line
1973 to 1977: Vice President, Marketing and Planning, Sitmar Cruises
1963 to 1973: Director, Commercial Marketing, TransWorld Airlines
1962 to 1963: Sales Representative, Continental Airlines

WHAT I LOOK FOR IN GENERAL IN A CANDIDATE:

Intelligence, thoughtfulness, strong people skills, and a predisposition to
action are the initial traits I am seeking in a candidate. Relevant skills sets/core
competencies/experience must be in place as well.

Next I dig for integrity, realism, and evidence of consistency and discipline.

Finally, I probe for innovativeness and the ability to think abstractly as well as
flexibility and maturity.

A good sense of humor is also a plus.

Evidence of the above qualities is sought in the interview and, very importantly, in thorough reference checking as well.

GEOGRAPHIC SCOPE OF RECRUITING ACTIVITIES:
Serve clients nationwide

TOTAL YEARS OF RETAINER-TYPE RECRUITING EXPERIENCE:
4 years

LINDA C. BIALECKI
President
Bialecki, Inc.
780 Third Avenue, Suite 4203
New York, NY 10017
Telephone: (212) 755-1090

Date of birth: March 28, 1947

EDUCATION:
University of California at Berkeley
    B.A., communication and
    public policy, 1969
Stanford University
    M.B.A., 1979

Buck Ennes/Institutional Investor

SPECIAL INTERESTS AND HOBBIES:
Board member, Association of Executive Search Consultants (AESC), head technology task force, head diversity task force, member finance committee; scuba diving, gardening, travel

EMPLOYMENT HISTORY:
1986 to present: Bialecki, Inc.
1986: Consultant, Ingram Inc.
1983 to 1986: Consultant, Jay Gaines & Co.
1979 to 1983: Assistant Vice President, Citicorp Credit Services, Inc.
1974 to 1977: Budget Analyst, University of California at Davis
1973 to 1974: Manager, University of California Employees Credit Union

WHAT I LOOK FOR IN GENERAL IN A CANDIDATE:

I look for "fabulous" or "incredible" when I'm tracking down a possible candidate's reputation. I let the marketplace tell me how good someone is at what they do, and I only call people who get raves. When I interview, my focus is on figuring out what kind of character the individual has and whether he or she would love the position and the culture of the firm I am recruiting for.

What I Look For is pretty simple, but it doesn't come together very often in one person:

Integrity. If someone can't be trusted, on even the smallest thing, I don't even call him or her for an interview—it doesn't matter if the individual is fabulous at new business, new products, etc. My clients are uncompromising on this issue.

Driven and serious about the business and about taking care of his or her clients. Does his or her homework. No shooting from the hip. No bullshit. Willing to say "I don't know" instead of cluttering the airwaves with what he or she "thinks" might be the answer to a fact question.

Straightforward and down-to-earth. Doesn't take him- or herself too seriously. Has a sense of humor, and can take being kidded. Wants to learn; has capacity to grow. Comfortable with him- or herself.

To sum it up, I look for really good human beings (who by definition have integrity) who are smart and driven.

GEOGRAPHIC SCOPE OF RECRUITING ACTIVITIES:
Serve clients nationwide and internationally

TOTAL YEARS OF RETAINER-TYPE RECRUITING EXPERIENCE:
11 years

LYNN TENDLER BIGNELL
Principal/Cofounder
Gilbert Tweed Associates, Inc.
415 Madison Avenue
New York, NY 10017
Telephone: (212) 758-3000

HONOREE: 1990, 1992, 1994

Date of birth: April 26, 1938

Gilbert Tweed Associates, Inc.

EDUCATION:
> University of Florida
> B.A., mathematics, 1959

SPECIAL INTERESTS AND HOBBIES:
> Family, friends, adventure travel, horseback riding, crafts, antique auctions, and flea markets; author, frequent lecturer, and seminar leader: "Picking Winners" and "Keeping Winners"

EMPLOYMENT HISTORY:
> 1972 to present: Gilbert Tweed Associates, Inc.
> 1963 to 1967 and 1970 to 1972: Director, Technical Recruiting, Dunhill Personnel
> 1960 to 1963: Associate, Personnel Associates

WHAT I LOOK FOR IN GENERAL IN A CANDIDATE:

Today, more than ever before, my candidates must be leaders—leaders who can engineer, implement, and manage change in order to meet the economic, technological, and competitive challenges that are bombarding business, industry, and the not-for-profit sector like never before.

Strategic, visionary leadership, whether as CEO or a functional head, must be coupled with strong communication and, more and more frequently, entrepreneurial skills.

Accordingly, I must make certain that my candidates have the something extra to contribute—perspective, insight, vision, innovation. They must have unique skills and experience beyond what is needed today. My candidates aren't just bodies that fill today's position specifications; they are value-added individuals who must be a resource to my clients, contributing to the future fabric of their organizations.

GEOGRAPHIC SCOPE OF RECRUITING ACTIVITIES:
> Serve clients nationwide and in Canada, Europe, Asia, Mexico, South and Central America, as well as through INESA's federation of offices in the United Kingdom, France, Belgium, Italy, Spain, Switzerland, Sweden, Germany, and Singapore

TOTAL YEARS OF RETAINER-TYPE RECRUITING EXPERIENCE:
> 22 years

SUSAN K. BISHOP
President
Bishop Partners
708 Third Avenue, Suite 2200
New York, NY 10017
Telephone: (212) 986-3419

Date of birth: April 3, 1946

Jennifer Bishop

EDUCATION:
Briarcliff College
    B.A., English literature, 1968
Fordham University
    M.B.A., 1986

SPECIAL INTERESTS AND HOBBIES:
Tennis, music, yoga, Childreach (foster parent for over 15 years); Economic Club of New York, Women in Cable, Cable Television Administration & Marketing Society, National Academy of Cable Programming, International Radio & Television Society, National Academy of Television Arts & Sciences

EMPLOYMENT HISTORY:
1988 to present: Bishop Partners
1982 to 1988: Partner, Johnson Smith & Knisely
1981 to 1982: Research Associate, Joe Sullivan & Associates
1968 to 1981: Various positions in theater, broadcasting, and cable TV in New York and Anchorage, Alaska, including the start-up of a pay TV company in Anchorage, Alaska

WHAT I LOOK FOR IN GENERAL IN A CANDIDATE:

Once a candidate is thoroughly prescreened by phone, I usually have a strong sense of whether or not the technical skills necessary to do the job are there. What then becomes most critical in the personal interview is whether or not this person is a good cultural match for the client and the organization. I am looking for things much less tangible than the facts on the resume—creative thinking, sense of humor, energy level, personal style, curiosity, listening skills, general intelligence, and common sense. I also look for someone who is confident and comfortable with him- or herself. An open and honest dialogue is critical.

GEOGRAPHIC SCOPE OF RECRUITING ACTIVITIES:
Serve clients nationwide

TOTAL YEARS OF RETAINER-TYPE RECRUITING EXPERIENCE:
14 years

OTIS H. BOWDEN II
Founder
Bowden & Company, Inc.
5000 Rockside Road, Suite 550
Cleveland, OH 44131
Telephone: (216) 447-1800

HONOREE: 1990, 1992, 1994

Date of birth: January 2, 1928

EDUCATION:
Washington University, St. Louis, Missouri
B.S.B.A., 1950
M.B.A., 1953

Bowden & Company, Inc.

MILITARY:
Officer Candidate, United States Marine Corps, 1951

SPECIAL INTERESTS AND HOBBIES:
Over 25 years' college and seminary board/trustee service; private pilot, tennis, sailing, photography, world travel

EMPLOYMENT HISTORY:
1972 to present: Bowden & Company, Inc.
1967 to 1971: Vice President, E.A. Butler Associates, Inc.
1963 to 1967: Director–Mass Transit Center, B.F. Goodrich Company
1953 to 1963: District Manager, TRW, Inc.
1950 to 1953: Financial Analyst, St. Louis Union Trust Co.

WHAT I LOOK FOR IN GENERAL IN A CANDIDATE:

Candidate evaluation with the goal of a client-candidate "Quality Match" begins with understanding the client and its decision maker's criteria—*listening* is crucial.

The candidate scrutiny begins with the careful evaluation of his or her professional experience based upon *intellect, knowledge, experience, creativity,* and *noteworthy accomplishments.*

The candidate's career track record is carefully examined to evaluate:
1. Leadership characteristics and style;
2. Persistent goal orientation and achievements;
3. Interpersonal skills, compatibility, and tact;
4. Communication, motivation, and technical skills;
5. Subtleties of strategic and tactical problem solving, including decisiveness where risks are involved;
6. Effects of past mistakes and failures;
7. Global perspective; and
8. Philosphy of "diversity."

Affirmation of his or her *integrity* and *honesty* based upon ethical values, coupled with self-confidence, positive attitude, and a high energy level are also vital probes in the evaluation process.

Only a "Quality Match," yielding long-term client and candidate satisfaction, also serves a search professional's best interest.

GEOGRAPHIC SCOPE OF RECRUITING ACTIVITIES:
Serve clients nationwide and in Canada, Mexico, Western Europe

TOTAL YEARS OF RETAINER-TYPE RECRUITING EXPERIENCE:
27 years

WILLIAM J. BOWEN
Vice Chairman
Heidrick & Struggles, Inc.
125 S. Wacker Drive, Suite 2800
Chicago, IL 60606
Telephone: (312) 372-8811

HONOREE: 1990, 1992, 1994

Date of Birth: May 13, 1934

Heidrick & Struggles, Inc.

EDUCATION:
Fordham University, New York
B.S., economics, 1956
New York University
M.B.A., investments, 1963

MILITARY:
First Lieutenant (pilot), United States Air Force, 1956 to 1959

SPECIAL INTERESTS AND HOBBIES:
Reading, music, photography, travel, baseball, jogging, golf

EMPLOYMENT HISTORY:
1973 to present: Heidrick & Struggles, Inc.
1969 to 1973: Vice President, Shearson, Hammill
1967 to 1969: Institutional Salesman, Hayden, Stone, Inc.
1962 to 1967: Assistant Vice President, Citibank
1960 to 1962: Trainee, Smith Barney & Co.

WHAT I LOOK FOR IN GENERAL IN A CANDIDATE:

Integrity, leadership; a person with a "can do" attitude. While executives should have a high degree of self-confidence, you want someone who can lead and motivate others as well as share the success—not an "I, I, I" type. A sense of humor doesn't hurt.

GEOGRAPHIC SCOPE OF RECRUITING ACTIVITIES:
Serve clients nationwide and internationally

TOTAL YEARS OF RETAINER-TYPE RECRUITING EXPERIENCE:
20+ years

MICHAEL D. BOXBERGER
President, North America
Korn/Ferry International
120 S. Riverside Plaza, Suite 918
Chicago, IL 60606
Telephone: (312) 726-1841

HONOREE: 1992, 1994

Date of birth: August 19, 1946

Korn/Ferry International

EDUCATION:
University of Denver
B.A., biological sciences, 1968
University of Texas at Austin
M.B.A., finance, 1972

SPECIAL INTERESTS AND HOBBIES:
Bird shooting, fishing, running, reading

EMPLOYMENT HISTORY:
1986 to present: Korn/Ferry International
1985 to 1986: Partner and Manager–Dallas, Heidrick & Struggles, Inc.
1983 to 1985: Vice President–Corporate Development, Kellogg-Rust, Inc.
1981 to 1983: President, McFaddin Ventures, Inc.
1977 to 1981: Senior Vice President and Manager, Heidrick & Struggles, Inc.
1974 to 1977: Senior Vice President, Capital National Bank

WHAT I LOOK FOR IN GENERAL IN A CANDIDATE:

To understand What I Look For in a candidate, one must start with the assumption that I genuinely understand my client's business and culture and the specific requirements of the position. Once I am "behind the client's eye" and feel competent as an extension of my client in the marketplace, I look for the following:

- A consistent history of success throughout one's entire life.
- The creativity to generate profits or truly "make a difference" regardless of the circumstances.
- Leadership by example.
- Self-confidence tempered with humility and tact.
- A high energy level coupled with a singular focus and commitment to accomplish one's objective.
- A proven ability to succeed in complex, difficult situations and to bounce back from adversity and win in the end.
- Through it all, the good judgment that maintains a balance in one's life.
- Values and ethics that are totally above reproach.

GEOGRAPHIC SCOPE OF RECRUITING ACTIVITIES:
Serve clients nationwide

TOTAL YEARS OF RETAINER-TYPE RECRUITING EXPERIENCE:
13 years

HOBSON BROWN, JR.
President and Chief Executive Officer
Russell Reynolds Associates, Inc.
200 Park Avenue, Suite 2300
New York, NY 10166-0002
Telephone: (212) 351-2000

Russell Reynolds Associates, Inc.

Date of birth: January 2, 1942

EDUCATION:
University of North Carolina
    B.A., economics, 1964
University of Pennsylvania,
    The Wharton School
    M.B.A., finance, 1969

MILITARY:
Lieutenant, United States Naval Reserves, 1964 to 1967

SPECIAL INTERESTS AND HOBBIES:
Fly-fishing, pheasant/grouse/quail shooting, hunting

EMPLOYMENT HISTORY:
1977 to present: Russell Reynolds Associates, Inc.
1970 to 1977: Vice President–National Division, Morgan Guaranty Trust
1969 to 1970: Associate–Corporate Finance, Dominick & Dominick

WHAT I LOOK FOR IN GENERAL IN A CANDIDATE:
For our clients, I look for candidates who would clearly be considered success-ful by any measure and who satisfy a number of criteria. First, one of our responsi-bilities is to understand a client's expectations, to assist a client in altering them if and when they are unrealistic, and to communicate them clearly to each other and to potential candidates. We have succeeded in managing our clients only when we have identified that individual who not only meets but *exceeds* client expectations.

Second, I look for candidates who can add significant value to their organiza-tions. In some cases, this value can be quantified. For example, when one of our clients recently announced the selection of our successful candidate, the stock market responded enthusiastically; the company's market valuation increased by almost $2 billion. In many cases, "value" is a quality that is difficult to measure. But in all cases, we seek to recruit individuals who make a very real difference in the organization. It may mean an executive who can lead a company into its next stage of growth. It may mean an executive who can lead a company through a restructuring effort. Whatever the company's situation, I look for the executive who truly makes a difference in the organization.

Finally, the positions I recruit for are at seniormost levels. To cope with the nature and constancy of change in today's business climate, organizations require not merely managers but *leaders*. These are two very different types of executives. Leaders are not merely administrators but innovators. They do not just maintain but develop. They are not system-oriented but people-oriented. They are not short-term thinkers but visionaries. Leaders are in greater demand than ever because they are the key to not just the success but the very *survival* of many orga-nizations in today's increasingly competitive environment.

GEOGRAPHIC SCOPE OF RECRUITING ACTIVITIES:
Serve clients nationwide and in Europe, Asia/Pacific

TOTAL YEARS OF RETAINER-TYPE RECRUITING EXPERIENCE:
17 years

DAVID ALAN BUESCHEL
Principal and Founder
Shepherd Bueschel & Provus, Inc.
One South Wacker Drive, Suite 2740
Chicago, IL 60606
Telephone: (312) 372-1142

Date of birth: May 6, 1942

Shepherd Bueschel & Provus, Inc.

EDUCATION:
Cornell University
B.S., mechanical engineering, 1965
Stanford Graduate School of Business
M.B.A., 1967

SPECIAL INTERESTS AND HOBBIES:
Association of Executive Search Consultants, Director; Chicago Theological
Seminary, Vice Chair; Cornell University Council, Administrative Board;
Lange Medical Products, Director

EMPLOYMENT HISTORY:
1992 to present: Shepherd Bueschel & Provus, Inc.
1986 to 1991: Principal and Founder, Sweeney Shepherd Bueschel Provus
Harbert & Mummert, Inc.
1983 to 1986: Vice President, Lamalie Associates
1981 to 1983: Vice President and General Manager, Austin Consulting
1975 to 1980: Various positions, Norlin Corporation
1967 to 1975: Senior Engagement Manager, McKinsey & Company, Inc.

WHAT I LOOK FOR IN GENERAL IN A CANDIDATE:
- Relevant professional history
- Integrity
- Vision and leadership
- Insight and creativity
- Communications effectiveness
- Stability and a healthy lifestyle
- Respect for human diversities
- Preparation and motivation
- Personality, especially a sense of humor

GEOGRAPHIC SCOPE OF RECRUITING ACTIVITIES:
Serve clients nationwide

TOTAL YEARS OF RETAINER-TYPE RECRUITING EXPERIENCE:
11 years

GERALD J. BUMP
Executive Managing Director
D.E. Foster Partners, Inc.
303 Peachtree Street, NE, Suite 2000
Atlanta, GA 30308
Telephone: (404) 222-3441

Date of birth: June 7, 1927

D.E. Foster Partners, Inc.

EDUCATION:
Purdue University
B.S., education, 1949
M.S., industrial sociology and psychology, 1950

MILITARY:
S 1/C, United States Naval Reserve, 1945 to 1946

SPECIAL INTERESTS AND HOBBIES:
Reading, golf, community service, gourmet cooking

EMPLOYMENT HISTORY:
1993 to present: D.E. Foster Partners, Inc.
1981 to 1992: Senior Director, SpencerStuart
1969 to 1981: President, Billington, Fox & Ellis
1960 to 1969: Regional Sales Manager, Trane Company
1950 to 1960: Manager, Staffing, Kimberly-Clark

WHAT I LOOK FOR IN GENERAL IN A CANDIDATE:

Executive search is involved in the business of predicting success. If there is any general rule for that prognosis, it could be William Shakespeare's line, "Past is prologue." Capturing, understanding, and reporting well on real achievement in a person's career, and in that individual's life, is the general platform for reading an executive's readiness and suitability for a new challenge.

GEOGRAPHIC SCOPE OF RECRUITING ACTIVITIES:
Serve clients nationwide

TOTAL YEARS OF RETAINER-TYPE RECRUITING EXPERIENCE:
25 years

SKOTT B. BURKLAND
President
Skott/Edwards Consultants
201 Route 17 North
Rutherford, NJ 07070
Telephone: (201) 935-8000

HONOREE: 1990, 1992, 1994

Date of birth: May 25, 1942

Skott/Edwards Consultants

EDUCATION:
   Dickinson College
      A.B., political science, 1964

MILITARY:
   Staff Sergeant, United States Army, 1965 to 1971

SPECIAL INTERESTS AND HOBBIES:
   Amateur race car driving

EMPLOYMENT HISTORY:
   1974 to present: Skott/Edwards Consultants
   1970 to 1974: Vice President–Personnel, U.S. Consumer Products, The
      Singer Company
   1969 to 1970: Personnel Manager–Area II Operating Group, Citibank
   1968 to 1969: Director of Recruiting, W.R. Grace & Co.
   1966 to 1967: Recruiter, The Sun Oil Company
   1964 to 1966: Financial Analyst, E.I. duPont de Nemours & Co.

WHAT I LOOK FOR IN GENERAL IN A CANDIDATE:

There are two very specific things I look for in a candidate. The first has to
do with an established, consistent track record of accomplishment—accomplishment in both professional and personal life. Secondly, and increasingly important,
are people who have good interpersonal skills. People who are capable of listening, who have developed strong communications skills, and who are clearly team
players. Of course, I look for high levels of intelligence, energy, and a strong sense
of humor. Unquestioned integrity is a must.

GEOGRAPHIC SCOPE OF RECRUITING ACTIVITIES:
   Serve clients nationwide and in Western Europe

TOTAL YEARS OF RETAINER-TYPE RECRUITING EXPERIENCE:
   20+ years

C. DOUGLAS CALDWELL
Chairman
The Caldwell Partners Amrop International
64 Prince Arthur Avenue
Toronto, Ontario M5R 1B4 Canada
Telephone: (416) 920-7702

HONOREE: 1992, 1994

Date of birth: January 26, 1937

EDUCATION:
> University of New Brunswick
> B.B.A., 1960

SPECIAL INTERESTS AND HOBBIES:

Brown, Melvin & Associates

> Skiing, sailing, and racket sports; Governor,
> Board of the Olympic Trust of Canada; Director, Corporate Council of
> Business Education; Director, Association of Executive Search Consul-
> tants, 1975–1979; Trustee, Lester B. Pearson College of the Pacific,
> 1984–1985; past Director, Lakefield College School; member of the
> Royal Canadian Yacht Club, Toronto

EMPLOYMENT HISTORY:
> 1970 to present: The Caldwell Partners Amrop International
> 1967 to 1970: Consultant, Hickling-Johnston Limited
> 1965 to 1967: Marketing Manager, Monsanto Fibers
> 1962 to 1965: Contract Specialist, Harding Carpets
> 1960 to 1962: Sales Representative, Shell Oil

WHAT I LOOK FOR IN GENERAL IN A CANDIDATE:

On the positive side:
- A person with few obvious flaws; a person who has an understanding of people and their frailties, who is good at dealing with people.
- Above-average *social skills* and *people skills* with the power to *influence.*
- High *self-confidence* but *subtle* in contests, *tactful* and *well mannered.*
- High integrity, *likes to work* and is a *hard worker,* great stamina.
- A good chairperson or *"head of meeting"* leader, yet detail-minded.

Early jobs and repeated ability to get things done. Strengths should include being intensely human, intelligent, and thoughtful—a giver, a touch of single-mindedness and toughness to handle today's challenges. Strategic thinker and planner. Team player who is innovative and ambitious. Participative with strong loyalties to people and community. Entrepreneurial spirit with commitment and dedication.

Then we look for attitudes and styles that fail:
- Any sign of *laziness,* which is often cunning and dangerous.
- A person whose *emphasis* is on appearance rather than substance.
- A process-oriented person rather than a *results-driven* one.
- Any fear of selling (one's ideas and leadership).
- Arrogance!
- Indication of failure to hire *strong, smart staff.*

GEOGRAPHIC SCOPE OF RECRUITING ACTIVITIES:
> Serve clients in Asia/Pacific, Europe, the Americas

TOTAL YEARS OF RETAINER-TYPE RECRUITING EXPERIENCE:
> 24 years

ROBERT M. CALLAN
Partner
Callan Associates, Ltd.
1550 Spring Road
Oak Brook, IL 60521
Telephone: (708) 832-7080

HONOREE: 1992, 1994

Date of birth: September 26, 1936

Callan Associates, Ltd.

EDUCATION:
Fordham University
B.S., business administration, 1958
New York University
M.B.A., 1966

MILITARY:
First Lieutenant, United States Army, 1958 to 1960

SPECIAL INTERESTS AND HOBBIES:
Family, hospital, and community college board memberships

EMPLOYMENT HISTORY:
1982 to present: Callan Associates, Ltd.
1981 to 1982: Partner, McFeely Wackerle
1973 to 1981: Senior Vice President and Partner, SpencerStuart Associates
1968 to 1973: Associate, Booz, Allen & Hamilton Inc.
1964 to 1968: Personnel Manager–Research, Hoffmann–La Roche, Inc.
1961 to 1964: Employee Relations Manager, Continental Can Company

WHAT I LOOK FOR IN GENERAL IN A CANDIDATE:

Integrity; high ethical standards.

Natural leadership; the ability to gain support and inspire loyalty.

Intelligence; a quick study who understands key issues and is able to identify the right course of action.

Excellent people skills; a reputation as a team player and a record of attracting, motivating, and keeping top talent.

Proven achievement; success in both an up and down economy, and the flexibility to react quickly to a changing environment.

Chemistry; someone who fits the client organization's style and can complement it.

A sense of humor; business can be difficult, but candidates must be able to laugh at themselves.

Balance; a healthy lifestyle and stable family environment that is supportive of senior executive responsibility.

High energy; one who thrives on the fast-paced schedule demanded of today's successful executives.

Global orientation; as the world gets smaller, executives must be able to grasp international opportunities.

GEOGRAPHIC SCOPE OF RECRUITING ACTIVITIES:
Serve clients nationally and worldwide

TOTAL YEARS OF RETAINER-TYPE RECRUITING EXPERIENCE:
26 years

JOHN H. CALLEN, JR.
Managing Director
Ward Howell International, Inc.
99 Park Avenue
New York, NY 10016
Telephone: (212) 697-3730

HONOREE: 1990, 1992, 1994

Date of birth: June 19, 1932

Ward Howell International, Inc.

EDUCATION:
Princeton University, 1951 to 1953
Trinity College
    B.A., 1955

MILITARY:
First Lieutenant, United States Marine Corps, 1955 to 1958

SPECIAL INTERESTS AND HOBBIES:
Golf, hiking, breeder of alpacas, Association of Executive Search Consultants

EMPLOYMENT HISTORY:
1977 to present: Ward Howell International, Inc.
1974 to 1977: President, Burlington Sportswear
1973 to 1974: President, Galey and Lord
1960 to 1973: Executive Vice President–Marketing, Burlington-Madison Yarn Co.
1958 to 1960: Sales Representative, Peerless Woolen Mills

WHAT I LOOK FOR IN GENERAL IN A CANDIDATE:

I look for signs of energy, intellect, self-motivation, and problem-solving abilities. In high-level assignments, stature and extraordinary leadership qualities become important. In this era, I look for proven ability in team building coupled with strong interpersonal skills and a sense of humor. I also look for candidates who have a commitment to some form of volunteerism away from work.

A competitive spirit is also an important attribute, particularly in high-level marketing and general management assignments.

GEOGRAPHIC SCOPE OF RECRUITING ACTIVITIES:
Serve clients nationwide and in Canada, Mexico, all South American countries, and Europe as well as the Middle East

TOTAL YEARS OF RETAINER-TYPE RECRUITING EXPERIENCE:
17 years

JOSEPH J. CARIDEO
Partner
Thorndike Deland Associates
275 Madison Avenue, Suite 1300
New York, NY 10016
Telephone: (212) 661-6200

Date of birth: May 5, 1948

Roberta A. Raeburn/Fotografia Studios

EDUCATION:
St. Joseph's University
B.S., psychology, 1970
Fairleigh Dickinson University
M.A., organizational psychology, 1972

EMPLOYMENT HISTORY:
1980 to present: Thorndike Deland Associates
1979 to 1980: Director, Organizational Development and Executive Placement, American Express Corporation
1974 to 1979: Corporate Director, Executive Staffing, R.J. Reynolds Industries
1972 to 1974: Human Resources Manager, Universal Manufacturing Division,
Northwest Industries, Inc.

WHAT I LOOK FOR IN GENERAL IN A CANDIDATE:

In the executives that I recruit, typically I look for someone who can size up a situation quickly and discern the key issues at hand. This should be someone who can then explain in clear and simplified language his strategies and actions. While they obviously have to be strategical, they must also be fully engaged in their areas of responsibility. Besides being technically sound, they must possess the quality of leadership. In other words, providing direction to their organization, organizing and motivating their people toward those objectives, and not letting the business get off course. All of the above traits must be manifested in a stellar track record of accomplishments and promotions.

GEOGRAPHIC SCOPE OF RECRUITING ACTIVITIES:
Serve clients nationwide and the United Kingdom, Western Europe,
Asia/Pacific

TOTAL YEARS OF RETAINER-TYPE RECRUITING EXPERIENCE:
14 years

ANTHONY B. CASHEN
Managing Partner
Lamalie Amrop International
489 Fifth Avenue, Suite 1400
New York, NY 10017
Telephone: (212) 953-7900

Date of birth: October 26, 1935

Jannick Grossman/Arista Photo Services

EDUCATION:
Cornell University
B.S., economics, 1957
Cornell University Johnson
School of Management
M.B.A., finance, 1958

SPECIAL INTERESTS AND HOBBIES:
Skiing, hiking, private pilot

EMPLOYMENT HISTORY:
1990 to present: Lamalie Amrop International
1980 to 1990: President, Flanagan & Webster
1970 to 1980: Vice President, Partner, Donaldson, Lufkin & Jenrette, Inc.
1964 to 1970: Vice President, Partner, A.G. Becker & Co.
1958 to 1964: Sales Manager, MD Publications, Inc.

WHAT I LOOK FOR IN GENERAL IN A CANDIDATE:

Candidates must possess the *technical* qualifications required by the position to be filled. It is essential to knowledgeably qualify candidates according to defined position specifications developed by each client.

Position requirements and knowledge of each client organization help define the personality and leadership characteristics required of successful candidates.

In general, the following are the characteristics that help define the selection of outstanding candidates:

High intellect—both native and as developed through education and experience.

Useful experience—the demanding events and assignments that teach success and failure.

Evidence of leadership—the qualities exemplified by peer recognition and achieved objectives throughout one's career.

Portrayal of strong personal values—as manifest in expressed importance of family, community, and perceptions of self.

GEOGRAPHIC SCOPE OF RECRUITING ACTIVITIES:
Serve clients nationwide and in Europe and Asia

TOTAL YEARS OF RETAINER-TYPE RECRUITING EXPERIENCE:
14 years

MICHAEL D. CAVER
Partner, Health Care Practice
Heidrick & Struggles, Inc.
125 S. Wacker Drive, Suite 2800
Chicago, IL 60606
Telephone: (312) 372-8811

HONOREE: 1990, 1992, 1994

Date of birth: April 7, 1942

Heidrick & Struggles, Inc.

EDUCATION:
> Hampden-Sydney College, Virginia
> > B.S., modern European history, 1964

SPECIAL INTERESTS AND HOBBIES:
Photography, classical music, international travel, fishing

EMPLOYMENT HISTORY:
> 1979 to present: Heidrick & Struggles, Inc.
> 1977 to 1979: Director, International Personnel, Baxter-Travenol Laboratories
> 1976 to 1977: Manager–International Personnel Administration, Procter & Gamble Co.
> 1972 to 1976: Director of Personnel Administration, Procter & Gamble Co. of Canada, Ltd.
> 1967 to 1972: Various Marketing, Sales, and Personnel, Procter & Gamble Co.

WHAT I LOOK FOR IN GENERAL IN A CANDIDATE:

My objective is to identify candidates whose unique blend of intellect, experiences, concrete accomplishments, values, personality, style, ambitions, and family goals most closely match my client's *total* opportunity.

Given that our client organizations are almost always undergoing fundamental change, we are retained to help them achieve "critical mass" in senior executive strength. Therefore, it is essential that candidates have demonstrated they consistently accomplish priority objectives while anticipating the future and properly positioning their organizations for future success.

Our clients depend on our ability to present candidates of conspicuous character, values, and integrity; well respected by their peers; committed to continuing professional development; balanced between collegial, participative, and directive styles as appropriate; with strong common sense and good humor; passionate about their commitments; and who inspire and develop others. Such candidates are thoughtful about their affiliations, reluctant to leave as long as they are contributing, and invariably make major impacts in all their involvements.

Especially appealing are those candidates who know themselves well and confidently share their limitations and frustrations as well as their strengths, accomplishments, and aspirations.

GEOGRAPHIC SCOPE OF RECRUITING ACTIVITIES:
Serve clients nationwide and internationally

TOTAL YEARS OF RETAINER-TYPE RECRUITING EXPERIENCE:
14 years

DAVID E. CHAMBERS
President
David Chambers & Associates, Inc.
2 Greenwich Plaza, Suite 100
Greenwich, CT 06830
Telephone: (203) 622-1333

HONOREE: 1990, 1992, 1994

Date of birth: March 6, 1938

David Chambers & Associates, Inc.

EDUCATION:
University of Arizona
B.S., business administration, 1961

MILITARY:
Specialist Fourth Class, United States Army, 1961 to 1963

SPECIAL INTERESTS AND HOBBIES:
Golf, travel, people, theater

EMPLOYMENT HISTORY:
1974 to present: David Chambers & Associates, Inc.
1973 to 1974: President, Executive Search Division, Fry Consultants
1969 to 1973: Partner, Antell, Wright & Nagel
1968 to 1969: Employment Director, Allied Chemical
1967 to 1968: President, David Chambers Company
1966 to 1967: Associate, Booz, Allen & Hamilton
1965 to 1966: Employment Supervisor, Xerox Corporation
1961 to 1965: Employment Representative, Pan American World Airways

WHAT I LOOK FOR IN GENERAL IN A CANDIDATE:

In addition to personal chemistry and specific background and experience required on each search assignment, I am interested in the candidate's maturity, energy level, appearance, leadership skills, and other personal attributes.

Other considerations include family home life, outside interests and other matters that show the person's "balance," and how he or she projects him- or herself.

GEOGRAPHIC SCOPE OF RECRUITING ACTIVITIES:
Serve clients nationwide and in Canada and in Europe through affiliates in London

TOTAL YEARS OF RETAINER-TYPE RECRUITING EXPERIENCE:
25 years

DAVID H. CHARLSON
President and Chief Executive Officer
Chestnut Hill Partners, Ltd.
2345 Waukegan Road, Suite S-165
Deerfield, IL 60015
Telephone: (708) 940-9690

HONOREE: 1990, 1992, 1994

Date of birth: May 26, 1947

Chestnut Hill Partners, Ltd.

EDUCATION:
University of Arizona, Tucson
B.S., business administration, 1969

SPECIAL INTERESTS AND HOBBIES:
Golf, tennis, auto racing, Tae Kwon Do

EMPLOYMENT HISTORY:
1989 to present: Chestnut Hill Partners
1984 to 1989: Executive Vice President–Managing Director, Richards Consultants
1976 to 1984: Managing Director and Senior Officer, Korn/Ferry International
1974 to 1976: Staff Vice President, Staub Warmbold & Associates
1973 to 1974: Manager–Employment, General Foods Corporation
1969 to 1973: Personnel Director–International, Bank of America

WHAT I LOOK FOR IN GENERAL IN A CANDIDATE:

To effectively evaluate a candidate, the executive recruiter must understand his or her client, the industry in which they operate, and the culture of the organization the potential candidate will work in. Thus, the ability to understand your client's business and the management skills necessary for success becomes dominant as I evaluate candidates and measure their style against my client's needs and desires.

In all cases, I look for a proven track record of success in more than one environment. The ability to lead, manage, control, and develop other professionals in a confident, nonthreatening manner is also key to most individuals' ability to succeed. I try to seek out candidates who are effective communicators, who can add value to my client's organization, with the ability and dedication to grow beyond the positions for which they have been recruited.

Finally, I look for individuals who are career-oriented, self-confident, goal-oriented, and self-motivated toward the achievement of corporate and individual goals.

GEOGRAPHIC SCOPE OF RECRUITING ACTIVITIES:
Serve clients nationwide and in the United Kingdom, Spain, Germany, Switzerland, Italy, Mexico, Venezuela, Argentina, Japan, and South Korea

TOTAL YEARS OF RETAINER-TYPE RECRUITING EXPERIENCE:
20 years

JEFFREY E. CHRISTIAN
President and CEO
Christian & Timbers
3201 Enterprise Parkway
Cleveland, OH 44124
Telephone: (216) 464-8710

Date of birth: January 10, 1956

Christian & Timbers

SPECIAL INTERESTS AND HOBBIES:
Founder of organization focused on building tomorrow's diverse work force called Diversity Works; skiing, basketball, and history

EMPLOYMENT HISTORY:
1980 to present: Christian & Timbers

WHAT I LOOK FOR IN GENERAL IN A CANDIDATE:

Through our research and initial screening, we tend to interview only candidates who possess most of the experience and skills required by our client. However, our philosophy is to be willing to make trade-offs in exact experience while never compromising on the following elements:

1. Integrity. How do I feel about this person as a human being? Does he or she have a good, honest value system?
2. Intelligence. I look for someone who is incredibly bright and has a "real-world" ability to apply this intellect.
3. Combination of spark, enthusiasm, energy, creativity, and the ability to create positive change and a passion for building things.
4. Leadership. Individuals who can drive an organization full-speed toward a vision while nurturing and growing that organization.

GEOGRAPHIC SCOPE OF RECRUITING ACTIVITIES:
Serve clients nationwide and internationally

TOTAL YEARS OF RETAINER-TYPE RECRUITING EXPERIENCE:
15 years

JOHN R. (JACK) CLAREY
Partner
Clarey & Andrews, Inc.
1200 Shermer Road, Suite 108
Northbrook, IL 60062
Telephone: (708) 498-2870

HONOREE: 1992, 1994

Date of birth: June 5, 1942

EDUCATION:
  Iowa State University
    B.S., industrial administration,
    1960 to 1965
  University of Pennsylvania, The Wharton   *Furla Studios*
    School M.B.A., corporate finance, 1972

MILITARY:
  Lieutenant, United States Navy, 1965 to 1970

SPECIAL INTERESTS AND HOBBIES:
  Flying, tennis, microcomputers, Lifeline Pilots (charity)

EMPLOYMENT HISTORY:
  1982 to present: Clarey & Andrews, Inc.
  1976 to 1982: Vice President and Partner, Heidrick & Struggles, Inc.
  1974 to 1976: Manager, Price Waterhouse
  1972 to 1974: Financial Analyst, Ford Motor Company

WHAT I LOOK FOR IN GENERAL IN A CANDIDATE:

Obviously, for each assignment the required background and experiences differ. Additionally, personal attributes will vary significantly depending on the client's "culture." For example, there must be compatibility in style, values, and priorities. On the other hand, regardless of the assignment, the following are characteristics I seek in a candidate:

- Absolute integrity.
- Pattern of consistent achievement.
- Common sense.
- High energy level and skill in focusing that energy.
- Balance between professional and personal interests.
- Sense of humor.
- Sense of responsibility and accountability for one's own actions.
- Realistic acknowledgment of own weaknesses as well as strengths.
- Breadth of perspective.
- Willingness to listen and to see the other person's point of view.
- Ability to deal with adversity or failure by becoming stronger for the experience.

GEOGRAPHIC SCOPE OF RECRUITING ACTIVITIES:
  Serve clients nationwide and in Canada

TOTAL YEARS OF RETAINER-TYPE RECRUITING EXPERIENCE:
  20 years

DONALD B. CLARK
Partner
Paul Ray Berndtson, Inc.
10 S. Riverside Plaza, Suite 720
Chicago, IL 60606
Telephone: (312) 876-0730

Date of birth: July 31, 1945

Raul Ray Berndston, Inc.

EDUCATION:
Northern Illinois University
B.S., finance, 1968

SPECIAL INTERESTS AND HOBBIES:
International travel, running, golf, skiing

EMPLOYMENT HISTORY:
1985 to present: Paul Ray Berndtson, Inc.
1977 to 1984: Vice President, Bankers Trust
1970 to 1977: Second Vice President, Continental Bank
1968 to 1970: Marketing Representative, Standard Oil of Indiana (Amoco)

WHAT I LOOK FOR IN GENERAL IN A CANDIDATE:

A self-assured, enthusiastic professional with demonstrated career success, strong communication skills, and solid academic credentials will always be a finalist. International experience, either academically or job-related, is also a plus. Culture fit is another key consideration. We assess our clients' corporate environments, including their history, values, politics, structure, attitude toward change, strategy, products, markets, and current management team—and we evaluate a candidate's ability to work within the unique cultural framework of the client organization.

The candidate's long-term potential and strategic orientation have become increasingly critical, particularly in the financial services field, where the transaction orientation of the 1980s has shifted to a longer-term focus.

Finally, creativity, resourcefulness, results orientation, and unquestioned integrity are essential characteristics of all candidates we recommend to clients. A sense of humor never hurts.

GEOGRAPHIC SCOPE OF RECRUITING ACTIVITIES:
Serve clients nationwide and Canada and England

TOTAL YEARS OF RETAINER-TYPE RECRUITING EXPERIENCE:
9 years

J. ROBERT CLARKE
Principal
Furst Group/MPI
421 South Mulford Road
Rockford, IL 61108
Telephone: (815) 229-9111

Date of birth: March 21, 1959

Kane Photo

EDUCATION:
University of Dubuque
B.S., 1980
American Managed Care Review Association
Certified Managed Care Executive, 1993

SPECIAL INTERESTS AND HOBBIES:
Aviation, outdoor activities

EMPLOYMENT HISTORY:
1991 to present: Furst Group/MPI
1984 to 1991: President, Healthcare Division, Furst Group
1979 to 1984: Vice President, Airmanship, Inc.
1978 to 1979: Swedish-American Hospital

WHAT I LOOK FOR IN GENERAL IN A CANDIDATE:

In the fast-paced world of health care, executives need a strong base of business and management skills as well as a healthy appetite for adventure. Comfort with change and ambiguity is a must in this ever-changing industry. Health care executives also must understand all aspects of health care delivery from provider to payor whether managing a large system or serving as an individual physician in a rural clinic.

In addition to understanding the industry, an individual must solidly understand the balance between the business of medical care and the human element. The successful executive must develop and lead teams and be willing to educate him- or herself. He or she must be a quick thinker, a mentor, and a leader who will always challenge, never underestimate, and consistently praise others' efforts. As a leader, respect for others and the utmost in professionalism is vital. Above all, honesty, self-confidence, and humility are perhaps the most sought-after attributes.

GEOGRAPHIC SCOPE OF RECRUITING ACTIVITIES:
Serve clients nationwide

TOTAL YEARS OF RETAINER-TYPE RECRUITING EXPERIENCE:
10 years

WILLIAM B. CLEMENS, JR.
Managing Director
Norman Broadbent International Inc.
200 Park Avenue
New York, NY 10166
Telephone: (212) 953-6990

HONOREE: 1990, 1992, 1994

Date of birth: May 6, 1944

Ken Korsh

EDUCATION:
Bloomfield College
B.A., political science, 1967

SPECIAL INTERESTS AND HOBBIES:
Sailing, skiing, racket sports, traveling, theater

EMPLOYMENT HISTORY:
1987 to present: Norman Broadbent International Inc.
1979 to 1987: Managing Director, Russell Reynolds Associates, Inc.
1972 to 1979: Director of Staffing, McKinsey & Company, Inc.
1969 to 1972: Personnel Manager, NL Industries
1967 to 1969: Recruiting Coordinator, Squibb Corporation

WHAT I LOOK FOR IN GENERAL IN A CANDIDATE:

Our profession is an art, not a science. The quality of creative thinking the recruiter brings to his art, the judgment he uses in assessing prospects against client requirements, and the skill to close in a manner beneficial to the client and candidate come only from experience. There is simply no substitute for experience.

One evaluates candidates against specific client needs; personal characteristics, business skills, and personality traits are in part driven by the nature of the organization and the role for which we are recruiting. Nonetheless, there are certain characteristics I look for in every candidate. Not necessarily in order, they are: stable personal and professional history, series of successive accomplishments in their chosen field, strong sense of self, sense of humor, personal and professional ambition, positive and genuine personality, but with a competitive edge, willingness to make decisions, ability to attract and develop people, intellectual curiosity, understanding the economics of a business and how to make money, get things done, self-directed, and highly motivated. To generalize is to overstate the obvious; where we add value is assisting a client within a given set of candidate parameters in selecting the most appropriate prospect in a timely fashion.

GEOGRAPHIC SCOPE OF RECRUITING ACTIVITIES:
Serve clients nationwide and in Europe

TOTAL YEARS OF RETAINER-TYPE RECRUITING EXPERIENCE:
25 years

W. HOYT COLTON
President
The Colton Partnership, Inc.
67 Wall Street
New York, NY 10005
Telephone: (212) 509-1800

HONOREE: 1992, 1994

Date of birth: September 13, 1939

Selwyn Fund Prestige Photography, Inc.

EDUCATION:
Rutgers University, 1960
Long Island University
B.S., business, 1966

MILITARY:
First Lieutenant, United States Army Reserves, 1962 to 1968

SPECIAL INTERESTS AND HOBBIES:
Golf, sailing, tennis, skiing, The Stony Brook School, the Seventh Regiment

EMPLOYMENT HISTORY:
1979 to present: The Colton Partnership, Inc.
1975 to 1979: Vice President–Human Resources, Smith Barney & Co.
1971 to 1975: Assistant Vice President, Regional Personnel Manager, Dean
    Witter & Co.
1970 to 1971: Employment Manager, Brown Brothers Harriman & Co.
1968 to 1970: Employment Manager, Walston & Co.
1966 to 1968: Employment Representative, United Airlines

WHAT I LOOK FOR IN GENERAL IN A CANDIDATE:

I look for people who command respect in their chosen vocation at their current level of achievement; people who will bring creativity, energy, leadership, and vision to the new assignment.

The criteria established in the candidate's ideal profile are a directed drive, presence, a strong work ethic, personal substance, and a progressively successful track record.

Excellent interpersonal skills, a sense of self, intelligence, stability, honesty, integrity, and personal balance are musts. But above all, that person should have common sense, a natural manner, and a style and direction that are consistent with the client's culture and management philosophy.

GEOGRAPHIC SCOPE OF RECRUITING ACTIVITIES:
Serve clients nationwide

TOTAL YEARS OF RETAINER-TYPE RECRUITING EXPERIENCE:
15 years

JAMES H. CORNEHLSEN
Partner
Lamalie Amrop International
245 Park Avenue, Suite 3230
New York, NY 10167
Telephone: (212) 867-9876

Lamalie Amrop International

HONOREE: 1990, 1994

Date of birth: June 11, 1942

EDUCATION:
Dartmouth College
B.A., English, psychology, 1964

MILITARY:
Yeoman First Class, United States
Coast Guard, 1967 to 1972

EMPLOYMENT HISTORY:
1994 to present: Lamalie Amrop International
1990 to 1994: Heidrick & Struggles, Inc.
1984 to 1989: Vice President, Handy Associates
1982 to 1983: Partner, Antel, Nagel, Moorhead
1980 to 1981: President, Las Americas Inc.
1975 to 1979: Vice President, Marketing, CBS, Inc.
1967 to 1974: Vice President, McGraw-Hill, Inc.
1964 to 1966: Marketing Director, General Electric Company

WHAT I LOOK FOR IN GENERAL IN A CANDIDATE:

The evaluation is based on ability to *learn* from success and failure; *creativity* in seeking solutions and new courses of action; *flexibility* in adapting to organization or marketplace change; and *leadership* of people.

Experience considerations are based on industry or market breadth, willingness to take on a new or risky assignment, ability to step back and set a vision, technology fluency, and international exposure.

Personal characteristics sought include sensitivity to diverse groups or geography, open communication, self-confidence with humor, sincere interest in people in new configurations for service teamwork, and work-family integration.

Personal involvement in managing change, determining strategies for real growth, expanding internationally, integrating new technology, building teams, developing partnerships or joint ventures, and board participation, philanthropic or corporate.

Honesty about weaknesses, current efforts to grow, judgment mistakes, political aptitude, and most difficult decisions.

Looks, presence, verbal quickness, and adaptability always win unless one can document intelligence, results, financial performance, aptitude for new challenges, and real humanity.

GEOGRAPHIC SCOPE OF RECRUITING ACTIVITIES:
Clients nationwide—Northeast (Washington, Boston), Midwest, West (Denver, Salt Lake City), San Francisco, and Seattle and internationally in Canada, Mexico, Spain, the United Kingdom, Australia, Tokyo, Hong Kong, and Singapore

TOTAL YEARS OF RETAINER-TYPE RECRUITING EXPERIENCE:
12 years

PETER D. CRIST
Managing Director and Co-Head of
North America
Russell Reynolds Associates, Inc.
200 S. Wacker Drive, Suite 3600
Chicago, IL 60606
Telephone: (312) 993-9696

HONOREE: 1992, 1994

Date of birth: March 8, 1952

Russell Reynolds Associates, Inc.

EDUCATION:
>   Brown University
>   A.B., political science, 1974

SPECIAL INTERESTS AND HOBBIES:
>   Coaching Little League baseball

EMPLOYMENT HISTORY:
>   1977 to present: Russell Reynolds Associates, Inc.
>   1976 to 1977: Manager of Public Relations, Household Finance Corporation
>   1974 to 1976: Director, E.F. McDonald Company

WHAT I LOOK FOR IN GENERAL IN A CANDIDATE:

There are certain characteristics that I look for in each and every candidate. Regardless of the project, I want a person who has a strong self-awareness and an ability to recognize his or her own strengths and weaknesses. The more the intellectual honesty, the more attractive the candidate.

A positive and genuine personality, intellectual curiosity, and motivation are important, as is a fundamental sense of humor.

Leadership traits such as the ability to assess risk, competitiveness, decision-making skills, energy, and professional ambition have to be balanced with common sense, humility, and the demeanor to relate with others. Good listeners with a strong sense of purpose are most attractive.

Strong morals and a balanced family life are pieces of the multidimensional personality that I seek.

GEOGRAPHIC SCOPE OF RECRUITING ACTIVITIES:
>   Serve clients nationally and internationally

TOTAL YEARS OF RETAINER-TYPE RECRUITING EXPERIENCE:
>   17 years

RICHARD J. CRONIN
President
Hodge-Cronin & Associates, Inc.
9575 West Higgins Road, Suite 904
Rosemont, IL 60018
Telephone: (708) 692-2041

HONOREE: 1992, 1994

Date of birth: October 4, 1930

Hodge-Cronin & Associates, Inc.

EDUCATION:
   Xavier University
      B.S., education, 1974

MILITARY:
   Specialist Third Class, United States Army, 1953 to 1955

SPECIAL INTERESTS AND HOBBIES:
   Family comprised of seven children and eight grandchildren; active in IACPR
      and I.I.C., our international partnership of U.S., Canadian, European,
      Mexican, and Pacific Rim executive search firms

EMPLOYMENT HISTORY:
   1963 to present: Hodge-Cronin & Associates, Inc.
   1958 to 1963: Manager–Employment, I.T.T. Telecommunications
   1956 to 1958: Manager–Employment, Admiral Corporation

WHAT I LOOK FOR IN GENERAL IN A CANDIDATE:

   There are four basic factors in each individual's makeup, namely, intelligence, motivation, personality, and knowledge/experience. Over the past thirty years, I have developed a structured interview format directed at determining a candidate's intellectual skills and aptitudes, motivational characteristics, personality strengths and limitations, and knowledge/experience. After coupling this with the particular position specifications we have developed during meetings with the client and after three to four hours spent in interviewing a candidate, we can and do make an objective decision as to whether this candidate is qualified for what our client is seeking. For those candidates we feel are qualified, we conduct extensive reference checks.

GEOGRAPHIC SCOPE OF RECRUITING ACTIVITIES:
   Serve clients nationwide and in North America, Europe, and Pacific Rim

TOTAL YEARS OF RETAINER-TYPE RECRUITING EXPERIENCE:
   30+ years

O.D. "DAN" CRUSE
Managing Director Worldwide
High Technology Practice
SpencerStuart
1717 Main Street, Suite 5300
Dallas, TX 75201
Telephone: (214) 658-1777

HONOREE: 1990, 1992, 1994

Date of birth: March 24, 1939

Gittings

EDUCATION:
> University of Dallas
>> B.A., liberal arts, 1961

SPECIAL INTERESTS AND HOBBIES:
> Golf, outdoor activities, including bird hunting and fishing

EMPLOYMENT HISTORY:
> 1977 to present: SpencerStuart
> 1975 to 1977: Vice President–Human Resources, Farah Manufacturing Company
> 1966 to 1975: Vice President–Central Services, Tracor, Inc.
> 1963 to 1966: Labor Relations Specialist, General Electric Company

WHAT I LOOK FOR IN GENERAL IN A CANDIDATE:

In general, we make a judgment regarding the executive's ability to make a difference in our client's results. Has the candidate demonstrated the capacity for producing results (beyond the norm of good performance) that will produce a sustainable positive impact within the client organization? Other traits we evaluate include energy and work ethic, self-image, judgment, interpersonal skills, and commitment/dedication. And, finally, will the candidate "fit" in the client's culture even if charged with being a "change agent"?

GEOGRAPHIC SCOPE OF RECRUITING ACTIVITIES:
> Serve clients nationwide and in Japan, Germany, France, Spain, Brazil, and Australia

TOTAL YEARS OF RETAINER-TYPE RECRUITING EXPERIENCE:
> 16+ years

W. MICHAEL DANFORTH
Executive Vice President
Hyde Danforth & Company
5950 Berkshire Lane, Suite 1600
Dallas, TX 75225
Telephone: (214) 691-5966

HONOREE: 1992, 1994

Date of birth: August 21, 1941

Hyde Danforth & Company

EDUCATION:
University of North Texas
B.S., psychology, 1963

MILITARY:
Staff Sergeant, United States Army, Texas
National Guard, 1964 to 1970

SPECIAL INTERESTS AND HOBBIES:
Antique collecting (European furniture and American primitives), travel,
theater, bridge

EMPLOYMENT HISTORY:
1974 to present: Hyde Danforth & Company
1973 to 1974: Vice President, Wescott Associates
1971 to 1973: Vice President and Corporate Secretary, CIC Corporation
1971: Consultant, Booz, Allen & Hamilton, PAR Technology Division
1969 to 1971: Consultant, Peat Marwick Mitchell & Co.
1963 to 1969: Various sales and marketing positions, Hartford Insurance,
Ford Motor Company, USM Corp.

WHAT I LOOK FOR IN GENERAL IN A CANDIDATE:
An individual who most closely matches the attributes identified by the client
at the inception of the engagement. This "picture" (specification) becomes the
standard against which all candidates are measured. Within this framework, spe-
cific attributes which I seek include:
- Personal and professional integrity.
- Chemistry "fit"—is he or she a proper match with the client?
- Proven track record as both a leader and decision maker.
- Perspective—an appropriate sense of the blend of professional, personal, and family values and needs.
- Potential—does the candidate have "upward mobility"?
- Sense of humor—ability to laugh at the foibles of life and its unique chal-
lenges.
- Ability to confront and answer the tough questions, the good sense to real-
istically identify personal and professional weaknesses, and the demon-
strated ability to address and rectify them.
- Vision and a sense of purpose—a candidate who can effectively communicate his or her goals, ambitions, dreams, and objectives.

A successfully completed search is one where the final candidate is challenged, excited about the opportunity, and strives to exceed expectations. Con-
currently, our client must have fairly presented the opportunity, be enthusiastic
about the "hire," and dedicated to providing an environment for success.

GEOGRAPHIC SCOPE OF RECRUITING ACTIVITIES:
Serve clients nationwide and in Mexico and Europe

TOTAL YEARS OF RETAINER-TYPE RECRUITING EXPERIENCE:
20 years

STEVEN M. DARTER
President
People Management Northeast, Inc.
One Darling Drive
Avon, CT 06001
Telephone: (203) 678-8900

Date of birth: August 25, 1949

Bruno of Newington

EDUCATION:

State University of New York at Oswego
B.A., sociology, 1971
State University of New York at Albany
M.S., education, 1975; Ed.S., counseling and personnel, 1975

SPECIAL INTERESTS AND HOBBIES:

Basketball, tennis

EMPLOYMENT HISTORY:

1976 to present: People Management Northeast, Inc.
1975 to 1985: Various positions, Saint Joseph College
1972: Sales Representative, Mutual Benefit Life Insurance Company

WHAT I LOOK FOR IN GENERAL IN A CANDIDATE:

I believe that each person possesses a unique and natural style and that the key to effective placement is to understand people and determine if they fit a situation.

I believe that when people are in jobs that play into their natural strengths and style, they excel and feel a positive flow, and when the same people are in poor job fit situations, they are demotivated, feel out of sync, and perform poorly.

Once I do the standard assessment of making sure that a person's background is appropriate, I focus on uncovering the heart and soul of the individual to see if they fit the essence of the job to be filled. I do this through a very detailed and in-depth interview of achievements that range over the candidate's life. Candidates as well as clients appreciate this focus. Each understands that when poor job fit decisions result, no one gains.

GEOGRAPHIC SCOPE OF RECRUITING ACTIVITIES:

Serve clients nationwide with a limited basis internationally

TOTAL YEARS OF RETAINER-TYPE RECRUITING EXPERIENCE:

17 years

DAVID M. deWILDE
Managing Director
Chartwell Partners International, Inc.
275 Battery Street, Suite 2180
San Francisco, CA 94111
Telephone: (415) 296-0600

HONOREE: 1992, 1994

Date of birth: August 11, 1940

EDUCATION:
Dartmouth College
A.B., government, 1962
University of Virginia
J.D., 1967

Chartwell Partners International, Inc.

Stanford University
M.S., management, 1984

MILITARY:
Lieutenant, United States Navy, 1962 to 1964

EMPLOYMENT HISTORY:
1989 to present: Chartwell Partners International, Inc.
1984 to 1988: Managing Director, Financial Services, Boyden International
1982 to 1984: President, DeWilde & Associates
1981 to 1982: Executive Vice President, Policy and Planning, Fannie Mae
1977 to 1981: Managing Director, Lepercq deNeuflize and Company
1976 to 1977: President, Ginnie Mae
1974 to 1976: Deputy Assistant Secretary/Deputy Commissioner, FHA, HUD
1972 to 1974: Investment Banker, Lehman Brothers
1969 to 1972: Associate General Counsel, HUD
1967 to 1969: Attorney, Curtis, Malet-Prevost, Colt & Mosle

WHAT I LOOK FOR IN GENERAL IN A CANDIDATE:

I focus on fit. Like Cinderella, it's not sufficient to be a first-rate person unless the glass slipper fits your foot. So, we work closely with our client to carefully define the need. That need, typically, breaks down to a combination of leadership, management, and expertise. We then recruit an executive whose qualities enable her or him to best meet our client's specific need.

Within that framework, I generally look for a consistent record of accomplishment and good judgment. Intelligence is important. Integrity is essential. Energy and enthusiasm should be coupled with commitment and discipline. In a world of imperfection, ability to learn from mistakes is a must.

One of my clients told me, "Don't bring us a peacetime general." Since then, I've looked for evidence of performance under fire. I am also impressed by executives who leverage themselves through information technology. Finally, the ability to communicate effectively is an essential skill in any organization. Without it, you cannot lead, manage, or share expertise.

GEOGRAPHIC SCOPE OF RECRUITING ACTIVITIES:
Serve clients nationwide and throughout North America

TOTAL YEARS OF RETAINER-TYPE RECRUITING EXPERIENCE:
10 years

RALPH E. DIECKMANN
President
Dieckmann & Associates, Ltd.
Two Prudential Plaza, Suite 5555
180 North Stetson Street
Chicago, IL 60601
Telephone: (312) 819-5900

HONOREE: 1990, 1992, 1994

Date of birth: March 30, 1944

John Reilly Photography

EDUCATION:

Northwestern University
B.A., psychology, 1966
Loyola University of Chicago
M.S., industrial relations, 1972

SPECIAL INTERESTS AND HOBBIES:

Opera, symphony, tennis, cycling, cross-country and downhill skiing, sailing, travel, civic and charity boards

EMPLOYMENT HISTORY:

1981 to present: Dieckmann & Associates, Ltd.
1973 to 1981: Manager, Executive Search Division, KPMG Peat Marwick
1966 to 1973: Director of Recruiting, R.R. Donnelley & Sons Co.

WHAT I LOOK FOR IN GENERAL IN A CANDIDATE:

An executive recruiter's greatest value-added service is helping determine which unique candidate talents will have a leveraging effect on client results. Necessary to this process are understanding the complexities of the position within its organizational context and determining the skill sets required to appropriately complement the existing management corps.

Notwithstanding the unique aspects of every search, fourteen characteristics build a foundation for outstanding executive performance.

Communications excellence is the essence of the executive function. *Leadership* requires charisma to mobilize the emotional support systems and *drive* to achieve what charisma won't. *Vision* provides the impetus for leadership and *realism* the boundaries to the vision. *Common sense* allows one to lead in the right direction and *intelligence* to lead briskly. *Diversified interests* are a sign of intelligence and foil for tunnel vision. *Perseverance* multiplies the effectiveness of new responsibilities by entrusting old ones to others. *Decisiveness* combats inertia, the cancer of organizations. *Flexibility* and *creativity* are the primary tools for coping with exponential change, with *staffing finesse* essential to frequent adaptation. Finally, a *sense of humor* is the best outlet for the inevitable stress with which all executives must cope.

GEOGRAPHIC SCOPE OF RECRUITING ACTIVITIES:

Serve clients nationally and in Canada, Mexico, Europe

TOTAL YEARS OF RETAINER-TYPE RECRUITING EXPERIENCE:

21 years

PAUL M. DiMARCHI
President
DiMarchi Partners
1225 17th Street, Suite 1460
Denver, CO 80202
Telephone: (303) 292-9300

Date of birth: December 8, 1949

DiMarchi Partners

EDUCATION:
University of Minnesota
B.S., economics/psychology, 1971

SPECIAL INTERESTS AND HOBBIES:
Water skiing, snow skiing, scuba diving

EMPLOYMENT HISTORY:
1983 to present: DiMarchi Partners
1980 to 1982: Search Consultant, Assistant Manager, Opportunities Unlimited
1972 to 1979: Regional Vice President, Topps & Trowsers

WHAT I LOOK FOR IN GENERAL IN A CANDIDATE:

The most important aspect of a search consultant's work is to understand the personality of the corporate client; understanding that "culture" and recruiting to that particular style are the keys to good management retention. Hiring for the "black and white" specifications is less critical than hiring for the specific emotional and relational characteristics of a company.

GEOGRAPHIC SCOPE OF RECRUITING ACTIVITIES:
Serve clients nationwide

TOTAL YEARS OF RETAINER-TYPE RECRUITING EXPERIENCE:
11 years

ROBERT W. DINGMAN
Chairman of the Board
Robert W. Dingman Company, Inc.
32129 West Lindero Canyon Road, #206
Westlake Village, CA 91361
Telephone: (818) 991-5950

Robert W. Dingman Company, Inc.

HONOREE: 1990, 1992, 1994

Date of birth: August 23, 1926

EDUCATION:
>   Houghton College, New York
>   B.A., 1950

MILITARY:
>   Private First Class, United States Army, 1944 to
>   1945

SPECIAL INTERESTS AND HOBBIES:
>   Tennis, World War II history, advising church search committees; author: *In
>   Search of a Leader: The Complete Search Committee Guide Book*

EMPLOYMENT HISTORY:
>   1979 to present: Robert W. Dingman Company, Inc.
>   1974 to 1979: Vice President and Partner, Billington, Fox & Ellis
>   1966 to 1974: Vice President and Partner, Wilkinson, Sedwick & Yelverton
>   1950 to 1966: Manager, Arthur Young & Company, Inc.
>   1951 to 1961: Personnel positions in industry, government, and education

WHAT I LOOK FOR IN GENERAL IN A CANDIDATE:

What I Look For in a candidate varies according to what I have learned about my client. One client may require a highly competitive, intense, and politically adept type of person, while another client may favor someone who is more of a team builder, or a values-oriented person who devotes time to the family and community.

The best possible fit is based on shared values, compatible style, and company goals that allow the candidate to see his or her own goals to be congruent. When there is a shared vision, then the other important factors lie in finding qualities that fit the client's "comfort zone." Search consultants seldom make errors in matters of basic technical competence because these are so easily checked out. Our judgments are of special value as we discern the crucial, though sometimes subtle, things in a firm's culture that make for success.

With all candidates, I look for evidence of leadership, decisiveness, integrity, and how they have rebounded from failure. I have little time for candidates who are less than open with me, cannot identify their limitations, or have only criticism for their past superiors. As I understand that ego space the candidates require, I can then relate it to that of my client, so that both can have their needs met as they work together.

GEOGRAPHIC SCOPE OF RECRUITING ACTIVITIES:
>   Serve clients nationwide

TOTAL YEARS OF RETAINER-TYPE RECRUITING EXPERIENCE:
>   33 years

PETER DROMESHAUSER
President
Dromeshauser Associates
20 William Street
Wellesley, MA 02181
Telephone: (617) 239-0222

Date of birth: September 19, 1933

Albert's Photo Studio

EDUCATION:
Dartmouth College
B.A., history, 1955
General Motors Institute
Graduate, business, 1956

MILITARY:
Captain, United States Air Force, 1956 to 1959

SPECIAL INTERESTS AND HOBBIES:
Golf, skiing, fly-fishing, and judo; board of directors, Ventex Technologies, Calgary, Canada; President (owner and operator), Pleasant Mountain Ski Area, Bridgton, ME

EMPLOYMENT HISTORY:
1968 to present: Dromeshauser Associates
1966 to 1968: Product Manager, IBM Corporation
1964 to 1966: Branch Manager, Itek Corporation
1961 to 1964: Marketing Manager, Xerox Corporation
1959 to 1961: Supervisory Training Instructor, General Motors Corporation (Cadillac & B.O.P. Division)

WHAT I LOOK FOR IN GENERAL IN A CANDIDATE:

There are several qualities I look for in a candidate, depending of course on the desires of the client. I call it my "CLIPPER" approach: *C*ommon sense, *L*eadership, *I*ntellect, *P*ersonality, *P*resence, *E*ducation, and *R*ecord.

The only criterion, in my opinion, that is essential in *all* engagements is the "Record." If an executive is presentable, smart, and self-confident, but has a mediocre track record, he or she won't make the cut. Someone once said, "They don't draw pictures on the scorecard." I think that adage is rather applicable to our business. Success makes up for a lot of shortcomings.

GEOGRAPHIC SCOPE OF RECRUITING ACTIVITIES:
Serve clients nationwide and in Europe, Asia (Pacific Rim) and South America

TOTAL YEARS OF RETAINER-TYPE RECRUITING EXPERIENCE:
15 years

PETER DRUMMOND-HAY
Managing Director
Russell Reynolds Associates, Inc.
200 Park Avenue, 23rd Floor
New York, NY 10166
Telephone: (212) 351-2000

Date of birth: November 18, 1948

Russell Reynolds Associates, Inc.

EDUCATION:
    Cambridge University
        B.A. and M.A., history, 1970

EMPLOYMENT HISTORY:
    1982 to present: Russell Reynolds Associates, Inc.
    1975 to 1982: Arbuthnot Latham & Co., London
    1980 to 1982: Senior Vice President, Arbuthnot Export Services, Inc., New
        York
    1970 to 1975: Manager, Balfour Williamson & Co. Ltd., London and New
        York

WHAT I LOOK FOR IN GENERAL IN A CANDIDATE:

    Curiosity, a gleam in the eye, a sense of urgency, a sense of humor—self-confidence without arrogance, a measurable record.

GEOGRAPHIC SCOPE OF RECRUITING ACTIVITIES:
    Serve clients nationwide and in Europe

TOTAL YEARS OF RETAINER-TYPE RECRUITING EXPERIENCE:
    12 years

JAMES (JIM) J. DRURY III
Managing Director, Midwest Practice
SpencerStuart
401 N. Michigan Avenue, Suite 3400
Chicago, IL 60611
Telephone: (312) 822-0080

HONOREE: 1992, 1994

Date of birth: March 10, 1942

SpencerStuart

EDUCATION:

University of Notre Dame
B.S., aeronautical engineering, 1964
University of Chicago
M.B.A., marketing and finance, 1966

EMPLOYMENT HISTORY:

1984 to present: SpencerStuart
1979 to 1984: Partner, Nordeman Grimm
1974 to 1979: Principal and Director, Marketing Consulting Practice, Arthur
Young & Co.
1969 to 1974: Management Consultant, Donald R. Booz & Associates
1966 to 1969: Manager of Strategic Planning, The Boeing Company

WHAT I LOOK FOR IN GENERAL IN A CANDIDATE:

The complex business problems our clients face will require more the recruitment of "leaders" than simply "managers." I believe that the 90s will hold the opportunity for some search consultants to serve their clients more as "leadership advisors" than simply as "recruiters." Not every leadership problem will be deserving of a search. Recruiters will have to possess a broader skill set and will need to become students of both leadership and their clients' businesses.

What do I look for in candidates? Leadership capability. Vision and insight. Raw intelligence and common sense. Energy. Self-awareness and assuredness. Honesty and integrity. Sense of urgency and competitive spirit. Humor, listening skills. Likes people. Physical fitness and good health. Sound business judgment.

GEOGRAPHIC SCOPE OF RECRUITING ACTIVITIES:

Serve clients nationally and occasionally internationally

TOTAL YEARS OF RETAINER-TYPE RECRUITING EXPERIENCE:

15 years

CRAIG J. DUDLEY
President
Conrey Paul Ray International
Palo Santo No. 6
Col. Lomas Altas
Mexico, D.F. 11950
Telephone: (525) 259-6010

HONOREE: 1992, 1994

Date of birth: July 19, 1930

Conrey Interamericana, S.A. de C.V.

EDUCATION:
American   ool of Foreign Trade, Thunderbird
    Bachel   eign Trade, 1958
University of Oregon
    B.A., psychology, political science, 1955

MILITARY:
Corporal, United States Army, 1952 to 1954

SPECIAL INTERESTS AND HOBBIES:
Golf, hiking, archaeological exploration

EMPLOYMENT HISTORY:
1975 to present: Conrey Paul Ray International
1969 to 1975: Vice President, Boyden Incorporation, Latin America
1958 to 1969: Vice President–Manager Mexico, ESB Inc.
1955 to 1957: Counselor, Marion County Juvenile Department

WHAT I LOOK FOR IN GENERAL IN A CANDIDATE:

The individual's professional growth and his contributions in each responsibility held are what has attracted us in the beginning. Next we compare his management style, communications skills, and team development history to the culture and expectations of our client. I always look at problem-solving analytical skills. They vary greatly in style or presentation from person to person.

Even though the individual has an outstanding record of accomplishments, will his management style and the client's requirements predict a compatible successful relationship?

GEOGRAPHIC SCOPE OF RECRUITING ACTIVITIES:
Serve clients in the United States, Mexico, Venezuela, and Brazil

TOTAL YEARS OF RETAINER-TYPE RECRUITING EXPERIENCE:
23 years

RONALD DUKES
Partner and Director
Heidrick & Struggles, Inc.
125 South Wacker Drive
Chicago, IL 60606
Telephone: (312) 781-3789

Date of birth: December 27, 1942

Heidrick & Struggles, Inc.

EDUCATION:
    Lincoln University
        B.S., 1964

MILITARY:
    Captain, United States Army, 1966 to 1969

SPECIAL INTERESTS AND HOBBIES:
    Jogging, computers

EMPLOYMENT HISTORY:
    1980 to present: Heidrick & Struggles, Inc.
    1978 to 1980: Associate, Booz Allen & Hamilton
    1974 to 1978: Corporate Director, Recruiting and Management Develop-
        ment, American Motors Corporation
    1971 to 1974: Senior Corporate Recruiter, Emerson Electric Company
    1969 to 1971: Training and Labor Relations Supervisor, Continental Can
        Company, Central Metals Division, St. Louis

WHAT I LOOK FOR IN GENERAL IN A CANDIDATE:

- Consistent track record
- Mental toughness
- Self-confidence in one's ability, and more important, a sense of self
- Professional and personal maturity
- A sense of humor and at least a modicum of humility
- Ability to delegate and get things done through others
- Good physical fitness
- Good oral skills
- Courage and willingness to take on tough issues and, if necessary, be a minority of one
- Personal integrity
- Possess a bottom-line focus without forgetting that it is achieved through people

GEOGRAPHIC SCOPE OF RECRUITING ACTIVITIES:
    Serve clients nationwide

TOTAL YEARS OF RETAINER-TYPE RECRUITING EXPERIENCE:
    16 years

MICHAEL S. DUNFORD
Vice President
Korn/Ferry International
120 S. Riverside Plaza, Suite 918
Chicago, IL 60606
Telephone: (312) 726-1841

Korn/Ferry International

HONOREE: 1990, 1992, 1994

Date of birth: October 7, 1944

EDUCATION:
Stout State University
B.S., business administration, 1968
University of Wisconsin
M.B.A., marketing, 1971

MILITARY:
Ensign, United States Navy, 1968 to 1969

SPECIAL INTERESTS AND HOBBIES:
Christian Business Men's Committee of USA, Knights of Columbus, church
programs, running, tennis

EMPLOYMENT HISTORY:
1992 to present: Korn/Ferry International
1989 to 1992: President, Michael S. Dunford, Inc.
1978 to 1989: Partner, Lamalie Associates, Inc.
1973 to 1978: Associate, Booz, Allen & Hamilton, Inc.
1971 to 1973: Marketing Manager, Refrigerated Foods Division, The Pillsbury
Co.
1971: Marketing Representative, Computer System Division, The RCA Corporation

WHAT I LOOK FOR IN GENERAL IN A CANDIDATE:

Each assignment naturally comes with its specific requirements; however, there
are several key elements that we look for in all executive candidates. These can be
divided into three categories: personality traits, professional capabilities, and personal interests. Our primary focus centers on the individual's personality and character. Integrity, positive attitude, maturity, and strong communication and listening
skills are heavily weighted. We look for a balance between these traits and humility,
common sense, demeanor, confidence, and the ability to relate with others.

Professionally speaking, we examine previous employment experience as an
indication of current functional and industry knowledge and future potential.
Decision-making abilities, judgment, leadership and management skills, a team
orientation, and how one handles financial and corporate success/disappoint-
ment are also key factors. The individual's major strengths and developmental
areas, along with career interests and motivations, are evaluated and identified.

Personal responsibilities and interests such as family, religious activities, community involvement, and hobbies demonstrate the balanced lifestyle that we seek
in a healthy, integrated executive.

GEOGRAPHIC SCOPE OF RECRUITING ACTIVITIES:
Serve clients nationwide and the Far East, Europe, Mexico, and Canada

TOTAL YEARS OF RETAINER-TYPE RECRUITING EXPERIENCE:
16 years

BERT H. EARLY
President
Early Cochran & Olson, Inc.
55 East Monroe Street, Suite 4530
Chicago, IL 60603-5805
Telephone: (312) 236-6868

HONOREE: 1992, 1994

Date of birth: July 17, 1922

EDUCATION:
Duke University
A.B., history, 1946
Harvard Law School
LL.B., converted to J.D., 1949

Stuart-Rodgers Reilly

MILITARY:
First Lieutenant, United States Army Air Corps, 1943 to 1945

SPECIAL INTERESTS AND HOBBIES:
Participation in activities of a number of legal education and legal research
organizations and Bar associations; music, theater, travel

EMPLOYMENT HISTORY:
1994 to present: Early Cochran & Olson, Inc.
1985 to 1994: Bert H. Early Associates, Inc.
1981 to 1985: President, Wells International
1962 to 1981: Executive Director, American Bar Association
1957 to 1962: Associate General Counsel, Island Creek Coal Company
1949 to 1957: Associate, Fitzpatrick, Marshall, Huddleston & Bolen

WHAT I LOOK FOR IN GENERAL IN A CANDIDATE:

After carefully evaluating and determining a client's needs through a series
of comprehensive interviews, we develop search specifications to guide our
research in identifying those who most closely match the needs of the client. We
evaluate practical experience and professional accomplishment evidenced by:

- Reputation for integrity and adherence to the highest standards of the
  legal profession.
- Broad and comprehensive legal practice experience.
- Affirmative approach to resolving legal issues.
- Managerial experience.
- Policy-level and government-service practice exposure.
- Reputation as a team player and for superior people skills.
- Academic achievement in both undergraduate and law schools.
- Community and professional organization participation.

Our goal is to present candidates who are qualified not only by academic
achievement and professional experience, but who are most likely to be compatible with the culture, style, and traditions of each client.

GEOGRAPHIC SCOPE OF RECRUITING ACTIVITIES:
Serve clients nationwide and occasionally Europe

TOTAL YEARS OF RETAINER-TYPE RECRUITING EXPERIENCE:
13 years

GEORGE R. ENNS
President
George Enns Partners Inc.
70 University Avenue, Suite 410
Toronto, Ontario M5J 2M4 Canada
Telephone: (416) 598-0012

HONOREE: 1992, 1994

Date of birth: August 10, 1936

George Enns Partners Inc.

EDUCATION:
University of Western Ontario, School of Business Administration
Honours B.A., marketing, 1959

SPECIAL INTERESTS AND HOBBIES:
Canadian art, skiing, tennis, fitness, travel

EMPLOYMENT HISTORY:
1983 to present: George Enns Partners Inc.
1978 to 1983: Partner, Herman Smith Inc.
1976 to 1978: President, Bigelow Canada Ltd.
1974 to 1976: President, Canadian Facts Ltd.
1970 to 1974: General Manager, The Mennen Company, Ltd.
1968 to 1970: Division Vice President Marketing, The Borden Company Ltd.
1959 to 1968: Various marketing positions, General Foods Ltd.

WHAT I LOOK FOR IN GENERAL IN A CANDIDATE:

In general, I look for consistency in the pattern of position and responsibility development and the quality of the organizations in which the individual has developed his or her career.

I also look for the behavior patterns and attitudes that will help me understand the candidate's basic values, judgment, drive and motivation, leadership qualities, and personality characteristics.

GEOGRAPHIC SCOPE OF RECRUITING ACTIVITIES:
Serve clients nationally and in Russia

TOTAL YEARS OF RETAINER-TYPE RECRUITING EXPERIENCE:
16 years

LEON A. FARLEY
Managing Partner
Leon A. Farley Associates
468 Jackson Street
San Francisco, CA 94111
Telephone: (415) 989-0989

HONOREE: 1990, 1992, 1994

Date of birth: May 6, 1935

Jock McDonald

EDUCATION:
University of California at Los Angeles
    B.A., English literature, 1956
University of California School of Law
    J.D., 1959

SPECIAL INTERESTS AND HOBBIES:
Theater, tennis, travel

EMPLOYMENT HISTORY:
1976 to present: Leon A. Farley Associates
1972 to 1976: Regional Vice President, Korn/Ferry International
1970 to 1972: Executive Vice President, Business Development, ITT
    Aerospace Optical Division
1969 to 1970: Marketing Manager, WDL Division, Ford Aerospace
1967 to 1968: Financial Operations Manager, WDL Division, Ford Aerospace
1963 to 1967: Contracts Manager, Ford Aeronutronic Division
1959 to 1963: Contract Supervisor, Hughes Aircraft

WHAT I LOOK FOR IN GENERAL IN A CANDIDATE:
We are challenged to deliver candidates compatible with our clients and capable of addressing their business needs. Most important, their success must be predictable and assured.

After establishing functional competence and relevant experience, I focus on management style and personal characteristics. Do we need a leader, manager, or an administrator? How intelligent? Intuitive or analytical? Deliberate or spontaneous in decision making? Confident or risk averse?

Today's technological advances demand the highest level of interpersonal skills. The old command-and-control management style won't work. Contemporary executives must communicate superbly and have the rare ability to listen—and hear!

By exploring the early years in depth, I try to understand character development. I favor candidates who have conquered adversity, as tough experiences temper the steel of executive performance.

Intellectual breadth, cultural sensitivity, and a sense of humor are all important, but two attributes are essential. One is motivation. Does the executive have the energy and will to give our client the full measure of performance? The ultimate requirement? Integrity! Integrity! Integrity!

GEOGRAPHIC SCOPE OF RECRUITING ACTIVITIES:
Serve clients nationwide and on occasion internationally. Most recruiting for international positions is effected through membership in Penrhyn International, our twelve-firm global affiliation with offices in London, New York, Los Angeles, Hong Kong, Melbourne, Brussels, Athens, Stockholm, Tokyo, Zurich, Montreal, Toronto, and Johannesburg.

TOTAL YEARS OF RETAINER-TYPE RECRUITING EXPERIENCE:
22 years

ANNE M. FAWCETT
Managing Partner
The Caldwell Partners Amrop International
64 Prince Arthur Avenue
Toronto, Ontario M5R 1B4 Canada
Telephone: (416) 920-7702

HONOREE: 1992, 1994

Date of birth: September 30, 1945

The Caldwell Partners Amrop International

EDUCATION:
> University of Western Ontario
>> B.S., 1967

SPECIAL INTERESTS AND HOBBIES:
> Swimming, hiking, reading; volunteer work: YMCA of Metropolitan Toronto, Director and Past Chair; Faculty of Administrative Studies, York University, member, Advisory Board; YMCA Canada, Director; Princess Margaret Hospital Foundation, Director

EMPLOYMENT HISTORY:
> 1975 to present: The Caldwell Partners Amrop International
> 1973 to 1975: Search Consultant, John D. Crawford & Co.
> 1969 to 1973: Search Consultant, Peat, Marwick & Partners
> 1967 to 1969: Accounting Assistant, The Bermudiana Hotel Group

WHAT I LOOK FOR IN GENERAL IN A CANDIDATE:

Personal qualities: Solid sense of self-worth, quality and duration of relationships, energy, stamina, hard work ethic, signs of striving and self-development, good listener, personal impact and salesmanship, a giver rather than a taker, optimist, pragmatist.

Track record: Life history of leadership, risk taking—successes/failures, development of people and productive, happy organizations, community contribution, family circumstances, signs of creativity/innovation.

Vision: Ability to dream, execution and achievement of dreams in any aspect of life, diverse interests, curiosity, sense of humor.

GEOGRAPHIC SCOPE OF RECRUITING ACTIVITIES:
> Serve clients nationwide and internationally, primarily the United States and Mexico

TOTAL YEARS OF RETAINER-TYPE RECRUITING EXPERIENCE:
> 24 years

JOHN R. FERNEBORG
President
Ferneborg & Associates Inc.
555 Twin Dolphin Drive, Suite 190
Redwood City, CA 94065
Telephone: (415) 637-8100

Date of birth: February 23, 1943

Ferneborg & Associates, Inc.

EDUCATION:
North Park College
B.S., 1964

SPECIAL INTERESTS AND HOBBIES:
Youth volunteer work, golf, bicycling, reading

EMPLOYMENT HISTORY:
1994 to present: Ferneborg & Associates Inc.
1980 to 1994: Cofounder and Partner, Smith, Goerss & Ferneborg
1974 to 1980: Senior Vice President, Heidrick & Struggles, Inc.
1973 to 1974: Vice President, Bateman Eichler & Co.
1968 to 1973: Assistant Vice President, Walston & Co.
1966 to 1968: Teacher, Chicago Board of Education

WHAT I LOOK FOR IN GENERAL IN A CANDIDATE:

Every search is unique, but there are certain general characteristics that I look for in all candidates. I look for a person who is bright, ethical, and of high integrity. I have found these attributes build confidence with co-workers. I also look for individuals who are good at developing team members and delegating responsibilities appropriately—good communication and people skills are key to this.

I identify candidates with a positive attitude who take a sense of pride and ownership in their organizations and are willing to go the distance through both good and bad times.

Finally, I look for candidates with an outstanding track record of success who come from highly regarded, well-managed industry leaders. These types of candidates bring an "added value" to my clients.

GEOGRAPHIC SCOPE OF RECRUITING ACTIVITIES:
Serve clients nationwide

TOTAL YEARS OF RETAINER-TYPE RECRUITING EXPERIENCE:
20 years

RICHARD M. FERRY
Chairman/CEO
Korn/Ferry International
1800 Century Park East, Suite 900
Los Angeles, CA 90067
Telephone: (310) 843-4111

HONOREE: 1990, 1992, 1994

Date of birth: September 26, 1937

Korn/Ferry International

EDUCATION:
> Kent State University
>> B.S., business administration, 1959

SPECIAL INTERESTS AND HOBBIES:
> Outside boards of directors, community service, education, golf

EMPLOYMENT HISTORY:
> 1969 to present: Korn/Ferry International
> 1965 to 1969: Partner, Peat, Marwick, Mitchell & Co.

WHAT I LOOK FOR IN GENERAL IN A CANDIDATE:

I believe that the men and women who will lead any enterprise of the 21st century must possess a broad understanding of history, culture, language, technology, and human relations. The future opportunities belong to those who can think globally, articulate vision, manage the nuts and bolts of everyday business, communicate with all levels of society and government, and not be influenced by conventional wisdom. They must be sensitive to the political and cultural realities of others and have a successful profit-making track record. Additionally, I look for a high level of intelligence, creativity, strong initiative, discipline, and good old-fashioned ethics.

GEOGRAPHIC SCOPE OF RECRUITING ACTIVITIES:
> Serve clients nationwide and worldwide—general management and director assignments

TOTAL YEARS OF RETAINER-TYPE RECRUITING EXPERIENCE:
> 25+ years

ROBERT M. FLANAGAN
President
Robert M. Flanagan & Associates, Ltd.
Fields Lane, JMK Building
North Salem, NY 10560
Telephone: (914) 277-7210

HONOREE: 1990, 1992, 1994

Date of birth: March 19, 1940

Robert M. Flanagan & Associates, Ltd.

EDUCATION:
Saint Anselm College, New Hampshire
A.B., economics, 1962

SPECIAL INTERESTS AND HOBBIES:
Golf

EMPLOYMENT HISTORY:
1991 to present: Robert M. Flanagan & Associates, Ltd.
1980 to 1991: Paul Stafford Associates, Ltd.
1966 to 1980: Principal, Booz, Allen & Hamilton
1965 to 1966: Operations Manager, Milton Bradley Co.
1963 to 1965: Systems Analyst, American Mutual Insurance Co.
1962 to 1963: Operations Trainee, New England Merchants National Bank

WHAT I LOOK FOR IN GENERAL IN A CANDIDATE:

- Specific accomplishments in his or her field of endeavor.
- Quality of the candidate's background vis-à-vis education; organizations he or she has been associated with; outside interests, including civic and public service activities.
- An appropriate "fit" with the client organization relative to his or her experience in dealing with issues, problems, and circumstances that the candidate will be facing if appointed to the position.
- A record of success in the candidate's background beginning early in his or her career and including academics, athletics, early work experience, and progression through his or her professional career.
- Leadership skills.

GEOGRAPHIC SCOPE OF RECRUITING ACTIVITIES:
Serve clients nationwide and in Europe and the United Kingdom

TOTAL YEARS OF RETAINER-TYPE RECRUITING EXPERIENCE:
20 years

J. DANIEL FORD
Executive Vice President and Partner
Witt/Kieffer, Ford, Hadelman & Lloyd
2015 Spring Road, Suite 510
Oak Brook, IL 60521
Telephone: (708) 990-1370

HONOREE: 1990, 1994

Date of birth: August 22, 1942

EDUCATION:
>   Jamestown College, North Dakota
>   B.S., mathematics, 1964
>   University of Chicago
>   M.B.A., health care administration, 1971

Witt/Kieffer, Ford, Hadelman & Lloyd

MILITARY:
>   Lieutenant (Naval Aviator), United States Naval Reserve, 1964 to 1969

SPECIAL INTERESTS AND HOBBIES:
>   Family, church, music, photography, travel, and sports

EMPLOYMENT HISTORY:
>   1984 to present: Witt/Kieffer, Ford, Hadelman & Lloyd
>   1977 to 1984: Vice President, Western Region, Witt Associates
>   1973 to 1976: Executive Director, Fox Valley Hospital Planning Council
>   1971 to 1973: Director, Emergency Medical Services Planning, Chicago Hospital Council

WHAT I LOOK FOR IN GENERAL IN A CANDIDATE:

Values the person lives by (personal and professional).
Self-esteem—the person feels good about himself or herself.
Positive attitude about life and people.
Key influences on the person during his or her life (e.g., who would comprise a personal board of directors?).
Self-assessment—person's ability to assess his or her own life.
Leadership, business, and communications skills (with strong emphasis on listening skills).
Self-starter, high energy level, assertive.
Quality of personal life, including marriage (if applicable).
Career path understandable, productive, and generally positive.
How he or she spends time when not working (hobbies, interests, personal-time activities).
Appropriate balance to life (work, personal, family, community, church, etc.).

GEOGRAPHIC SCOPE OF RECRUITING ACTIVITIES:
>   Clients nationwide

TOTAL YEARS OF RETAINER-TYPE RECRUITING EXPERIENCE:
>   16 years

DULANY "DUKE" FOSTER, JR.
Managing Director
Korn/Ferry International
1 Landmark Square
Stamford, CT 06901
Telephone: (203) 359-3350

HONOREE: 1992, 1994

Date of birth: October 28, 1934

Korn/Ferry International

EDUCATION:
> Colgate University
>   B.A., liberal arts, 1956
> Hofstra University
>   M.B.A., management, 1964

MILITARY:
> First Lieutenant/Pilot, United States Air Force, 1956 to 1959

SPECIAL INTERESTS AND HOBBIES:
> Tennis, water sports, travel, board of directors service

EMPLOYMENT HISTORY:
> 1971 to present: Korn/Ferry International
> 1965 to 1971: Manager, Executive Search, Touche Ross & Co.
> 1959 to 1965: Manager, Planning and Control, Grumman Aircraft Engineer-
>   ing Corp.

WHAT I LOOK FOR IN GENERAL IN A CANDIDATE:

> The very best fit between individual, the position, and the hiring executive.
> The general areas that are key to my candidate evaluation include:

> First impression—appearance, confidence, presence, openness, friendliness,
>   and honesty.
> Leadership—ability to articulate a vision, gain the team's support, organize,
>   inspire, and lead the team.
> Management—a track record of planning, controlling, recruiting, develop-
>   ing, and winning in a competitive business environment.
> Knowledge—having accumulated through education and experience the
>   required body of knowledge to excel.
> Balance—between family, personal, and business needs and pressures.
> Fit—with the company management and culture, or if required, the ability to
>   change both.
> Intelligence—quickly grasps the essentials; demonstrably bright, intuitive.
> Communications—superior oral and written skills.
> Luck—"to deserve victory."

GEOGRAPHIC SCOPE OF RECRUITING ACTIVITIES:
> Serve clients nationwide

TOTAL YEARS OF RETAINER-TYPE RECRUITING EXPERIENCE:
> 28 years

AMANDA C. FOX
Partner
Paul Ray Berndtson, Inc.
10 S. Riverside Plaza, Suite 720
Chicago, IL 60606
Telephone: (312) 876-0730

Date of birth: November 8, 1945

EDUCATION:
Randolph-Macon Woman's College
B.A., 1967

SPECIAL INTERESTS AND HOBBIES:
Opera, classical music, art

EMPLOYMENT HISTORY:

Paul Ray Berndtson, Inc.

1988 to present: Paul Ray Berndtson, Inc.
1986 to 1988: Partner, Lamalie Associates
1980 to 1986: Vice President, Human Resources & Administration, Blue Cross/Blue Shield Association
1978 to 1980: Manager, Employee Services, Standard Oil Company (AMOCO)
1974 to 1978: Employee Relations Manager, *Chicago Sun-Times/Daily News*
1972 to 1974: Labor Relations Manager, New York Post Corporation
1969 to 1972: Assistant Personnel Manager, American Home Products Corporation
1967 to 1969: Personnel Recruiter, Home Life Insurance Company

WHAT I LOOK FOR IN GENERAL IN A CANDIDATE:

Several factors are key in the identification of a leader. The first is focus: Executives who are able to tell their story in a straightforward manner and think of their efforts in terms of results are likely to use the same discipline when focusing on a business issue. Intellectual capacity and curiosity are important. They need to be combined with integrated thinking: the ability to see the whole from the parts. Without integrated thinking, an executive's capacity to "think outside the box" may be limited.

An executive's track record should demonstrate that he or she can deal with ambiguity and uncertainty. Successful executives can not only deal with these issues, they can guide others through them. An executive's ability to make commitments both professionally and personally is important to ascertain. The capacity to commit on both levels can provide a key insight on the executive's prospects for long-term success.

Finally, and most important, is determining the value system that drives the executive. It must be consistent with the client's value system if the relationship between the two will stand the test of time. Without common values, the pressures of business will eventually crack the relationship.

GEOGRAPHIC SCOPE OF RECRUITING ACTIVITIES:
Serve clients nationwide

TOTAL YEARS OF RETAINER-TYPE RECRUITING EXPERIENCE:
8 years

DAVID P. FRANCIS
Partner/Director
Heidrick & Struggles, Inc.
245 Park Avenue
New York, NY 10167
Telephone: (212) 867-9876

Date of birth: April 24, 1940

Heidrick & Struggles, Inc.

EDUCATION:
United States Military Academy
B.S., engineering, 1962
Harvard Business School
M.B.A., 1970

MILITARY:
Captain, United States Air Force, 1962 to 1968

EMPLOYMENT HISTORY:
1981 to present: Heidrick & Struggles, Inc.
1978 to 1981: Manager, Consumer Financing, GE Capital Corp., General Electric Co.
1975 to 1978: Vice President, BDSI (Venture Capital Subsidiary), General Electric Co.
1972 to 1975: Manager, Planning, Corporate Research & Development, General Electric Co.
1968 to 1972: Manager, Manufacturing, Inertial Instrumentation Division, Systron-Donner Corp.

WHAT I LOOK FOR IN GENERAL IN A CANDIDATE:

In three words: background, balance, and leadership. Background includes education and what they have done with it as well as early career experience, especially "hands-on" roles where in-depth knowledge of management process is developed. Balance encompasses the whole person, not just the business person. Family, personal interests, achievements, and goals outside of the work environment are "quality" indicators as well as indicators of how someone can adapt in a complex organization in changing times.

Leadership is the quality that moves a candidate ahead of other excellent managers on my slate. The insight and understanding of the process of leadership and the ability to effectively employ this process is what truly differentiates candidates.

GEOGRAPHIC SCOPE OF RECRUITING ACTIVITIES:
Serve clients nationwide and in Europe

TOTAL YEARS OF RETAINER-TYPE RECRUITING EXPERIENCE:
12 years

JOHN W. FRANKLIN, JR.
Managing Director
Russell Reynolds Associates, Inc.
1700 Pennsylvania Avenue, N.W., Suite 850
Washington, DC 20006
Telephone: (202) 628-2150

HONOREE: 1992, 1994

Date of birth: May 24, 1941

EDUCATION:
Amherst College
B.A., English, 1963
Johns Hopkins School of Advanced
International Studies
M.A., 1968

SPECIAL INTERESTS AND HOBBIES:
Sailing, bicycling, reading, opera

EMPLOYMENT HISTORY:
1979 to present: Russell Reynolds Associates, Inc.
1973 to 1979: Executive Vice President and Director, Simmons Associates
1968 to 1973: Management Consultant, American Technical Assistance Corp.
1967 to 1968: International Relations Officer, U.S. Department of State,
Agency for International Development
1963 to 1965: Volunteer, Nepal Group II, Peace Corps

WHAT I LOOK FOR IN GENERAL IN A CANDIDATE:

After twenty years in the business, one is struck by four things. First, native intelligence often correlates to success, of course depending on the function. Put differently, a hard driver without a quick and sharp brain can be dangerous. I find myself listening to the orderliness and logic of a person's thought process. Second, energy and enthusiasm are contagious and often characteristics of a strong leader. The higher the level of recruiting one does, the more one recognizes the need for these infectious characteristics. Third, interviewing skills are distinctly different from professional competence. I put less emphasis on the interview and more on third-party referrals. In this day of significant job movement, unemployment, and "high-level" people looking hard for jobs, there are a number of mediocre executives who become quite skillful at interviewing. The guts of the recruiting business lies in referencing. Fourth, long-term client relationships to us in the recruiting business permit recognition of the personal characteristics which work within a given organization. If one is unfortunate enough to have lots of clients where one-time transactions are the rule, this calibration is not possible. However, with companies with significant hiring appetites, the recruiter has the opportunity to apply value-added judgments in depth and on a consistent basis.

GEOGRAPHIC SCOPE OF RECRUITING ACTIVITIES:
Serve clients nationwide and in Europe and Asia

TOTAL YEARS OF RETAINER-TYPE RECRUITING EXPERIENCE:
20 years

SANFORD I. GADIENT
President
Huntress Real Estate Executive Search
P.O. Box 8667
Kansas City, MO 64114
Telephone: (913) 451-0464

HONOREE: 1990, 1994

Date of birth: February 7, 1936

Huntress Real Estate Executive Search

EDUCATION:
Arizona State University
B.S., business administration, 1956
University of Pennsylvania, The Wharton School
M.B.A., finance and banking, 1978

SPECIAL INTERESTS AND HOBBIES:
Antique collecting (particularly Oriental pieces and art glass), golf, tennis, skin diving, travel

EMPLOYMENT HISTORY:
1979 to present: Huntress Real Estate Executive Search
1966 to 1979: President, Condominium-Commercial Mortgages, Inc.
1962 to 1966: Executive Vice President, Financial Corp. of Arizona
1961 to 1962: Controller, Guaranty Bank
1960 to 1961: Manager, Administrative Services, Arthur Anderson & Company
1959 to 1960: Management Consultant, McKinsey & Company
1957 to 1958: Budget Specialist, General Electric Co., Computer Department

WHAT I LOOK FOR IN GENERAL IN A CANDIDATE:

In general, in recruiting candidates I try to determine the proper organizational fit for candidates to match clients' needs and objectives. Particular attention should be given to the value-added concept whereby candidates would be able to demonstrate specific accomplishments achieved to produce bottom-line earnings and positive results for every employer. Obvious factors such as age, education, experience, references, appearance, willingness to travel, aggressiveness, people skills, teamwork approach, and interviewing presence are important. Equally important, but sometimes more difficult to assess, are leadership skills, loyalty, perseverance in the face of adversity, stability, family support, negotiating abilities, work habits, and problem-solving skills. Perfect candidates are few and far between; it is the executive recruiter's responsibility to fully advise the client on each candidate's strengths and weaknesses relative to the position being filled.

GEOGRAPHIC SCOPE OF RECRUITING ACTIVITIES:
Serve clients nationwide and in English-language countries

TOTAL YEARS OF RETAINER-TYPE RECRUITING EXPERIENCE:
14 years

JAY GAINES
President
Jay Gaines & Company, Inc.
598 Madison Avenue
New York, NY 10022
Telephone: (212) 308-9222

HONOREE: 1990, 1992, 1994

Date of birth: April 18, 1947

Fred Marcus Inc.

EDUCATION:
>   George Washington University
>   B.A., psychology, 1968
>   Columbia University
>   M.A., industrial psychology, 1970

SPECIAL INTERESTS AND HOBBIES:
>   Boating, skiing, bicycling, reading

EMPLOYMENT HISTORY:
>   1982 to present: Jay Gaines & Co., Inc.
>   1976 to 1982: Vice President, Oliver and Rozner
>   1972 to 1976: Associate Recruiter, Halbrecht Associates
>   1968 to 1972: Teacher, Sixth Grade Special Service School, NY Board of
>   Education

WHAT I LOOK FOR IN GENERAL IN A CANDIDATE:

We look first for performance. The individual should be performing at or near the top of her peer group with a demonstrated record of substantive accomplishments relative to the needs of the particular client and assignment. Accomplishments must demonstrate initiative, staying power, and consistency. Personal and professional integrity are of absolute importance. We are most comfortable with individuals who have a well-developed sense of themselves. That includes understanding where they are today, why they have been successful in the past, recognizing the situations in which they operate best, and understanding the characteristics that differentiate them from their peers.

It also includes an ability to define and articulate a professional value system—what one wants to achieve, the rewards that are meaningful, and how they generally go about achieving it. We place an extremely high premium on thoughtfulness and insight. We look for and value in-depth professional/functional expertise combined with the instincts that come with seasoning and successful experience. We seek out a work ethic and commitment level that is substantially higher than the norm. However, we value the individual who has successfully managed his or her career along with their personal lives. We want someone who ideally can bring an additional dimension and add substantial value to our client's organization. We want that person to deliver and be counted upon over a long period of time.

GEOGRAPHIC SCOPE OF RECRUITING ACTIVITIES:
>   Serve clients nationwide and United Kingdom, Europe

TOTAL YEARS OF RETAINER-TYPE RECRUITING EXPERIENCE:
>   21 years

JOHN T. GARDNER
Managing Partner–Industrial Practice
Heidrick & Struggles, Inc.
125 S. Wacker Drive, Suite 2800
Chicago, IL 60606
Telephone: (312) 372-8811

HONOREE: 1992, 1994

Date of birth: June 21, 1943

EDUCATION:
Georgia Institute of Technology
B.S., industrial management, 1965
Harvard University, Graduate School
of Business

John Reilly Photography

M.B.A., 1970

MILITARY:
First Lieutenant, United States Army, 1966 to 1968

SPECIAL INTERESTS AND HOBBIES:
Tennis, reading

EMPLOYMENT HISTORY:
1992 to present: Heidrick & Struggles, Inc.
1986 to 1992: Managing Partner, Lamalie Associates, Inc.
1982 to 1986: Vice President, Ceramics and Planning Manager, Lighting,
General Electric Co.
1980 to 1982: Senior Vice President, Fotomat Corporation
1977 to 1980: General Manager, Ophthalmic Instrument Business, Director
of Marketing, American Optical Group, Warner Lambert Company
1973 to 1977: Engagement Manager, McKinsey & Company
1972 to 1973: Vice President, Cole National Corporation
1970 to 1972: Divisional Merchandise Manager, Rike's, Federated
Department Stores

WHAT I LOOK FOR IN GENERAL IN A CANDIDATE:

Before any candidate is evaluated, it is important to develop a comprehensive
knowledge of the business, the culture of the client, and the job content of the
specific position. I then assess the candidate's experience base to ensure the requisite technical skills and background. Second, through a combination of in-
depth interviewing and extensive reference checking, I look for a compatible style
and value system. Finally, I look for certain individual characteristics that are
essential for virtually all successful senior executive placements:

- Mental capacity and toughness—the intellect and "street smarts" to get
the job done.
- Vision and passion—the ability to see and internally feel where the business needs to go and an unswerving drive to get there.
- Leadership, self-confidence, communication skills, and maturity—the
ability to motivate others through diplomacy and personal example.
- Integrity—unquestioned on both a personal and professional level.

GEOGRAPHIC SCOPE OF RECRUITING ACTIVITIES:
Serve clients nationwide

TOTAL YEARS OF RETAINER-TYPE RECRUITING EXPERIENCE:
9 years

CLAIRE W. GARGALLI
Vice Chairman
The Diversified Search Companies
One Commerce Square
2005 Market Street, Suite 3300
Philadelphia, PA 19103
Telephone: (215) 656-3555

Date of birth: December 3, 1942

The Diversified Search Companies

EDUCATION:
Middlebury College
B.A., economics, 1964

SPECIAL INTERESTS AND HOBBIES:
Travel, art, music, reading, cooking, tennis, golf

EMPLOYMENT HISTORY:
1990 to present: The Diversified Search Companies
1984 to 1990: Chief Operating Officer, Equimark
1964 to 1984: Executive Vice President, Fidelity Bank

WHAT I LOOK FOR IN GENERAL IN A CANDIDATE:

When I look for a candidate, it is always most critical to understand all of the dimensions that the client is actually seeking. Aligning these needs with candidate qualifications and capabilities is critical to a successful search. In general, when seeking candidates for leadership positions, I am looking for specific experiences in which the individual can be credited with having achieved an outcome as a result of his or her direction. Other evidences of leadership include the ability to create a vision that will move the organization forward, to change an organization, and to communicate in a fashion that others will follow. The ability to communicate one's own experience is often a good indicator of the ability to communicate well within an organization. A sense of self-confidence, personal integrity, and commitment to the mission of the organization are key ingredients for success.

GEOGRAPHIC SCOPE OF RECRUITING ACTIVITIES:
Serve clients nationwide

TOTAL YEARS OF RETAINER-TYPE RECRUITING EXPERIENCE:
4 years

DEBRA S. GERMAINE
Vice President
Gilbert Tweed Associates, Inc.
233 Needham Street
Newton, MA 02164
Telephone: (617) 965-5770

Date of birth: August 9, 1953

Gilbert Tweed Associates, Inc.

SPECIAL INTERESTS AND HOBBIES:
Scuba diving, reading

EMPLOYMENT HISTORY:
1990 to present: Gilbert Tweed Associates, Inc.
1977 to 1990: Director, Executive Search, Digital Equipment, Inc. Corporation

WHAT I LOOK FOR IN GENERAL IN A CANDIDATE:

The pace of technology change, competitive challenges, and a global environment require a combination of technical and management skills. Problem-solving ability, use of available resources, ability to be effective under pressure, agility, creativity, and the ability to manage the whole spectrum of alliances.

Personal characteristics that cut across all functions include integrity, intelligence, perseverance, social graces, and understanding of human behavior.

GEOGRAPHIC SCOPE OF RECRUITING ACTIVITIES:
Serve clients nationwide and internationally

TOTAL YEARS OF RETAINER-TYPE RECRUITING EXPERIENCE:
4 years

RONALD G. GOERSS
President
Ronald G. Goerss & Associates, Inc.
388 Market Street, Suite 500
San Francisco, CA 94111
Telephone: (415) 296-3899

HONOREE: 1992, 1994

Date of birth: April 10, 1929

EDUCATION:
Concordia Seminary, St. Louis
B.A., 1951; Master of Divinity, 1954
University of Southern California
M.A., 1961

Expressly Portraits

SPECIAL INTERESTS AND HOBBIES:
Tennis, reading, music (jazz and classical), travel, family activities

EMPLOYMENT HISTORY:
1994 to present: Ronald G. Goerss & Associates, Inc.
1980 to 1994: Smith, Goerss & Ferneborg, Inc.
1971 to 1980: Associate and Vice President, Heidrick & Struggles, Inc.
1970 to 1971: Vice President, MRG Corporation
1966 to 1970: Manager of Staff Recruitment, McKinsey & Company, Inc.
1963 to 1966: Pastor, University Lutheran Chapel, UCLA
1960 to 1963: Pastor, Immanuel Lutheran Church, Valparaiso, Indiana
1954 to 1960: Lutheran Campus Pastor, UCLA and USC

WHAT I LOOK FOR IN GENERAL IN A CANDIDATE:
Does this candidate have the appropriate skills and experience for the position the client seeks to fill?

Is this person bright, and what is the quality of his or her education?

Does he or she have a career to date which demonstrates accomplishment, progression, and leadership ability that portend well for a future with the client organization?

Has the candidate stayed abreast of industry, economic, and societal developments that are pertinent? Is he or she curious about changes taking place and how to deal with them?

What are this person's outside interests?

What personal traits and values does this person have? Are they fitting for the client culture?

Does this person have self-confidence, poise, self-esteem, energy, and a sense of humor?

Are there any personal constraints that would prevent this person from relocating?

Is this a presentable candidate, and how does he or she measure up to the panel of candidates being developed?

GEOGRAPHIC SCOPE OF RECRUITING ACTIVITIES:
Serve clients nationwide

TOTAL YEARS OF RETAINER-TYPE RECRUITING EXPERIENCE:
23 years

TRINA D. GORDON
Partner
Boyden
180 N. Stetson, Suite 5050
Chicago, IL 60601
Telephone: (312) 565-1300

Boyden

Date of birth: December 9, 1954

EDUCATION:
Auburn University
B.S., 1975; M.A., 1976

SPECIAL INTERESTS AND HOBBIES:
Running, strength training, riding,
travel, music, reading

EMPLOYMENT HISTORY:
1989 to present: Boyden
1977 to 1989: Vice President, William H. Clark Associates, Inc.

WHAT I LOOK FOR IN GENERAL IN A CANDIDATE:

In an interview, I seek to identify and assess the following:

- A management and personal style that is complementary to the client organization.
- Depth of intellect, a clear, strategic thought process that employs excellent communications skills.
- Creativity, flexibility, energy—traits that exemplify leadership.
- A capacity for introspection that reveals a strong sense of self—both professionally and personally.
- Evidence of the functional experience requisite to the defined position as well as to the organization's future needs.

As executive search consultants, we act in partnership with clients in the selection of executive leadership, the most important resource of any organization. A successful search process is predicated on our ability to thoroughly understand, and subsequently represent, the client's culture, mission, and strategy within the context of a candidate evaluation. As an extension of the client, it is our responsibility to exercise value-added judgment in our assessment of all the variables that comprise an interview, and that responsibility extends to both client and candidate. Our reputation may rest on the successful completion of an assignment and ultimately on our candidate's contribution to the client's organization, but our value lies in the integrity and commitment we bring to the client and consultant partnership.

GEOGRAPHIC SCOPE OF RECRUITING ACTIVITIES:
Serve clients nationwide and the United Kingdom, Europe, Asia

TOTAL YEARS OF RETAINER-TYPE RECRUITING EXPERIENCE:
17 years

WILLIAM E. GOULD
Managing Director
Gould & McCoy, Inc.
300 Park Avenue
New York, NY 10022
Telephone: (212) 688-8671

Gould & McCoy, Inc.

HONOREE: 1990, 1992, 1994

Date of birth: October 23, 1932

EDUCATION:
Williams College, Massachusetts
B.A., chemistry, physics, 1957
Harvard Business School
M.B.A. with distinction, 1965

MILITARY:
Sergeant, 101st Airborne, United States Army, 1953 to 1955

SPECIAL INTERESTS AND HOBBIES:
International business/cultural relations, life planning, fly-fishing, hiking, skiing, Morgan cars

EMPLOYMENT HISTORY:
1973 to present: Gould & McCoy, Inc.
1969 to 1973: Vice President, Heidrick & Struggles, Inc.
1965 to 1969: Commercial Director, MackAmax Aluminum Ltd., Subsidiary of Amax Corp.
1961 to 1965: Sales Manager, Varcum Chemical Division, Reichhold Chemicals Corp.
1957 to 1961: New Products Marketing Engineer, Carborundum Company

WHAT I LOOK FOR IN GENERAL IN A CANDIDATE:

As my practice has included a blend of North America and Eastern Europe, the Middle East, and South America, cultural fit with the client is even more important due to greater potential for misunderstanding the client's culture and values. I continue to look at the person's evolvement as a human being. How does he or she cope with adversity? How mature is the person to handle complex decisions without close supervision? What is the person's track record—did he or she really do what they claimed to do? Is the person a leader or follower, and how does that fit the client's requirements? What is the person's "life plan"? Does his or her goals fit within the client's strategy, or will there be an eventual conflict? Does the person have an active life outside of business? Is he or she fulfilled, balanced, and have a positive attitude? In my many years of retainer search experience, the successful candidates have always had a healthy sense of humor.

GEOGRAPHIC SCOPE OF RECRUITING ACTIVITIES:
Serve clients nationwide and in Western Europe, Poland, Hungary, Czech Republic, Russia, Ukraine, Middle East, South America, Asia

TOTAL YEARS OF RETAINER-TYPE RECRUITING EXPERIENCE:
24 years

JOSEPH E. GRIESEDIECK
U.S. Managing Director
SpencerStuart
333 Bush Street
San Francisco, CA 94104
Telephone: (415) 495-4141

HONOREE: 1992, 1994

Date of birth: July 3, 1944

SpencerStuart

EDUCATION:
Brown University
A.B., classics, 1966

SPECIAL INTERESTS AND HOBBIES:
Automobile racing (interest; former hobby)

EMPLOYMENT HISTORY:
1985 to present: SpencerStuart
1979 to 1985: Managing Director, Russell Reynolds Associates, Inc.
1978 to 1979: Group Vice President, Alexander & Baldwin, Inc.
1966 to 1978: President and Chief Operating Officer, Falstaff Brewing Corporation

WHAT I LOOK FOR IN GENERAL IN A CANDIDATE:

Competence, spontaneity, energy level, track record, broad range of interests, education, integrity, intellectual toughness, intellectual curiosity, sense of humor, empathy, sense of self.

I have found that my most successful candidates for CEO/COO-held positions are those who have strong determination and personal self-balance. They are decisive, but interested in seeking the views of others. They are people who gravitate to a leadership role in the things which they undertake, job-related or otherwise, based on sound judgment, strong interpersonal skills, high integrity, and a drive to succeed. They are highly competitive, but not purely in an individual sense.

GEOGRAPHIC SCOPE OF RECRUITING ACTIVITIES:
Serve clients nationwide and in Europe

TOTAL YEARS OF RETAINER-TYPE RECRUITING EXPERIENCE:
15 years

PETER G. GRIMM
Managing Partner
Nordeman Grimm, Inc.
717 Fifth Avenue, 26th Floor
New York, NY 10022
Telephone: (212) 935-1000

HONOREE: 1990, 1992, 1994

Date of birth: May 23, 1933

Nordeman Grimm, Inc.

EDUCATION:
Cornell University
B.S., hotel administration, 1955

MILITARY:
First Lieutenant, Single Engine Jet Instructor Pilot, U.S. Air Force, 1956 to 1959

SPECIAL INTERESTS AND HOBBIES:
Golf, sailing, travel, reading

EMPLOYMENT HISTORY:
1968 to present: Nordeman Grimm, Inc.
1966 to 1968: Partner, Antell Wright & Nagel
1961 to 1966: Senior Associate, Cresap McCormick & Paget
1959 to 1961: Registered Representative, Merrill Lynch
1955 to 1956: Sales, General Foods

WHAT I LOOK FOR IN GENERAL IN A CANDIDATE:

The things I look for are:

Creative intelligence—a sound and logical thought process mixed with creativity.
Presence—the ability to present persuasively, one-on-one and in groups.
Energy—high energy is essential in today's competitive environment.
Work ethic—goes hand in hand with high energy.
Competitive—in whatever he or she has done in school, business, sports.
Risk tolerance—able to make decision based on incomplete analysis.
Success—the earlier the better.
Luck—I look for "lucky" executives; they usually make their own luck.
Sound basic values—honesty, sensitivity to others.
Consistency—some pattern in their lives/careers.
Balance—something to balance the business part of their lives—home, sports, travel or the like.

GEOGRAPHIC SCOPE OF RECRUITING ACTIVITIES:
Serve clients nationally and in Great Britain and Europe

TOTAL YEARS OF RETAINER-TYPE RECRUITING EXPERIENCE:
28 years

JACK L. GROBAN
Vice President and Managing Director
A.T. Kearney Executive Search
500 S. Grand, 19th Floor
Los Angeles, CA 90071
Telephone: (213) 624-8328

Date of birth: August 19, 1945

A.T. Kearney Executive Search

EDUCATION:
California State University at San Jose
B.A., advertising; minors economics and humanities, 1967
University of Southern California
M.B.A., management and organizational behavior, 1971

EMPLOYMENT HISTORY:
1993 to present: A.T. Kearney Executive Search
1989 to 1993: Founder, Jack Groban & Associates Executive Search
1982 to 1989: Senior Vice President and Manager, Los Angeles Office, Boyden International
1980 to 1981: Vice President, William H. Clark & Associates
1974 to 1980: Senior Manager, Price Waterhouse & Company
1973 to 1974: Senior Associate, Korn/Ferry International

WHAT I LOOK FOR IN GENERAL IN A CANDIDATE:

The world is full of executives with great potential who, for plausible reasons, have failed to achieve their potential.

In evaluating candidates, I look for (1) a record of accomplishment, or track record of successes; (2) demonstrated ability to overcome adversity—economic, political, legislative, competitive, personal; (3) clear thinking, ability to articulate a well-considered point of view, to stay on point in a discussion; (4) balanced personality, neither everybody's friend nor a take-no-prisoners attitude, and interests and concerns beyond work; (5) agility, demonstrated ability to make course corrections as circumstances demand; and (6) expertise in their field.

GEOGRAPHIC SCOPE OF RECRUITING ACTIVITIES:
Serve clients nationwide

TOTAL YEARS OF RETAINER-TYPE RECRUITING EXPERIENCE:
21 years

JORDAN M. HADELMAN
President/Chief Operating Officer
Witt/Kieffer, Ford, Hadelman & Lloyd
2015 Spring Road, Suite 510
Oak Brook, IL 60521
Telephone: (708) 990-1370

Date of birth: December 27, 1953

Witt/Kieffer, Ford, Hadelman & Lloyd

EDUCATION:
  Georgetown University
    B.S., business administration, 1976
  George Washington University
    M.H.A., 1978

MILITARY:
  Lieutenant, United States Navy, 1978 to 1981

SPECIAL INTERESTS AND HOBBIES:
  Serve on several boards for not-for-profit organizations and play golf

EMPLOYMENT HISTORY:
  1992 to present: Witt/Kieffer, Ford, Hadelman & Lloyd
  1983 to 1992: Executive Vice President, Kieffer, Ford & Hadelman
  1981 to 1983: Senior Recruiter, Witt Associates

WHAT I LOOK FOR IN GENERAL IN A CANDIDATE:

As the nation focuses on health care reform, certain skills become more important in the selection of executives. Included in the list are candidates with strong leadership skills, a vision that is grounded in reality, strong communication skills, and an ability to manage change in a very turbulent environment. Additionally, candidates need to have uncompromising commitment to high standards of excellence, the ability to inspire organizations, empower subordinates, and push decision making as far down in an organization as possible. In addition, candidates must demonstrate courage to challenge traditional thinking, be willing to take a leadership role in the communities they serve, and have the ability to partner with other providers and institutions that, historically, at times may have been viewed as adversarial. Last, and most important, candidates must be able to integrate personal and organizational values, be able to translate the definition of values into a practical reality in order to mobilize organizations, and monitor a scope of balance in a fast-shifting, competitive marketplace.

GEOGRAPHIC SCOPE OF RECRUITING ACTIVITIES:
  Serve clients nationwide

TOTAL YEARS OF RETAINER-TYPE RECRUITING EXPERIENCE:
  13 years

PETER V. HALL
Managing Director
Chartwell Partners International, Inc.
275 Battery Street, Suite 2180
San Francisco, CA 94111
Telephone: (415) 296-0600

Date of birth: April 14, 1934

EDUCATION:
Georgetown University
B.A., economics, 1957
Stanford University
M.B.A., 1962

MILITARY: *Romaine Photography*
Ensign, United States Navy, 1957 to 1958

SPECIAL INTERESTS AND HOBBIES:
Tennis, squash

EMPLOYMENT HISTORY:
1990 to present: Chartwell Partners International, Inc.
1987 to 1990: Consultant, business planning and real estate consulting to
major California thrifts
1984 to 1986: Executive Vice President–Real Estate, Bank of America
1982 to 1984: President and Chief Operating Officer, PMI Mortgage Insurance Co.
1979 to 1982: General Partner, Weyerhaeuser Venture Company
1972 to 1979: Various positions, PMI Mortgage Corporation
1971 to 1972: President and Founder, Argus Financial Corporation
1962 to 1970: President and Founder, Chairman, Colonial Mortgage Company
1960 to 1962: Vice President, General Equity Investment Corporation
1959: Assistant Vice President, Advance Mortgage Corporation
1958: Manager, Hearth Homes

WHAT I LOOK FOR IN GENERAL IN A CANDIDATE:

I make a concerted effort to develop a thorough understanding of our client,
its business strategy and culture. Then I attempt to match closely the candidate's
personality and management style with the needs of the company.

I also look beyond the usual assignment specifications for:

- Motivation, energy and a sense of urgency.
- Solid interpersonal and team-building skills.
- Sound personal characteristics and self-awareness.
- A willingness to accept risk and make decisions.
- An ability to initiate and manage change.

The candidate should be able to present, in an orderly and logical manner, a
track record that will convince me that he or she will make a particularly valuable
contribution to my client's business. I have a bias toward those who have learned
from adversity.

GEOGRAPHIC SCOPE OF RECRUITING ACTIVITIES:
Serve clients nationwide

TOTAL YEARS OF RETAINER-TYPE RECRUITING EXPERIENCE:
4 years

DAVID G. HANSEN
Executive Vice President
Ott & Hansen, Inc.
136 S. Oak Knoll, Suite 300
Pasadena, CA 91101
Telephone: (818) 578-0551

Date of birth: February 18, 1942

Ott & Hansen, Inc.

EDUCATION:
Wheaton College
B.A., business administration, 1963
Northwestern University
M.B.A., industrial relations, 1971

MILITARY:
Lieutenant, United States Navy, 1963 to 1968

SPECIAL INTERESTS AND HOBBIES:
Biking, golf, reading, board member for various nonprofit organizations

EMPLOYMENT HISTORY:
1980 to present: Ott & Hansen, Inc.
1969 to 1980: Principal, A.T. Kearney, Inc.
1968 to 1969: Associate, Touche Ross & Co.

WHAT I LOOK FOR IN GENERAL IN A CANDIDATE:

The first thing I always look for is the match between the client's specific experience, industry, and education requirements and those of the candidate. If we have a match here, it rarely matters if the rest of the candidates can walk on water.

Once this match is found, I look for a variety of attributes, among them being:
- A demonstrated record of success.
- Chemistry—the often elusive aligning of the candidate's management style, personality, work habits, and ethics with the culture of both the corporation and the individual to whom he or she will report.
- Leadership skills as evidenced by the ability to mobilize others toward achieving a given set of objectives.
- A realistic self-assessment of who they are and where they are going. A sense of humor helps, as does a candid appraisal of their own strengths and limitations.
- Personal integrity.

GEOGRAPHIC SCOPE OF RECRUITING ACTIVITIES:
Serve clients nationwide

TOTAL YEARS OF RETAINER-TYPE RECRUITING EXPERIENCE:
26 years

DAVID O. HARBERT
President
Sweeney, Harbert & Mummert, Inc.
777 S. Harbour Island Boulevard, Suite 130
Tampa, FL 33602
Telephone: (813) 229-5360

HONOREE: 1990, 1992, 1994

Date of birth: April 14, 1940

Sweeney Harbert & Mummert, Inc.

EDUCATION:
> University of Michigan
> > B.B.A., engineering and business, 1962
> > M.B.A., finance and statistical methods, 1963

SPECIAL INTERESTS AND HOBBIES:
> Physical fitness, classical music, audio/video equipment, performance automobiles, movies, national economic policy, travel

EMPLOYMENT HISTORY:
> 1992 to present: Sweeney, Harbert & Mummert, Inc.
> 1986 to 1991: President, Sweeney Shepherd Bueschel Provus Harbert & Mummert, Inc.
> 1981 to 1986: Vice President/Managing Director, Lamalie Associates, Inc.
> 1979 to 1981: Vice President–Finance, Austin Powder Corporation
> 1977 to 1979: Vice President–Finance, Stanwood Corporation
> 1972 to 1977: President, Advisory Services Inc.
> 1968 to 1972: Manager–Finance, Celanese Corporation
> 1965 to 1968: Senior Financial Analyst, Standard Oil Company New Jersey
> 1964 to 1965: Auditor/Consultant, Arthur Andersen & Company

WHAT I LOOK FOR IN GENERAL IN A CANDIDATE:

Every search assignment is unique, based on the client involved and their specific requirements for the position. To truly achieve a successful, long-term match, candidate evaluations are necessarily comprehensive and move through several levels. The chronology tends to be the following: (1) Technical skills—does the candidate meet the position's technical requirements? Have the appropriate career steps and professional accomplishments successfully taken place? If so, I will then concentrate on: (2) Interpersonal skills and chemistry with my client—does the candidate present him- or herself in a manner compatible with the position and the environment? Typically this will include an evaluation of intelligence, aggressiveness, purpose, professionalism, poise, articulation, candor, and sense of humor. Physical presentation is also considered: clothing, physical fitness, mannerisms, and so on. I will then make judgments on: (3) The candidate's interest—will it be served? If not, he or she will probably fail in the position and therefore our client's needs will not be satisfied. (4) Recruitability—as I gain knowledge of the candidate, is it clear he or she can, in fact, be recruited, or we are wasting my client's time? (5) Promotability—what is his or her potential to grow beyond the initial position? Will this be a match in everyone's long-term interest?

GEOGRAPHIC SCOPE OF RECRUITING ACTIVITIES:
> Serve clients nationwide and selectively in Canada and Latin America

TOTAL YEARS OF RETAINER-TYPE RECRUITING EXPERIENCE:
> 13 years

ANDREW D. HART, JR.
Managing Director
Russell Reynolds Associates, Inc.
200 Park Avenue
New York, NY 10166
Telephone: (212) 351-2000

HONOREE: 1990, 1992, 1994

Date of birth: May 3, 1929

Stanford Golob

MILITARY:
First Lieutenant, United States Army, 1951 to 1954

SPECIAL INTERESTS AND HOBBIES:
Education, Republican Party politics, fund-raising, skiing, golf, tennis, reading, the arts

EMPLOYMENT HISTORY:
1970 to present: Russell Reynolds Associates, Inc.
1969 to 1970: Associate, Boyden Associates, Inc.
1962 to 1969: General Sales Manager–Carton Division, Westvaco Corp.
1958 to 1962: Eastern Regional Sales Manager–Carton Division, Federal Paper Board Co.
1954 to 1958: Sales Representative, Federal Paper Board Company

WHAT I LOOK FOR IN GENERAL IN A CANDIDATE:

In personal terms, I look for leadership ability, interpersonal/communication skills, dedication, ambition, self-confidence, integrity, and good judgment. As to professional qualifications, I am interested in self-assessment of one's principal skills and accomplishments, the results of performance appraisals, and one's management philosophy. In general management positions, I probe the extent of one's marketing, manufacturing, financial, and administrative experience as well as the achievements over a period of time in terms of financial results and the steps taken to bring those about. I am looking for individuals with a proven record of performance in jobs matching the position requirements.

GEOGRAPHIC SCOPE OF RECRUITING ACTIVITIES:
Serve clients nationwide and in Europe, the Far East, and Latin America

TOTAL YEARS OF RETAINER-TYPE RECRUITING EXPERIENCE:
24 years

JOHN HAWKINS
Managing Director
Russell Reynolds Associates, Inc.
1700 Pennsylvania Avenue, N.W., Suite 850
Washington, DC 20006
Telephone: (202) 628-2150

Date of birth: June 11, 1954

Russell Reynolds Associates, Inc.

EDUCATION:
University of Virginia
B.A., history, 1976
Amos Tuck School–Dartmouth College
M.B.A., 1982

SPECIAL INTERESTS AND HOBBIES:
My family

EMPLOYMENT HISTORY:
1990 to present: Russell Reynolds Associates, Inc.
1987 to 1990: Senior Vice President, Invitron Corporation
1982 to 1987: Vice President–Investment Banking, Alex Brown & Sons
1976 to 1980: Assistant Vice President, Irving Trust Co.

WHAT I LOOK FOR IN GENERAL IN A CANDIDATE:

Depends on the search assignment. Always look for:

- Integrity
- Intellect
- Problem-solving ability

GEOGRAPHIC SCOPE OF RECRUITING ACTIVITIES:
Serve clients nationwide and particular interest in Asia/Pacific and Western
Europe

TOTAL YEARS OF RETAINER-TYPE RECRUITING EXPERIENCE:
4 years

GARDNER W. HEIDRICK
Chairman
The Heidrick Partners, Inc.
20 N. Wacker Drive, Suite 2850
Chicago, IL 60606-3171
Telephone: (312) 845-9700

HONOREE: 1990, 1992, 1994

Date of birth: October 7, 1911

The Heidrick Partners, Inc.

EDUCATION:
University of Illinois
B.S., banking and finance, 1935

MILITARY:
United States Naval Reserve, 1945 to 1946

SPECIAL INTERESTS AND HOBBIES:
Golf, coin collecting

EMPLOYMENT HISTORY:
1982 to present: The Heidrick Partners, Inc.
1953 to 1982: Cofounder/Chairman, Heidrick & Struggles, Inc.
1951 to 1953: Associate, Booz, Allen & Hamilton
1942 to 1951: Director of Personnel, Farmland Industries
1935 to 1942: Industrial District Manager, Scott Paper Company

WHAT I LOOK FOR IN GENERAL IN A CANDIDATE:

In corporate director assignments, what the candidate will bring to the board and his or her visibility. Generally, this is a chairman or a president. Overall, it is compatibility.

Targeted are industries, functional position, geography (ability to attend meetings), minorities, and women.

In general management executives, it is primarily the same. The pattern of the past indicates the pattern of the future.

GEOGRAPHIC SCOPE OF RECRUITING ACTIVITIES:
Serve clients nationwide

TOTAL YEARS OF RETAINER-TYPE RECRUITING EXPERIENCE:
42 years

ROBERT L. HEIDRICK
President
The Heidrick Partners, Inc.
20 N. Wacker Drive, Suite 2850
Chicago, IL 60606-3171
Telephone: (312) 845-9700

HONOREE: 1990, 1992, 1994

Date of birth: June 8, 1941

The Heidrick Partners, Inc.

EDUCATION:
Duke University
    B.A., economics, 1963
University of Chicago, Graduate School of Business
    M.B.A., 1971

SPECIAL INTERESTS AND HOBBIES:
Golf, numismatics

EMPLOYMENT HISTORY:
1982 to present: The Heidrick Partners, Inc.
1977 to 1982: President, Robert Heidrick Associates, Inc.
1975 to 1977: Vice President, Spriggs & Company
1963 to 1975: Division Vice President–Marketing, American Hospital Supply
    Corp.

WHAT I LOOK FOR IN GENERAL IN A CANDIDATE:

First is the executive's image: How well groomed? The person's demeanor: assertive/retiring, etc.? In short, the individual's executive presence. Second, education and compensation are considerations. In most instances, it is important that the individual have a college degree with graduate work being a plus. However, education becomes less important as the executive gains experience and demonstrates examples of success. In terms of compensation, there should be a pattern of good upward progression. For younger people, earnings should be three or four times the person's age. Ultimately, the compatibility of the candidate with the client and the client organization is important. The individual should have "street smarts" along with leadership skills. Finally, background and experience. Does the person have a track record of success? Is he or she able to articulate accomplishments without overstating or taking too much personal credit? Is there humility? Does the career progress in a logical fashion? Do the mistakes make sense?

GEOGRAPHIC SCOPE OF RECRUITING ACTIVITIES:
Serve clients nationwide

TOTAL YEARS OF RETAINER-TYPE RECRUITING EXPERIENCE:
19 years

DONALD A. HENEGHAN
Partner
Allerton Heneghan & O'Neill
70 West Madison Street, Suite 2015
Chicago, IL 60602
Telephone: (312) 263-1075

Date of birth: June 14, 1949

Stuart-Rodgers-Reilly Photography

EDUCATION:
>   Rockhurst College
>   A.B., English, 1972
>   Northeast Missouri State University
>   M.A., English, 1977

SPECIAL INTERESTS AND HOBBIES:
>   International Association of Professional & Corporate Recruiters; University
>   of Chicago–Steering Committee, Library Society

EMPLOYMENT HISTORY:
>   1991 to present: Allerton Heneghan & O'Neill
>   1988 to 1991: Partner, Ernst & Young
>   1984 to 1988: Manager and Senior Manager, Ernst & Young
>   1980 to 1984: Research Manager, Boyden Associates Inc.
>   1976 to 1979: Writing Lab Director, Bowling Green State University

WHAT I LOOK FOR IN GENERAL IN A CANDIDATE:

Like corporations, individuals are shaped by experiences, time, and a variety of influences. Finding the right fit between client and candidate is at the center of the recruiting process. Although each individual is unique, several characteristics are consistent among those considered the *best*.

They are problem solvers; they possess the ability to listen and synthesize information effectively. The *best* can apply creativity in solving problems; essentially they can think outside of the box.

Equally important is the ability to succeed and persevere in difficult situations. I look for individuals who don't quit and possess a "can do" attitude. They know how to leave yesterday's problems behind and move forward in a positive way.

The *best* possess initiative and drive. They know how to make things happen and show results. They lead by example and are able to win support at all levels within the organization.

Above all, the *best* possess a strong sense of honesty and integrity.

GEOGRAPHIC SCOPE OF RECRUITING ACTIVITIES:
>   Serve clients nationwide and in Canada, Mexico, and Europe

TOTAL YEARS OF RETAINER-TYPE RECRUITING EXPERIENCE:
>   14 years

GEORGE W. HENN, JR.
President
G.W. Henn & Company
42 E. Gay Street, Suite 1312
Columbus, OH 43215-3119
Telephone: (614) 469-9666

HONOREE: 1990, 1992, 1994

Date of birth: November 13, 1936

G.W. Henn & Company

EDUCATION:
    Rutgers University
        B.A., American civilization, 1958

MILITARY:
    E-4 (Reserve), United States Army, 1959

SPECIAL INTERESTS AND HOBBIES:
    Breeding and exhibiting American saddlebred horses

EMPLOYMENT HISTORY:
    1987 to present: G.W. Henn & Company
    1980 to 1987: Managing Director–Cleveland, SpencerStuart Associates
    1971 to 1980: Partner, Booz, Allen & Hamilton Inc.
    1969 to 1971: Associate, David North & Associates
    1958 to 1969: Personnel Director, Great American Insurance Co.

WHAT I LOOK FOR IN GENERAL IN A CANDIDATE:

Our objective in all client assignments is to recruit the best possible candidate for the position—the candidate who can best contribute to the client's organization—short and long term.

Leading candidates have a record of significant progression through larger, well-managed companies. In addition to functional skills, the candidates have demonstrated the personal dimension to work effectively in a corporate setting while aggressively and energetically pursuing business goals and objectives.

Successful candidates consistently demonstrate leadership skills and the strategic understanding of key business issues. They are also known and regarded within their industry.

GEOGRAPHIC SCOPE OF RECRUITING ACTIVITIES:
    Serve clients nationwide and in Canada

TOTAL YEARS OF RETAINER-TYPE RECRUITING EXPERIENCE:
    24 years

RICHARD L. HERTAN
President
Executive Manning Corporation
3000 NE 30th Place, Suite 405
Fort Lauderdale, FL 33306
Telephone: (305) 561-5100

Date of birth: March 30, 1949

Executive Manning Corporation

EDUCATION:
Jacksonville University
B.S., business management, 1971

SPECIAL INTERESTS AND HOBBIES:
Fly-fishing, travel

EMPLOYMENT HISTORY:
1975 to present: Executive Manning Corporation
1973 to 1975: President, Hertan Enterprises
1972 to 1973: Expediter, Pratt & Whitney Aircraft

WHAT I LOOK FOR IN GENERAL IN A CANDIDATE:

The keys to finding the right candidate in an executive retained search are balanced between the candidate's learned skill levels and the intuitive natural leadership abilities. A harmonious whole. At the executive level, 80 percent of the time it is that intuitive learned natural ability and mutual cultural interface that make for a successful match. I also look for the following traits:

- The ability to be proficient in handling people.
- The ability to communicate and originate ideas.
- The ability to maintain a high level of energy.
- The ability to organize and run large projects.
- The ability to conceptualize objectivity and efficiency.
- The ability to generate confidence and marshal the support mechanism to ensure success.

GEOGRAPHIC SCOPE OF RECRUITING ACTIVITIES:
Serve clients nationwide

TOTAL YEARS OF RETAINER-TYPE RECRUITING EXPERIENCE:
19 years

WILLIAM A. HERTAN
Chairman and Chief Executive Officer
Executive Manning Corporation
3000 N.E. 30th Place, Suite 405
Fort Lauderdale, FL 33306
Telephone: (305) 561-5100

HONOREE: 1990, 1992, 1994

Date of birth: July 15, 1921

Executive Manning Corporation

EDUCATION:
    New York University
        B.S., industrial relations, 1943

MILITARY:
    Lieutenant Commander, United States Navy Reserve, 1941 to 1957

SPECIAL INTERESTS AND HOBBIES:
    Boating, fishing, world traveler

EMPLOYMENT HISTORY:
    1956 to present: Executive Manning Corporation
    1948 to 1956: Owner/President, Harper Associates Employment Agency

WHAT I LOOK FOR IN GENERAL IN A CANDIDATE:

    A candidate must possess a unique ability to communicate skills both verbally and in writing. This would include the ability to be open, truthful, and frank in all discussions. Stability of employment is an integral part of the evaluation as well as diversity of assignments showing a continual responsibility growth pattern. Loyalty and sincerity to both employer and subordinates, family stability, and the lack of external constraints are essential. Character and business references are part and parcel of the evaluation process; not merely references supplied by a candidate but also an in-depth check of past and present employment, scholastic, and credit records are necessary. An ability to exude confidence and convey a superior knowledge of the candidate's chosen field of endeavor is mandatory.

GEOGRAPHIC SCOPE OF RECRUITING ACTIVITIES:
    Serve clients nationwide and internationally

TOTAL YEARS OF RETAINER-TYPE RECRUITING EXPERIENCE:
    38 years

JAMES N. HEUERMAN
Vice President and Senior Partner
Korn/Ferry International
600 Montgomery Street, 31st Floor
San Francisco, CA 94111
Telephone: (415) 956-1834

HONOREE: 1990, 1992, 1994

Date of birth: August 9, 1940

Korn/Ferry International

EDUCATION:
University of Minnesota
B.S., business, 1965
M.A., hospital and health care administration, 1971

MILITARY:
Spec 4, United States Army, 1960 to 1962

SPECIAL INTERESTS AND HOBBIES:
Tennis, running, cycling, reading

EMPLOYMENT HISTORY:
1983 to present: Korn/Ferry International
1977 to 1983: Vice President and Partner, Booz, Allen & Hamilton
1972 to 1977: Principal, Arthur Young & Company
1971 to 1972: Assistant Administrator, Evanston Hospital, Illinois
1965 to 1970: Marketing Representative, IBM

WHAT I LOOK FOR IN GENERAL IN A CANDIDATE:

A series of milestones over time, which include:

- Work ethic, usually developed at a young age.
- Solid education, good schools, and accomplishment.
- Early jobs that refine analytical skills.
- Mentors who contribute to style and character.
- Employer organizations of quality and reputation.
- Demonstrated profit-and-loss responsibility and results.
- A well-developed management philosophy and style.
- A vision of one's industry that demonstrates depth of thinking.
- An ability to communicate in a clear and meaningful fashion.

GEOGRAPHIC SCOPE OF RECRUITING ACTIVITIES:
Serve clients nationwide

TOTAL YEARS OF RETAINER-TYPE RECRUITING EXPERIENCE:
10 years

HENRY G. HIGDON
Managing Partner
Higdon Associates, Inc.
230 Park Avenue, Suite 1455
New York, NY 10169
Telephone: (212) 986-4662

HONOREE: 1990, 1992, 1994

Date of birth: June 1, 1941

Higdon Associates, Inc.

EDUCATION:
> Yale University
> > B.A., American studies, 1964

MILITARY:
> Staff Sergeant, United States Marine Corps Reserve, 1964 to 1970

SPECIAL INTERESTS AND HOBBIES:
> Sports: skiing, running, squash, rugby, coaching; active in church and alumni affairs of Andover and Yale

EMPLOYMENT HISTORY:
> 1992 to present: Higdon Associates, Inc.
> 1986 to 1992: Managing Partner, Higdon, Joys & Mingle, Inc.
> 1971 to 1986: Executive Vice President, Russell Reynolds Associates, Inc.
> 1964 to 1971: Associate, Massachusetts Mutual Life Insurance Co.

WHAT I LOOK FOR IN GENERAL IN A CANDIDATE:

In general, I look for the following characteristics in candidates:

Integrity. While it would appear that this would go without saying, it can never be assumed and is the single most important characteristic for any candidate.

Intelligence. While a high level of intellect is clearly preferred, basic street smarts, savvy, and instincts are as important.

High level of energy. Energy is critically important, and assumes great stamina and endurance, and even physical fitness.

Team leadership. While most people look for team players, which is important, I believe that it is important for someone to be able to be a team builder and a team leader.

Self-confidence and inner security. I look for self-confidence, which also means that an individual can admit that one can make mistakes and realize that one is fallible.

Communications ability. People who are organized in their thought process and can present ideas with clarity and brevity.

A sense of humor. A sense of humor is absolutely essential, as it enables people to not take themselves too seriously, to have some grace under pressure, and to laugh at themselves.

Humility. Self-effacement can be an important characteristic, especially in today's world of occasionally superarrogant CEOs who may feel they can do absolutely no wrong.

Balance. I look for people who have their lives in balance, meaning that their personal, family, business, intellectual, and even spiritual existences blend well together. I am not impressed with people who are single-dimensional or monomaniacal.

GEOGRAPHIC SCOPE OF RECRUITING ACTIVITIES:
> Serve clients nationally and in North America and Europe

TOTAL YEARS OF RETAINER-TYPE RECRUITING EXPERIENCE: 24 years

MICHAEL J. HOEVEL
Partner
Poirier, Hoevel & Company
12400 Wilshire Blvd., Suite 1250
Los Angeles, CA 90025
Telephone: (310) 207-3427

HONOREE: 1990, 1992, 1994

Date of birth: September 16, 1944

Denis Trantham/Westside Studio

EDUCATION:
California State University
B.S., science, 1967

SPECIAL INTERESTS AND HOBBIES:
Family, travel, river rafting, scuba diving, snow skiing, golf

EMPLOYMENT HISTORY:
1975 to present: Poirier, Hoevel & Company
1972 to 1975: Consultant–Executive Search, Peat Marwick Main & Company
1967 to 1972: Manager of Recruiting, City of Los Angeles
1967: Management Trainee, Shell Oil Company

WHAT I LOOK FOR IN GENERAL IN A CANDIDATE:

The first and most important element that a candidate must possess is *fit*. Fit is that nondefinable asset that makes any candidate a front runner for my client. I measure this subjectively without regard to what is on an individual's resume. Since each client usually requires a different fit, I spend as much time as possible meeting and interviewing all of the people with my client who may effect or be effected by the individual who accepts this position. In addition, I look for:

- A solid employment history with excellent progression.
- Good articulation, intelligence, a sense of humor, a life outside of business, and honesty.
- An easy but assertive manner.
- Experience that meets or exceeds what my client is looking for.

GEOGRAPHIC SCOPE OF RECRUITING ACTIVITIES:
Serve clients nationwide and in Europe and Latin America

TOTAL YEARS OF RETAINER-TYPE RECRUITING EXPERIENCE:
22 years

DAVID H. HOFFMANN
President
DHR International, Inc.
10 S. Riverside Plaza, Suite 1650
Chicago, IL 60606
Telephone: (312) 782-1581

HONOREE: 1990, 1992, 1994

Date of birth: August 7, 1952

Stuart-Rodgers-Reilly Photography

EDUCATION:
> Central Missouri State University
>> B.S., 1974
>
> Pennsylvania State University
>> Executive Management Program, 1980

SPECIAL INTERESTS AND HOBBIES:
> Board member, Lawrence Hall School for Boys; youth athletics (coach various Little League organizations)

EMPLOYMENT HISTORY:
> 1989 to present: DHR International, Inc.
> 1985 to 1989: Senior Vice President/Managing Partner, Boyden International
> 1983 to 1985: Vice President/Partner, Korn/Ferry International
> 1977 to 1983: Director of Employee Relations, GATX Corporation
> 1975 to 1977: Various Human Resource positions, Pullman Inc.
> 1974 to 1975: Various Human Resource positions, Clark Equipment Company

WHAT I LOOK FOR IN GENERAL IN A CANDIDATE:

An individual who can effect change and be perceived as a change agent. A charismatic leader who achieves results. Exceptional track record of accomplishment. Exceptional communication skills, oral and written. Strong people skills—a total business acumen. A career orientation. Interests outside the job—family, civic, philanthropic, etc. A well-rounded and grounded individual. A visionary.

GEOGRAPHIC SCOPE OF RECRUITING ACTIVITIES:
> Serve clients nationwide and in Europe and Latin America

TOTAL YEARS OF RETAINER-TYPE RECRUITING EXPERIENCE:
> 11 years

JONATHAN S. HOLMAN
President and Founder
The Holman Group, Inc.
1592 Union Street, #239
San Francisco, CA 94123
Telephone: (415) 751-2700

HONOREE: 1992, 1994

Date of birth: May 26, 1945

The Holman Group, Inc.

EDUCATION:
Princeton University
A.B., politics, 1966
Stanford University Graduate School of Business
M.B.A., 1968

EMPLOYMENT HISTORY:
1981 to present: The Holman Group, Inc.
1978 to 1981: Partner, Bacci, Bennett, Gould & McCoy
1971 to 1978: Director of Human Resources, E & J Gallo Winery
1968 to 1971: Personnel Director, Pfizer, Inc.

WHAT I LOOK FOR IN GENERAL IN A CANDIDATE:

Those of us who focus our efforts on CEO-level searches face some special dilemmas, most notably the need to satisfy an entire board of directors rather than a single individual making a hiring decision. This means that there will be countervailing forces as to what defines the "perfect" candidate. The good CEO recruiter will take a strong hand in helping the board define perfection for their special set of circumstances, and then seek candidates whose strengths are the essential ones and whose weaknesses are irrelevant, fixable, or counterbalanced elsewhere in the organization.

All searches seek candidates with intelligence, diligence, and other obvious attributes. I would add four specific ones for CEOs. First, he or she must know how to make money for the enterprise; all other skills are irrelevant if this one is lacking. Second, there cannot be the slightest question about business or personal integrity. Third, references from subordinates and peers must be at least as good as those from above; bosses are the easiest to fool. Finally, a sense of humor is essential.

GEOGRAPHIC SCOPE OF RECRUITING ACTIVITIES:
Serve clients nationwide and have recruited personally for international positions, but in general I believe that these searches should be conducted by recruiters on the scene

TOTAL YEARS OF RETAINER-TYPE RECRUITING EXPERIENCE:
16 years

LAWRENCE J. HOLMES
Managing Principal
Columbia Consulting Group
Sun Life Building, 9th Floor
20 South Charles Street
Baltimore, MD 21201
Telephone: (410) 997-2525

HONOREE: 1990, 1994

Date of birth: December 19, 1941

James Ferry Photography

EDUCATION:
Old Dominion University
B.S., science/education, 1964

SPECIAL INTERESTS AND HOBBIES:
Sports, reading, Key West

EMPLOYMENT HISTORY:
1978 to present: Columbia Consulting Group (formerly Consulting Associates, Inc.)
1977 to 1978: Partner, Harold Denton Associates
1973 to 1977: President, Cantrell Associates
1969 to 1973: Director of Training and Development, Maryland Casualty Company
1966 to 1969: Loss Control Engineer, Aetna Life & Casualty
1965 to 1966: Science Teacher, Norfolk School System

WHAT I LOOK FOR IN GENERAL IN A CANDIDATE:

The primary traits and characteristics I look for in an individual are:

A successful track record.
The ability to listen.
The quality of questions the individual asks.
The direct related experience that the client wants.
A sense of humor and a personality.
An independent and competitive nature.
The technical and educational experience as it relates to the opportunity.

GEOGRAPHIC SCOPE OF RECRUITING ACTIVITIES:
Clients nationwide and through international affiliates

TOTAL YEARS OF RETAINER-TYPE RECRUITING EXPERIENCE:
20 years

WILLIAM C. HOUZE
Partner
William C. Houze & Company
48249 Vista de Nopal
La Quinta, CA 92253
Telephone: (619) 564-6400

William C. Houze & Company

HONOREE: 1992, 1994

Date of birth: November 26, 1921

EDUCATION:
> Chase College
>> B.S., commerce, personnel, 1955
>
> University of Southern California
>> M.A., liberal arts, 1976

MILITARY:
> Captain, United States Air Force, 1942 to 1945

SPECIAL INTERESTS AND HOBBIES:
> Classical and jazz music, writing, mountaineering, cross-country skiing, Anglophilia, travel

EMPLOYMENT HISTORY:
> 1984 to present: William C. Houze & Company
> 1977 to 1984: President, Houze, Shourds & Montgomery, Inc.
> 1973 to 1977: Partner and Vice President–Operations, Hergenrather & Company
> 1967 to 1973: Executive Director–Management Personnel, Rockwell International
> 1963 to 1967: Manager–Employee Relations, Computer Division, General Electric Company
> 1951 to 1963: Various Human Resource positions, Jet Engine Division, General Electric Company

WHAT I LOOK FOR IN GENERAL IN A CANDIDATE:

Over the years I have developed a sequential, three-stage process of evaluating candidates. The first stage is the easiest to complete because it measures objective data, pertinent skills, work experiences, and education—the professional requisites for the position.

Second, a candidate is then evaluated on his or her management style and how that style will mesh (or clash) with the culture of my client's organization. This stage requires in-depth analysis of the candidate plus several assessments to determine the organization's actual culture.

The third stage serves as a safety net. It assumes that my assessments in the earlier stages may not have been totally correct. Therefore, before my final "stamp of approval," I probe for bedrock attitudes and behavior patterns: work ethic, honesty, loyalty, team play, and dedication to the Golden Rule. Experience suggests that a man or woman steeped in such behavior can usually overcome marginal shortcomings in specific skills or culture compatibility.

GEOGRAPHIC SCOPE OF RECRUITING ACTIVITIES:
> Serve clients nationwide and in England, Western Europe, and the Pacific Rim

TOTAL YEARS OF RETAINER-TYPE RECRUITING EXPERIENCE:
> 20 years

EDWARD R. HOWE, JR.
Managing Partner/President
Howe, Lawlor & Associates
5 Radnor Corporate Center, Suite 448
Radnor, PA 19087
Telephone: (215) 975-9124

HONOREE: 1990, 1994

Date of birth: March 13, 1947

Bachrach

EDUCATION:
University of Denver
B.S., marketing, 1970

SPECIAL INTERESTS AND HOBBIES:
Sports, fishing, hiking

EMPLOYMENT HISTORY:
1993 to 1994: Howe, McMahon & Lawlor
1981 to 1993: Partner, Diversified Search Inc.
1979 to 1981: Chief Operating Officer, United Nesco Steel
1974 to 1979: Sales Manager, Polaroid Corp.
1970 to 1974: National Sales Manager, Burlington Industries

WHAT I LOOK FOR IN GENERAL IN A CANDIDATE:

At the top-level search work that I do I look for:

Candidate's ability to make a decision that would effect his or her company's
bottom line.
Chemistry with my client.
Leadership abilities.
Sense of humor, intellect, family values.
People skills, listening ability, comprehension.
Personality traits.
Ability to answer a tough question regarding his failures, problems in both
work and social worlds.

I do not spend time (in great detail) exploring a candidate's technical knowledge of his job. When he becomes a top executive—Senior Vice President or
higher—he has the technical ability. I find out about personal and management
and worldly aspects.

GEOGRAPHIC SCOPE OF RECRUITING ACTIVITIES:
Clients nationwide

TOTAL YEARS OF RETAINER-TYPE RECRUITING EXPERIENCE:
12 years

SIDNEY A. HUMPHREYS
President
Korn/Ferry International
Scotia Plaza, Suite 3918
40 King Street, West
Toronto, Ontario, M5H 3Y2 Canada
Telephone: (416) 366-1300

HONOREE: 1992, 1994

Date of birth: August 13, 1933

EDUCATION:
>University of Manitoba
>>Chartered Accountant, 1959

Peter Caton/Gerald Campbell Studios

SPECIAL INTERESTS AND HOBBIES:
>Christian ministries, youth counseling, sports (golf, hockey), reading, fitness/nutrition

EMPLOYMENT HISTORY:
>1990 to present: Korn/Ferry International
>1978 to 1990: Managing Director, SpencerStuart, Toronto
>1962 to 1978: Various positions, Xerox Corporation in Canada and United States
>1960 to 1962: Comptroller, Branch Operation Manager–Monarch Lumber Company, Winnipeg
>1958 to 1960: Chartered Accountant, James N. Chalmers & Co., Winnipeg
>1954 to 1958: Student-Manager, Deloitte Haskins & Sells, Chartered Accountants

WHAT I LOOK FOR IN GENERAL IN A CANDIDATE:

My first priority is to identify candidates who come as close to the mutually agreed upon client's position specification as possible. Once I have accomplished this, I have no hesitation in also introducing any candidates who do not completely meet the client's specification, but who I feel have the successful relevant track records that indicate they could do the job. It is important here to know the client culture well—the personalities, strengths, and weaknesses of the executive team.

The major characteristics I look for in candidates are the qualities of leadership and integrity. A positive, can-do attitude and a track record of building organizations and attaining consistent bottom-line results are good indicators. Other personal characteristics that I look for are basic social and communication skills, strong personal drive, and a solid work ethic.

Relative to education, I look for people who are very bright and "street smart," and although university degrees are positive attributes, they are not critical. More and more candidates are required to have international experience and ideally the capability to converse in more than one language. I also look for individuals who keep fit (don't smoke) and take care of their appearance (not flashy). A history of developing subordinates is an advantage, as are candidates who are respected for taking the "high ground."

GEOGRAPHIC SCOPE OF RECRUITING ACTIVITIES:
>Serve clients in Canada, the United States, France, the United Kingdom, Germany, Switzerland, Holland, Japan, and Hong Kong

TOTAL YEARS OF RETAINER-TYPE RECRUITING EXPERIENCE:
>15 years

WILLIAM M. HUMPHREYS
Managing Partner
Robison Humphreys & Associates, Inc.
295 The West Mall, 7th Floor
Etobicoke, Ontario, M9C 4Z4 Canada
Telephone: (416) 626-6346

Date of birth: November 27, 1935

EDUCATION:
> University of Manitoba
> > Chartered Accountant, 1962

SPECIAL INTERESTS AND HOBBIES:
> Golf, wildlife photography, travel

Robison Humphreys & Associates, Inc.

EMPLOYMENT HISTORY:
> 1987 to present: Robison Humphreys & Associates, Inc.
> 1980 to 1987: Partner, Touch Ross
> 1976 to 1978: Vice President–Finance, Thomson Newspapers (International Thomson)
> 1974 to 1976: Vice President–Finance, J. Walter Thompson Co. Ltd.
> 1965 to 1974: Regional Vice President–Marketing, Great-West Life Assurance Company
> 1956 to 1965: Staff Supervisor (Audit), Deloitte Haskins & Sells, Public Accountants

WHAT I LOOK FOR IN GENERAL IN A CANDIDATE:

Our professional commitment is to recruit the best-qualified candidates who can be attracted to the client position based on a refined set of techniques and standards that we have established over the years.

At the outset of each search assignment, we:

1. Gain an understanding of the client's business, organization, environment, and objectives.
2. Learn the characteristics of management, the key executives, and their interrelationships.

STRUCTURED SOURCING. The source call is one of our most valuable skills. Over the years, we have developed a network of knowledgeable sources—ex-associates, industry leaders, association executives.

Accordingly, we think through and plan the sourcing phase of each assignment. Thus, we can develop the kind of information needed to help us confirm, prescreen, and qualify the best possible candidates in the shortest possible time.

DISCIPLINED STRATEGY. We approach each assignment with a search plan tailored to meet the client's specific requirements. In a carefully documented position description, we spell out the concept, major thrust, and principal tasks of the position, together with an ideal candidate profile.

ONGOING COMMUNICATION. We emphasize continual communication with the client to ensure an open and straightforward working relationship.

GEOGRAPHIC SCOPE OF RECRUITING ACTIVITIES:
> Coast and south to Florida and Canada, United States, United Kingdom, and Germany

TOTAL YEARS OF RETAINER-TYPE RECRUITING EXPERIENCE:
> 16 years

JAMES E. HUNT
Partner
Kenny, Kindler, Hunt & Howe
1 Dag Hammarskjold Plaza, 34th Floor
New York, NY 10017
Telephone: (212) 355-5560

Date of birth: December 14, 1930

Kenny, Kindler, Hunt & Howe

EDUCATION:
> University of Cincinnati
> > B.B.A., marketing, 1953

SPECIAL INTERESTS AND HOBBIES:
> Tennis, golf, bicycling, travel, cooking

EMPLOYMENT HISTORY:
> 1983 to present: Kenny, Kindler, Hunt & Howe
> 1976 to 1983: Vice President, Russell Reynolds Associates, Inc.
> 1953 to 1976: District Manager–Financial Salaries, NCR Corporation

WHAT I LOOK FOR IN GENERAL IN A CANDIDATE:

I look for a pattern of consistent growth and accomplishment, ideally in a changing environment. Someone who has made a difference. The former chairman of NCR Corporation, where I began my career, once said: "We have too many twenty-year veterans who have one year's experience twenty times."

Once the core competence and skill levels are confirmed, I look for a value system that is compatible with the client. From that point on, it's the personal characteristics that count:

> Integrity, intelligence, curiosity, focus
> Leadership, energy, motivation, candor
> Humor, communications skills, decisiveness

GEOGRAPHIC SCOPE OF RECRUITING ACTIVITIES:
> Serve clients nationwide and on occasion internationally

TOTAL YEARS OF RETAINER-TYPE RECRUITING EXPERIENCE:
> 18 years

DURANT A. (ANDY) HUNTER
Partner
Pendleton James and Associates, Inc.
One International Place
Boston, MA 02110
Telephone: (617) 261-9696

HONOREE: 1992, 1994

Date of birth: November 25, 1948

Pendleton James and Associates, Inc.

EDUCATION:
University of North Carolina, Chapel Hill
A.B., American studies, 1971
George Washington University
M.P.A., public administration, 1973

SPECIAL INTERESTS AND HOBBIES:
Boys & Girls Clubs of Boston, international affairs, politics, skiing, golf

EMPLOYMENT HISTORY:
1992 to present: Pendleton James and Associates, Inc.
1989 to 1992: Partner, Gardiner Stone Hunter International
1985 to 1989: Senior Vice President, Boyden International
1983 to 1985: Executive Vice President, HM Consultants International
1981 to 1983: Vice President, James Hunter Machine Company
1974 to 1981: Assistant Vice President, J.P. Morgan
1973 to 1974: Program Director, International Management and Development Institute

WHAT I LOOK FOR IN GENERAL IN A CANDIDATE:

The search for the right executive, much like the search for a marriage partner, is not done "in general." The goal of the recruiter is to find the best available candidate by matching an individual to the unique needs of each client. Having said this, there are qualities and attributes which appear consistently in successful candidates: intelligence, straightforwardness, strong communication and interpersonal skills, organization, energy, focus, humor, professionalism, and motivation.

In matching a candidate to a company, I examine proven accomplishments and potential fit. First, I am looking for a solid record of achievement in a given industry or function. I look much deeper than words on a resume or what a candidate tells me during an interview.

Second, I try to assess whether the match makes sense for everybody. Is the move progressive for the candidate in terms of his or her goals, values, and strengths? Does the candidate measure up to the requirements of the particular industry, company, job, and prospective superiors? Finally, I ask myself, would I like to work with this individual?

GEOGRAPHIC SCOPE OF RECRUITING ACTIVITIES:
Serve clients nationwide and in Europe, Latin America, and Asia

TOTAL YEARS OF RETAINER-TYPE RECRUITING EXPERIENCE:
9 years

W. JERRY HYDE
President
Hyde Danforth & Company
5950 Berkshire Lane, Suite 1600
Dallas, TX 75225
Telephone: (214) 691-5966

HONOREE: 1992, 1994

Date of birth: December 23, 1933

Hyde Danforth & Company

EDUCATION:
> East Texas State University
> > B.B.A., general business, 1954
> > M.B.A., human resources management, 1958

MILITARY:
> Personnel Specialist Third Class, United States Army, 1954 to 1956

SPECIAL INTERESTS AND HOBBIES:
> Native American history, vegetable gardening, golf

EMPLOYMENT HISTORY:
> 1973 to present: Hyde Danforth & Company
> 1968 to 1973: Manager, Human Resources Consulting, Peat Marwick Mitchell & Company
> 1962 to 1967: Manager–Southwest, Preferred Business Service Corporation
> 1958 to 1962: Assistant Director of Personnel, Republic National Life Insurance Co.
> 1957 to 1958: Teaching Assistant, East Texas State University
> 1956 to 1957: Principal, Bland High School

WHAT I LOOK FOR IN GENERAL IN A CANDIDATE:

Whether a candidate is for an entry-level management position or for chief executive officer, certain qualities are requisite for on-the-job success.

1. Professional manner and bearing—a visual presence for leadership.
2. Polished communications skills—the ability to sell an idea orally, to present it succinctly in writing, and to listen objectively.
3. Previous demonstrated leadership—a track record that historically indicates the ability to motivate and control.
4. Positive client chemistry—the empathy to effectively relate to client personnel, goals, and objectives.
5. Proven integrity—an individual of principle.
6. Practiced technical knowledge—the experience necessary for excellence.

GEOGRAPHIC SCOPE OF RECRUITING ACTIVITIES:
> Serve clients nationwide and Mexico, Europe, and Canada

TOTAL YEARS OF RETAINER-TYPE RECRUITING EXPERIENCE:
> 25 years

HUGH ILLSLEY
President
Ward Howell Illsley & Partners
141 Adelaide Street West, Suite 1800
Toronto, Ontario, M5H 3L5 Canada
Telephone: (416) 862-1273

HONOREE: 1992, 1994

Date of birth: November 6, 1949

Ward Howell Illsley & Partners

EDUCATION:
Florida State University
B.S.C., economic geography, 1972

SPECIAL INTERESTS AND HOBBIES:
Golf, squash, family

EMPLOYMENT HISTORY:
1977 to present: Ward Howell Illsley & Partners
1975 to 1977: Consultant, H.V. Chapman & Associates

WHAT I LOOK FOR IN GENERAL IN A CANDIDATE:

Values. What the person stands for. How they go about accomplishing things! What they are really interested in. What they are not good at. What good performance means to them. Large amount of time discussing family history and value system.

GEOGRAPHIC SCOPE OF RECRUITING ACTIVITIES:
Serve clients nationwide and in North America and Europe

TOTAL YEARS OF RETAINER-TYPE RECRUITING EXPERIENCE:
20 years

D. JOHN INGRAM
Partner
Ingram & Aydelotte Inc.
430 Park Avenue, 7th Floor
New York, NY 10022
Telephone: (212) 319-7777

HONOREE: 1990, 1992, 1994

Date of birth: May 15, 1939

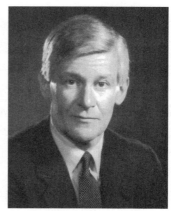

Ingram & Aydelotte, Inc.

EDUCATION:
> Michigan State University
> > B.S., 1964
> > M.S., 1965

MILITARY:
> L/Corporal, United States Marines, 1958 to 1964

EMPLOYMENT HISTORY:
> 1984 to present: Ingram & Aydelotte Inc.
> 1980 to 1984: Partner, Heidrick & Struggles, Inc.
> 1969 to 1980: Senior Vice President, American Express Company (Fireman's Fund)
> 1966 to 1969: Supervisor, Bell Telephone Labs
> 1965 to 1966: Industrial Relations Analyst, Ford Motor Company

WHAT I LOOK FOR IN GENERAL IN A CANDIDATE:

Leadership, integrity, preparation, implementation results.

GEOGRAPHIC SCOPE OF RECRUITING ACTIVITIES:
Serve clients nationwide

TOTAL YEARS OF RETAINER-TYPE RECRUITING EXPERIENCE:
14 years

JOHN ISAACSON
Managing Director
Isaacson, Miller
334 Boylston Street, Suite 500
Boston, MA 02116
Telephone: (617) 262-6500

Date of birth: November 7, 1946

Isaacson, Miller

EDUCATION:
Dartmouth College
B.A., English, 1968
Oxford University
B.A., politics, philosophy, and economics, 1970
Harvard Law School
J.D., 1973

SPECIAL INTERESTS AND HOBBIES:
Skiing, European history, my children

EMPLOYMENT HISTORY:
1982 to present: Isaacson, Miller
1980 to 1982: Project Manager, Pequod Associates
1978 to 1980: Director, Commonwealth of Massachusetts, Office for Children
1975 to 1978: Assistant Commissioner, Commonwealth of Massachusetts,
Department of Youth Services
1973 to 1975: Assistant to the Secretary, Commonwealth of Massachusetts,
Executive Office of Human Services

WHAT I LOOK FOR IN GENERAL IN A CANDIDATE:

I have a series of chronological biographical tests. I look early in a career for technical mastery, preferably in many varied disciplines and at the conceptual level, in manipulating concepts, and at the level of detailed memory. As the career advances, I look for the capacity to develop values and share mission and to reassure bosses. In the later phases, I am interested in the uses of control combined with the capacity to sell mission under strenuous conditions. Finally, I am interested in the ability to sell, conceptually in and out of the organization, to widely varied and hostile constituencies.

GEOGRAPHIC SCOPE OF RECRUITING ACTIVITIES:
Serve clients nationwide

TOTAL YEARS OF RETAINER-TYPE RECRUITING EXPERIENCE:
12 years

RICHARD K. IVES
Partner
Wilkinson & Ives
One Bush Street, Suite 550
San Francisco, CA 94104
Telephone: (415) 433-2155

Wilkinson & Ives

HONOREE: 1990, 1992, 1994

Date of birth: October 22, 1929

EDUCATION:
University of Southern California
    B.S., commerce, 1952
Stanford University Graduate
    School of Business
    M.B.A., 1954

MILITARY:
Lieutenant, United States Navy, 1954 to 1957

SPECIAL INTERESTS AND HOBBIES:
Golf, travel, gourmet cooking, reading

EMPLOYMENT HISTORY:
1984 to present: Wilkinson & Ives
1975 to 1984: Principal, Richard K. Ives & Company
1972 to 1975: Partner, Bacchi, Bentley, Evans & Gould, Inc.
1970 to 1972: Western Regional Manager, DPF&G
1957 to 1970: Various sales and marketing management positions, IBM Corporation

WHAT I LOOK FOR IN GENERAL IN A CANDIDATE:

The following characteristics or traits, not necessarily in this order, are what I try to assess in potential candidates for senior-level positions:

Personal chemistry
Intelligence and vision
Maturity and objectivity
Leadership qualities, interpersonal skills
Work ethic—energy, drive, enthusiasm, ambition
Integrity
Judgment and common sense
Sense of humor
Creative and innovative abilities
Communication skills
Education
Professional and personal balance

GEOGRAPHIC SCOPE OF RECRUITING ACTIVITIES:
Serve clients nationwide, the United Kingdom, and Europe

TOTAL YEARS OF RETAINER-TYPE RECRUITING EXPERIENCE:
22 years

MIKE JACOBS
President
Thorne, Brieger Associates Inc.
11 East 44th Street
New York, NY 10017
Telephone: (212) 682-5424

Thorne, Brieger Associates Inc.

HONOREE: 1990, 1992, 1994

Date of birth: June 6, 1932

EDUCATION:
>Brooklyn College
>>B.A., psychology, 1953
>City College of New York
>>Ph.D. candidate, industrial psychology,
>>1956–1959, no degree

MILITARY:
>Corporal, United States Army, 1953 to 1955

SPECIAL INTERESTS AND HOBBIES:
>Tennis

EMPLOYMENT HISTORY:
>1989 to present: Thorne, Brieger Associates
>1975 to 1989: President, The Thorne Group
>1979 to 1981: Chairman, Kien, Jacobs & Associates
>1960 to 1975: President, Garnet Associates
>1957 to 1960: Counsellor, Allen Employment
>1955 to 1957: Personnel Assistant, Rotobroil Corp. of America

WHAT I LOOK FOR IN GENERAL IN A CANDIDATE:

I look for candidates who are strong enough and smart enough not to be intimidated by the search process or by me.

I look for people who bring the same objectivity to our discussions that I do. They know how to listen. They focus on what is important and ask good questions. They are not turned off by negatives, but instead put them in perspective.

I look for individuals who will try to manage me—people who will come to the interview prepared—who know what they want me to discover about them and what they want to learn about the position—and who, before the meeting is over, will find a way to accomplish their agenda.

I look for people with a sense of humor who can laugh at themselves but still take their work seriously.

Ultimately, what I always look for in a candidate is someone who not only meets the needs of my client but whose own needs will be equally satisfied by the new position.

GEOGRAPHIC SCOPE OF RECRUITING ACTIVITIES:
>Serve clients nationwide and in Europe

TOTAL YEARS OF RETAINER-TYPE RECRUITING EXPERIENCE:
>19 years

THEODORE JADICK
**Partner and Member of Executive
Committee
Heidrick & Struggles, Inc.
245 Park Avenue
New York, NY 10167
Telephone: (212) 867-9876**

HONOREE: 1990, 1992, 1994

Date of birth: July 16, 1939

Bachrach

EDUCATION:
University of Scranton
B.S., business administration/accounting, 1961

MILITARY:
Specialist, Fourth Class, United States Army, 1962 to 1968

SPECIAL INTERESTS AND HOBBIES:
Squash, tennis, golf; Board of Directors, Calvary Hospital Foundation, Bronx, NY

EMPLOYMENT HISTORY:
1975 to present: Heidrick & Struggles, Inc.
1965 to 1975: Senior Vice President, F.W. Hastings Associates
1962 to 1965: Senior Accountant, Deloitte Haskins & Sells

WHAT I LOOK FOR IN GENERAL IN A CANDIDATE:

As I address potential candidates against predetermined search criteria, my prime concern centers around specific, direct, and quantifiable accomplishments. All of us live and function in a competitive marketplace. What sets some individuals apart are their accomplishments and the environment in which these results are produced. Personal characteristics also play a major role in my evaluation. Much attention is given to integrity, values, people skills, creativity, drive, and initiative. Obviously the ability to get the job done through and with people is an important measure of success. These qualities are certainly tested in flat organizations, where the best thinking by a group of people working together in a positive fashion can result in a well-defined team effort. Today's shrinking world also places a premium on a global outlook and candidates with international expertise. More and more the international thread is woven into the fabric of many of our position specifications.

GEOGRAPHIC SCOPE OF RECRUITING ACTIVITIES:
Serve clients nationwide and in Europe

TOTAL YEARS OF RETAINER-TYPE RECRUITING EXPERIENCE:
18 years

E. PENDLETON JAMES
Chairman
Pendleton James and Associates
200 Park Avenue, Suite 4520
New York, NY 10166
Telephone: (212) 557-1599

HONOREE: 1990, 1992, 1994

Date of birth: October 23, 1929

John F. Robben

EDUCATION:
University of the Pacific
B.A., 1954

MILITARY:
United States Army, 1950 to 1952

SPECIAL INTERESTS AND HOBBIES:
Golf, tennis, skiing, reading

EMPLOYMENT HISTORY:
1978 to present: Pendleton James and Associates
Prior employment: Heidrick & Struggles, Inc., Russell Reynolds Associates,
Inc.

WHAT I LOOK FOR IN GENERAL IN A CANDIDATE:

Initial overall appearance—both physical and verbal. How well does candidate present him or herself—his or her background, experiences? What are his or
her career goals? What are his or her outside interests? Is his or her personal life
stable? Is he or she smart in life? Can he or she handle him- or herself at all levels
and in all situations? Is the candidate flexible? Does the candidate respond well to
change (not job-hopping change but changes within his or her environment)?
Does he or she have a stable work background?

GEOGRAPHIC SCOPE OF RECRUITING ACTIVITIES:
Serve clients worldwide

TOTAL YEARS OF RETAINER-TYPE RECRUITING EXPERIENCE:
28 years

CAROL S. JEFFERS
Vice President and Partner
John Sibbald Associates, Inc.
8725 W. Higgins Road, Suite 575
Chicago, IL 60631
Telephone: (312) 693-0575

HONOREE: 1992, 1994

Date of birth: July 13, 1942

John Sibbald Associates, Inc.

SPECIAL INTERESTS AND HOBBIES:
Collecting cookbooks, modern jazz, entertaining

EMPLOYMENT HISTORY:
1975 to present: John Sibbald Associates, Inc.
1974 to 1975: Associate, Booz, Allen & Hamilton
1969 to 1974: Real Estate Administrator, Midas International
1964 to 1969: Credit Manager, U.S. Leasing Corp.

WHAT I LOOK FOR IN GENERAL IN A CANDIDATE:

I attempt to spot in every candidate I interview for a given client the qualities which suggest that the candidate will make a genuine difference to the client's organization. My work is highly specialized in that I serve only the hospitality industry, especially private clubs and resorts throughout the Western Hemisphere. In seeking people for this field, then, my focus must not only be on the professional skills and credentials they possess but on their sociability and service quotients as well. In these latter aspects, hospitality professionals are different from other managers and executives. These service-oriented qualities are as necessary for a club's head golf professional as they are for a club general manager. It is not enough for a candidate just to fit a club's distinctive culture. What I get paid for is finding a manager who counts. This is that rare individual who over the years does everything the club called for in its job description but also multiplies the members' pleasure and satisfaction with his or her own good taste, professional skills, and personal character. On top of this, a truly top club manager must always recognize that he or she is ever the employee and—regardless of tenure, reputation, ego, or caliber of clubs—never like a member.

GEOGRAPHIC SCOPE OF RECRUITING ACTIVITIES:
Serve clients nationwide and in Canada and the Caribbean

TOTAL YEARS OF RETAINER-TYPE RECRUITING EXPERIENCE:
14 years

HAROLD E. JOHNSON
Managing Director
Norman Broadbent International
200 Park Avenue
New York, NY 10166-1898
Telephone: (212) 953-6900

Date of birth: July 11, 1939

Ken Korsh

EDUCATION:
> University of Nebraska
> > B.S., business administration, 1962

SPECIAL INTERESTS AND HOBBIES:
> I have a particular interest in large-scale organizational change—and the
> influence that executive leadership can have in empowering and
> unleashing organizations

EMPLOYMENT HISTORY:
> 1991 to present: Norman Broadbent International
> 1988 to 1991: Managing Vice President, Korn/Ferry International
> 1985 to 1988: Senior Vice President, Human Resources and Corporate
> Administration, The Travelers Companies, Inc.
> 1980 to 1985: Senior Vice President, Human Resources, Federated Depart-
> ment Stores, Inc.
> 1975 to 1980: Senior Vice President, Human Resources INA (CIGNA) Corpo-
> ration
> 1973 to 1975: Vice President, Human Resources, American Medicorp Inc.
> 1968 to 1973: Director Recruiting and Management Development, Kennicott
> Copper
> 1962 to 1968: Various positions, American Can Company

WHAT I LOOK FOR IN GENERAL IN A CANDIDATE:

As both a buyer and provider of executive search for more than twenty years,
there is one key element I look for in evaluating candidates, beyond purely technical qualifications. I look for a record of specific accomplishments. For me, the
only predictor of future performance is past performance, so I concentrate on
finding people who have actually done something, made it happen, taken the
accountability, and moved the ball positively down the field. What has the candidate made of what life and experience and opportunity have handed him or her?
While there is a certain element of maintenance and status quo in every job, I
want to know what my candidates have specifically done in their previous positions—other than warm a chair!

GEOGRAPHIC SCOPE OF RECRUITING ACTIVITIES:
> Serve clients nationwide and in Europe, Asia, and Latin America

TOTAL YEARS OF RETAINER-TYPE RECRUITING EXPERIENCE:
> 20 years

JOHN F. JOHNSON
President
Lamalie Amrop International
One Cleveland Center
1375 East Ninth Street
Cleveland, OH 44114
Telephone: (216) 694-3000

Lamalie Amrop International

HONOREE: 1990, 1992, 1994

Date of birth: April 23, 1942

EDUCATION:
   Tufts University
      B.A., economics, 1963
   Columbia University
      M.B.A., industrial relations, 1964

SPECIAL INTERESTS AND HOBBIES:
   Wine collecting, big-game fishing, thoroughbred racing

EMPLOYMENT HISTORY:
   1976 to present: Lamalie Amrop International
   1967 to 1976: Various Human Resource positions, General Electric Company
   1964 to 1967: Industrial Relations Analyst, Ford Motor Company

WHAT I LOOK FOR IN GENERAL IN A CANDIDATE:

When evaluating candidates for a senior search assignment, I believe that there are four areas which must be explored in detail:

- Intellectual capability.
- Functional/technical/industry experience.
- Personal values.
- Management/leadership style.

Each of these factors must be evaluated against both the specification that I develop with my client and my knowledge of the hiring manager and the organization.

Based upon education and work history, intellect and experience are the easiest to assess. Values and management/leadership capabilities are harder to evaluate and must be sorted out over the course of a two- to three-hour interview. The candidate's value system needs to be compatible with that of the organization, and his or her management/leadership style must enable the individual to function effectively not only in the immediate role but also in broader responsibilities as the individual moves higher in the organization.

Management and leadership skills can become the Achilles' heel of many executives as they rise through an organization. They are the toughest issues to quantify in an interview; and, therefore, I address them in detail when referencing finalist candidates.

GEOGRAPHIC SCOPE OF RECRUITING ACTIVITIES:
   Serve clients nationwide and internationally

TOTAL YEARS OF RETAINER-TYPE RECRUITING EXPERIENCE:
   18 years

STANLEY C. JOHNSON
President
Johnson & Company
11 Grumman Hill Road
Wilton, CT 06897
Telephone: (203) 761-1212

Date of birth: August 15, 1947

Johnson & Company

EDUCATION:
   Oregon State University
      B.S., business administration, 1969

SPECIAL INTERESTS AND HOBBIES:
   Golf, tennis, and most other outdoor activities

EMPLOYMENT HISTORY:
   1992 to present: Johnson & Company
   1976 to 1992: Partner, Goodrich & Sherwood Company
   1970 to 1976: Various positions in General Advertising and Sales, The Procter
      & Gamble Company

WHAT I LOOK FOR IN GENERAL IN A CANDIDATE:

In general I look for the following broadly described attributes that are common to successful senior managers in all fields.

1. Intelligence: In addition to how smart, common sense, an open mind, and the ability to quickly understand and articulate the big picture are keys.
2. Communications: They should listen well, ask good questions, and, therefore, respond articulately even in areas that are unfamiliar.
3. People skills: The individual should demonstrate leadership and team-building success. This would include developing and promoting talent under them and engendering a level of confidence and integrity.
4. Passion: It is manifested in an intellectual curiosity about business in general and involvement in their current industry, and it conveys the feeling they are motivated.
5. Successes: The best performers add value to the bottom line even in their early years or in staff functions. They are able to explain their personal involvement in the significant achievements of their careers.

GEOGRAPHIC SCOPE OF RECRUITING ACTIVITIES:
   Serve clients nationwide and in the United States, Canada, Mexico, and the
      Caribbean

TOTAL YEARS OF RETAINER-TYPE RECRUITING EXPERIENCE:
   18 years

DAVID S. JOYS
Partner and Director
Heidrick & Struggles, Inc.
245 Park Avenue
New York, NY 10167-0152
Telephone: (212) 973-4846

Bachrach

HONOREE: 1992, 1994

Date of birth: July 17, 1943

EDUCATION:
> Amherst College
> > B.A., economics and psychology, 1965
> Columbia University Graduate
> > School of Business
> > M.B.A., finance and marketing, 1967

SPECIAL INTERESTS AND HOBBIES:
> Hunting/shooting, fly-fishing, golf, squash, Impressionist and post-Impressionist art

EMPLOYMENT HISTORY:
> 1992 to present: Heidrick & Struggles, Inc.
> 1986 to 1992: Managing Director, Higdon, Joys & Mingle, Inc.
> 1974 to 1986: Executive Vice President, Russell Reynolds Associates, Inc.
> 1972 to 1974: Vice President–Marketing Operations and Services, The Hertz Corporation
> 1967 to 1972: Assistant Vice President–General Sales, American Airlines, Inc.

WHAT I LOOK FOR IN GENERAL IN A CANDIDATE:

While each client assignment is unique and requires a tailored solution, most of our senior general management projects require assessment of the following candidate traits, characteristics, and background issues:

- Leadership and team-building skills.
- Intelligence and common sense.
- Personal and professional integrity.
- Self-confidence with humility.
- Interpersonal and communication skills.
- Flexibility/adaptability.
- Initiative/motivation/energy/drive.
- Judgment.
- Ability to listen.
- Vision and creativity.
- Positive outlook/"can-do" attitude.
- Action/results orientation.
- Progressive and successful track record of relevant accomplishments.
- Balance in life/breadth of interests.
- Sense of humor.

GEOGRAPHIC SCOPE OF RECRUITING ACTIVITIES:
> Serve clients nationwide and in the United Kingdom, Western Europe, Canada, and the Pacific Rim

TOTAL YEARS OF RETAINER-TYPE RECRUITING EXPERIENCE:
> 20 years

HOWARD L. KARR
President
Howard Karr & Associates, Inc.
1777 Borel Place, Suite 408
San Mateo, CA 94402
Telephone: (415) 574-5277

Date of birth: April 4, 1938

EDUCATION:
University of California at Berkeley
B.A., labor and industrial relations, 1960
Wharton School, University of Pennsylvania
M.B.A., finance, 1962

MILITARY:
First Lieutenant, United States Army, 1962
to 1964

Howard Karr & Associates, Inc.

SPECIAL INTERESTS AND HOBBIES:
Family, Cal (UC Berkeley) athletics and alumni activities, Rotary Club of San
Mateo, golf, travel, skiing

EMPLOYMENT HISTORY:
1983 to present: Howard Karr & Associates, Inc.
1973 to 1983: President, Karr Bartel & Adams
1972: Corporate Finance, Hambrecht & Quist
1971 to 1972: Chief Financial Officer, Telfon Communications Corporation, Inc.
1970 to 1971: Chief Financial Officer, Continental Telephone (Subsidiary:
Continental Data Services Corporation)
1968 to 1970: Manager–Executive Search, Touche Ross & Company
1967 to 1968: Director of Personnel and Distribution, Del Monte Corporation (Subsidiary: O'Brien, Spotorno & Mitchell, Inc.)
1964 to 1967: Certified Public Accountant, Arthur Young & Company

WHAT I LOOK FOR IN GENERAL IN A CANDIDATE:
I search for candidates who have a strong sense of self. This includes self-
awareness, high personal integrity, and realistic confidence in both their professional career and personal life.

I assess for effective communication skills as an indicator of intelligence,
organized thought, and leadership potential.

I review a candidate's career in order to evaluate accomplishments and level
of expertise. I gauge the quality of organizations and mentors, note successes and
challenges, follow the logic for career changes, appraise motivation, and observe a
candidate's sense of reality.

I look for outstanding references regarding the individual, professional accomplishments, creative abilities, leadership skills, and the ability to work with the
management team.

Candidates must be honest about themselves, learning from both their successes and their mistakes. Their career objectives should be compatible with their
ability, professional experience, and personal reputation.

GEOGRAPHIC SCOPE OF RECRUITING ACTIVITIES:
Serve clients in the western states

TOTAL YEARS OF RETAINER-TYPE RECRUITING EXPERIENCE:
23 years

ROGER M. KENNY
Partner
**Kenny, Kindler, Hunt & Howe/Boardroom
    Consultants**
One Dag Hammarskjold Plaza, 34th Floor
New York, NY 10017
Telephone: (212) 355-5560

HONOREE: 1990, 1992, 1994

Date of birth: October 3, 1938

Kenny, Kindler, Hunt & Howe

EDUCATION:
    Manhattan College
        B.B.A., 1959
    New York University Graduate School of Business
        M.B.A., 1961

MILITARY:
    Specialist Fourth Class, United States Army/National Guard, 1962 to 1968

SPECIAL INTERESTS AND HOBBIES:
    Hiking, travel, reading, scuba diving

EMPLOYMENT HISTORY:
    1982 to present: Kenny, Kindler, Hunt & Howe/Boardroom Consultants
    1967 to 1982: Senior Vice President and Partner, SpencerStuart, Inc.
    1959 to 1967: Manager of Operations and various positions, Port Authority of
        New York and New Jersey

WHAT I LOOK FOR IN GENERAL IN A CANDIDATE:

We insist on getting a special handle on each candidate. Every person in every function is different. We look for "winners": What is their track record as perceived by superiors—and subordinates?

We pose varied questions related to leadership: How does a person handle adversity, willingness to experiment? Do they know what is really happening in their company/industry?

Since we deal with the 95th percentile of corporate executives, we insist on intelligent and current contributions, so we request speeches and articles. We challenge candidates as to their thinking on current trends: How do they distinguish themselves as executives? What special ideas do they have in approaching their business? What would the candidate have done differently during his or her career?

GEOGRAPHIC SCOPE OF RECRUITING ACTIVITIES:
    Serve clients nationwide and in Europe, Asia/Far East, Mexico, Canada

TOTAL YEARS OF RETAINER-TYPE RECRUITING EXPERIENCE:
    27 years

CHARLES W. KEPLER
Executive Vice President
Russell Reynolds Associates, Inc.
200 South Wacker Drive
Chicago, IL 60606
Telephone: (312) 993-0701

Date of birth: December 29, 1930

Russell Reynolds Associates, Inc.

EDUCATION:
University of Michigan
B.B.A., 1953
M.B.A., 1953

MILITARY:
Sergeant, United States Army, 1953 to 1955

SPECIAL INTERESTS AND HOBBIES:
Family activities, tennis, travel, collectibles

EMPLOYMENT HISTORY:
1978 to present: Russell Reynolds Associates, Inc.
1973 to 1978: Group Vice President, Gould, Inc.
1968 to 1973: Assistant GM–Consumer Electronics, Motorola, Inc.
1955 to 1968: Manager–Marketing Consumer Electronics, General Electric
Company

WHAT I LOOK FOR IN GENERAL IN A CANDIDATE:

I look for the dimension of the individual over just functional skills. Leadership, adaptability, values, and communication skills are among the traits my clients and I seek for the senior positions I serve. Also, my successful candidates will have had a steady progression of positions in well-regarded companies and, importantly, will have been in positions long enough to have had measurable performance.

GEOGRAPHIC SCOPE OF RECRUITING ACTIVITIES:
Serve clients nationwide and in Europe and Asia

TOTAL YEARS OF RETAINER-TYPE RECRUITING EXPERIENCE:
16 years

JAMES F. KERESEY
President
James Keresey Associates, Inc.
342 Madison Avenue, Suite 817
New York, NY 10173
Telephone: (212) 867-0391

Date of birth: December 30, 1925

Harry Benson

MILITARY:
Sergeant, United States Marine Corps, 1943 to 1945, Guam and Iwo Jima campaigns, selected out of the field for Officer Candidate School

SPECIAL INTERESTS AND HOBBIES:
Competitive sports

EMPLOYMENT HISTORY:
1976 to present: James Keresey Associates, Inc.
1950 to 1976: Securities industry

WHAT I LOOK FOR IN GENERAL IN A CANDIDATE:

Every search assignment is unique, and at the outset we work with our clients to understand and define their needs as precisely as possible. Our goal is then to find candidates with the highest level of professional competence in their given fields, as well as the best match in terms of chemistry and outlook.

Professional competence and technical skills are only the first part, and in many ways the simplest, of a complex equation. The character and integrity of our candidates must be indisputable, and we prefer to recruit men and women with a balanced outlook on work, family, and community affairs. We seek to establish a long-term and sound relationship with our clients, with the individuals we recruit, and with the influential executives in the world of business community. Therefore each assignment begins uniquely, but with the foundation of the work and the trust that has preceded it.

GEOGRAPHIC SCOPE OF RECRUITING ACTIVITIES:
Serve clients nationwide and in Europe

TOTAL YEARS OF RETAINER-TYPE RECRUITING EXPERIENCE:
17 years

MICHAEL C. KIEFFER
Chairman
Witt/Kieffer, Ford, Hadelman & Lloyd
2015 Spring Road, Suite 510
Oak Brook, IL 60521
Telephone: (708) 990-1370

HONOREE: 1990, 1992, 1994

Date of birth: December 23, 1942

Witt/Kieffer, Ford, Hadelman & Lloyd

EDUCATION:
Marist College
    B.A., liberal arts, 1969
Central Michigan University
    M.A., management (health care concentration), 1979

MILITARY:
E-4 SSGT, United States Air Force, 1963 to 1967

SPECIAL INTERESTS AND HOBBIES:
Golf, sailing, international travel, skiing, tennis

EMPLOYMENT HISTORY:
1992 to present: Witt/Kieffer, Ford, Hadelman & Lloyd
1983 to 1992: President, Kieffer, Ford & Hadelman, Ltd.
1977 to 1983: Regional Vice President, Witt Associates
1975 to 1977: Vice President, Human Resources, Geneva General Hospital
1971 to 1975: Vice President, Human Resources, St. Francis Hospital
1970 to 1971: Assistant Director, Mid Hudson Career Development Center

WHAT I LOOK FOR IN GENERAL IN A CANDIDATE:

Naturally, the requisite skills and experience to do the job. But, just as important, the right personality, style, and value match for the organization's culture. A collaborative style and the ego strength to share power and control. Intelligence, sense of vision, relational skills. Well balanced in his or her life; combining leisure time with work time. Executive poise and presence. Quick thinker, i.e., "good on his or her feet." Sense of wit and humor. A LEADER! Politically astute, socially adept. Ability to establish quick trust and high credibility.

GEOGRAPHIC SCOPE OF RECRUITING ACTIVITIES:
Serve clients nationwide

TOTAL YEARS OF RETAINER-TYPE RECRUITING EXPERIENCE:
17 years

RICHARD E. KINSER
President
Kinser & Associates
919 Third Avenue, Suite 2140
New York, NY 10022
Telephone: (212) 735-2740

HONOREE: 1992, 1994

Date of birth: May 14, 1936

Ingram & Aydelotte, Inc.

EDUCATION:
Michigan State University
B.S., 1964
M.S., 1965

MILITARY:
L/Corporal, United States Marines, 1958 to 1964

EMPLOYMENT HISTORY:
1984 to present: Ingram & Aydelotte Inc.
1980 to 1984: Partner, Heidrick & Struggles, Inc.
1969 to 1980: Senior Vice President, American Express Company (Fireman's Fund)
1966 to 1969: Supervisor, Bell Telephone Labs
1965 to 1966: Industrial Relations Analyst, Ford Motor Company

WHAT I LOOK FOR IN GENERAL IN A CANDIDATE:

Leadership, integrity, preparation, implementation results.

GEOGRAPHIC SCOPE OF RECRUITING ACTIVITIES:
Serve clients nationwide

TOTAL YEARS OF RETAINER-TYPE RECRUITING EXPERIENCE:
14 years

GARY KNISELY
Chief Executive Officer
Johnson Smith & Knisely Accord
475 Fifth Avenue, 14th Floor
New York, NY 10017
Telephone: (212) 686-9760

Date of birth: June 29, 1942

Johnson Smith & Knisely Accord

EDUCATION:
Trinity College
B.A., history, 1963

MILITARY:
Reserves, United States Army, 1963 to 1969

SPECIAL INTERESTS AND HOBBIES:
Tennis, squash, physical training, French, piano

EMPLOYMENT HISTORY:
1976 to present: Johnson Smith & Knisely Accord
1975 to 1976: Special Assistant, John D. Rockefeller III
1972 to 1975: President, Tarrytown Conference Center
1969 to 1972: Head of Marketing and Sales, Technology Communication Inc.
1963 to 1969: Midwest Manager, Time-Life International, Time, Incorporated

WHAT I LOOK FOR IN GENERAL IN A CANDIDATE:

- Intelligence
- Applied intelligence
- Self-confidence and a controlled ego
- Ability to communicate
- Ability to see the larger context of an issue
- A breadth of experience
- Interpersonal management skills (motivation, team-building, etc.)
- Flexibility in approaching problems

GEOGRAPHIC SCOPE OF RECRUITING ACTIVITIES:
Serve clients nationwide and Europe

TOTAL YEARS OF RETAINER-TYPE RECRUITING EXPERIENCE:
17 years

R. PAUL KORS
Partner
Kors Montgomery International
1980 Post Oak Boulevard, Suite 2280
Houston, TX 77056
Telephone: (713) 840-7101

HONOREE: 1990, 1992, 1994

Date of birth: June 12, 1935

Kaye Marvins Photography, Inc.

EDUCATION:
University of Michigan
B.B.A., 1958
University of Southern California
M.B.A., marketing, 1965

MILITARY:
First Lieutenant, United States Army Reserve, 1958 to 1966

SPECIAL INTERESTS AND HOBBIES:
Skiing, mountain climbing, tennis, golf, classic films

EMPLOYMENT HISTORY:
1978 to present: Kors Montgomery International
1973 to 1978: Managing Partner, Korn/Ferry International
1966 to 1972: Account Manager, Dean Witter & Company
1958 to 1966: Salesman, Nalco Chemical Company

WHAT I LOOK FOR IN GENERAL IN A CANDIDATE:

There is a compelling need for change in today's corporate environment. I look for executives who understand the momentum behind the changes and who can translate these shifting forces into success factors for a specific position.

Most of our assignments have a high international content. Generally, candidates must convince me that they not only understand the global marketplace but also that they can be effective with a variety of overseas managers.

Clients today also want final candidates who can get things done rather than just fill a box. This means looking at how candidates prioritize and act on their objectives. It requires evaluating whether they have the capacity and the knowledge required to lead their new team across the goal line. In addition, candidates need to demonstrate that they can grasp the issues involved and can articulate how their past accomplishments will enable them to be successful in their new position.

GEOGRAPHIC SCOPE OF RECRUITING ACTIVITIES:
Serve clients nationally and internationally

TOTAL YEARS OF RETAINER-TYPE RECRUITING EXPERIENCE:
21 years

IRA W. KRINSKY
Managing Vice President
Korn/Ferry International
1800 Century Park East, Suite 900
Los Angeles, CA 90067
Telephone: (310) 552-1834

HONOREE: 1992, 1994

Date of birth: January 15, 1949

John Swede Studio

EDUCATION:
Hofstra University
B.A., 1971
New York University
M.A., 1974
Harvard University
Doctor of Education, 1978

MILITARY:
Specialist 5th Class, United States Army, 1966 to 1979

SPECIAL INTERESTS AND HOBBIES:
Military history, weight training, stamp collecting

EMPLOYMENT HISTORY:
1992 to present: Korn/Ferry International
1988 to 1992: President, Ira W. Krinsky & Associates
1982 to 1988: Managing Vice President, Korn/Ferry International
1979 to 1982: Deputy Superintendent, Pomona Unified School District
1978 to 1979: Assistant Superintendent, Levittown Public Schools, New York
1972 to 1975: Various administrative and teaching assignments, Huntington
Public Schools, New York

WHAT I LOOK FOR IN GENERAL IN A CANDIDATE:

I look for four general qualities in all candidates: intelligence, compassion, courage, and integrity. I also look for sensitivity and exceptional communication skills. What is important is how an individual integrates these qualities with his or her personality in each unique career situation. I try to envision the candidate in the specific role I'm recruiting on-site and then form a "gut-level" reaction which forms the basis of my recommendation.

GEOGRAPHIC SCOPE OF RECRUITING ACTIVITIES:
Serve clients nationwide, but with a Western focus and in Mexico, Latin
America, and Asia

TOTAL YEARS OF RETAINER-TYPE RECRUITING EXPERIENCE:
12 years

RICHARD F. LARSEN
President
Larsen, Zilliacus and Associates, Inc.
601 West Fifth Street, Suite 710
Los Angeles, CA 90071
Telephone: (213) 243-0033

Date of birth: August 12, 1936

Larsen Zilliacus & Associates/Boyden

EDUCATION:
  Harvard College
    B.A., economics, 1960
  London School of Economics
    Ph.D., economics, 1963

MILITARY:
  E-4, United States Army, 1956 to 1958

SPECIAL INTERESTS AND HOBBIES:
  Reading, roller-skating, finance, farming

EMPLOYMENT HISTORY:
  1983 to present: Larsen, Zilliacus and Associates, Inc.
  1979 to 1982: Vice President, Russell Reynolds & Associates, Inc.
  1975 to 1979: Vice President, Bank of America
  1972 to 1974: Deputy Assistant Secretary, U.S. Treasury
  1969 to 1972: Lt. Governor, State of North Dakota
  1963 to 1969: State Senator and State Representative, North Dakota;
    farmer and college professor

WHAT I LOOK FOR IN GENERAL IN A CANDIDATE:

  Competence and a proven track record in function/industry
  Honesty

GEOGRAPHIC SCOPE OF RECRUITING ACTIVITIES:
  Serve clients nationwide and in Asia, Europe, and Latin America

TOTAL YEARS OF RETAINER-TYPE RECRUITING EXPERIENCE:
  14 years

DAVID R. LAUDERBACK
Vice President and National Practice Leader
A.T. Kearney Executive Search,
Division of A.T. Kearney, Inc.
600 Superior Avenue East
Cleveland, OH 44114
Telephone: (216) 241-6880

Date of birth: November 2, 1938

Mort Tucker Photography

EDUCATION:
> The Ohio State University
> > B.A., English Literature, 1963

SPECIAL INTERESTS AND HOBBIES:
> Psychology and personality profiles of "leaders"; anthropology, macroeconomics, golf, tennis, exercise/music, art, literature

EMPLOYMENT HISTORY:
> 1990 to present: A.T. Kearney Executive Search
> 1987 to 1990: Vice President/Managing Director, Korn/Ferry International
> 1984 to 1987: Vice President, Korn/Ferry International
> 1983 to 1984: Founder/President, Intercable
> 1979 to 1983: Group Vice President, WYSE Advertising
> 1977 to 1979: Director Marketing and Strategic Planning, ESB Incorporated, Automotive Group
> 1975 to 1977: Vice President/General Manager, Enterprises Division, Penton Publishing Company
> 1963 to 1975: Vice President/Account Supervisor, Lang, Fisher & Stashower Advertising

WHAT I LOOK FOR IN GENERAL IN A CANDIDATE:

My personal challenge for each search is to find the candidate who can achieve beyond the rational expectations of the client organization. I call such people "leaders," for want of a better word.

My years in search have taught me that "leaders" come in many different forms, from many different circumstances, and they are recognizable, even through barriers of language and culture.

In general, these extraordinary people will show consistent patterns of accomplishment, will be in harmony with themselves and their surroundings, and will project "light" through their eyes. One wise teacher said, "They have the look of eagles."

There is an "eagle" for every situation.

GEOGRAPHIC SCOPE OF RECRUITING ACTIVITIES:
> Serve clients nationwide; I am very active in Asia, including Japan, Hong Kong, and Singapore

TOTAL YEARS OF RETAINER-TYPE RECRUITING EXPERIENCE:
> 10 years

BEVERLY A. LIEBERMAN
President
Halbrecht Lieberman Associates, Inc.
1200 Summer Street
Stamford, CT 06905
Telephone: (203) 327-5630

Date of birth: August 6, 1949

Halbrecht Lieberman Associates, Inc.

EDUCATION:
University of Michigan
B.A., Spanish, 1971
M.A., Spanish language and literature, 1973

SPECIAL INTERESTS AND HOBBIES:
Flying, sailing, theater, travel

EMPLOYMENT HISTORY:
1986 to present: Halbrecht Lieberman Associates, Inc.
1984 to 1986: Vice President Human Resources, Baybank Systems Company
1978 to 1983: Personnel Manager, United Brands Company
1975 to 1978: Personnel Recruiter, Lynn Evans Associates
1974 to 1975: Personnel Recruiter, Sanford Rose Associates

WHAT I LOOK FOR IN GENERAL IN A CANDIDATE:

In a candidate, I look for a track record of success and accomplishments. I look for excellent oral and written communications skills, flexibility, and the ability to have strong positive impact. I also look for managerial skill, technical competency, and the ability to lead others through personality, strength, and vision. I look to see if the individual is a team player and has the persistence to "stick it out" when the pressure is high and get the job done. I look for the quality of the person's performance and results and the ability to work within a budget and deadlines. I also look for promotability and the ability to learn and adapt in different cultures.

GEOGRAPHIC SCOPE OF RECRUITING ACTIVITIES:
Serve clients nationwide and in Europe and Asia

TOTAL YEARS OF RETAINER-TYPE RECRUITING EXPERIENCE:
8 years

RICHARD E. LINDE
Partner
The Ogdon Partnership
375 Park Avenue, Suite 2409
New York, NY 10152
Telephone: (212) 308-1600

Date of birth: April 8, 1953

The Ogdon Partnership

EDUCATION:
Tufts University
B.A., political science, 1976
Northwestern University
M.B.A., 1982

SPECIAL INTERESTS AND HOBBIES:
Vestry member, Church of the Heavenly Rest, New York City; marathoner,
Union Club member

EMPLOYMENT HISTORY:
1989 to present: The Ogdon Partnership
1986 to 1989: Associate, Russell Reynolds Associates, Inc.
1984 to 1986: Associate Product Manager, Nabisco Brands
1982 to 1984: Associate Product Manager, Pepsi-Cola
1978 to 1980: Chief Legislative Assistant, U.S. Congress/Office of Congressman Robert Daniel
1976 to 1978: Admissions Counselor/Alumni Director, Tufts University

WHAT I LOOK FOR IN GENERAL IN A CANDIDATE:

The key to a successful search is correctly assessing the candidate's "fit" in the client's organization. Uncovering candidates with the right technical proficiencies is usually not the hard part. The recruiter can add the most value by carefully sizing up the corporate culture and determining which candidates have the right chemistry in order to succeed.

GEOGRAPHIC SCOPE OF RECRUITING ACTIVITIES:
Serve clients nationwide

TOTAL YEARS OF RETAINER-TYPE RECRUITING EXPERIENCE:
8 years

KAI LINDHOLST
Managing Partner
Egon Zehnder International Inc.
21 S. Clark Street
One First National Plaza, Suite 3300
Chicago, Illinois 60603
Telephone: (312) 782-4500

HONOREE: 1992, 1994

Date of birth: August 25, 1942

John Howell

EDUCATION:
Copenhagen School of Business Administration
    M.B.A., marketing, 1966
Wharton School of Finance
    M.B.A., marketing, 1968

EMPLOYMENT HISTORY:
1972 to present: Egon Zehnder International, Inc.
1968 to 1972: Associate/Sr. Associate, McKinsey & Co., Inc.
1961 to 1963: Sales Representative, Lindholst & Company

WHAT I LOOK FOR IN GENERAL IN A CANDIDATE:

Each client organization has a management style and culture which must be well understood by the search consultant in order to advise successfully on senior-level appointments. However, irrespective of the size of the company, industry, and function, the key characteristics which I value in particular are: a high energy level, a balanced self-appraisal, an ability to create enthusiasm, and a "can-do" attitude. The more senior the position, such personality characteristics become more and more sought after. Truly great executives have no bad days. At least, none that others can see. They impart an optimism and resilience to the organization that allows employees to do more than they ever thought themselves capable of. It is this personal capacity to touch employees and to unleash their talents that I seek. While intellectual capacity and certain functional/technical skills are required to even be considered, leaders who have demonstrated an above-average ability to attract, retain, and motivate good people at many levels within an organization are particularly sought after.

GEOGRAPHIC SCOPE OF RECRUITING ACTIVITIES:
Serve clients worldwide

TOTAL YEARS OF RETAINER-TYPE RECRUITING EXPERIENCE:
22 years

JOHN S. LLOYD
Vice Chairman
Witt/Kieffer, Ford, Hadelman & Lloyd
2015 Spring Road, Suite 510
Oak Brook, IL 60521
Telephone: (708) 990-1370

HONOREE: 1990, 1992, 1994

Date of birth: February 18, 1946

Stuart-Rodgers-Reilly Photography

EDUCATION:
University of Missouri
B.S., business administration, 1968
M.B.A. and M.S.P.H., health care management, 1970

SPECIAL INTERESTS AND HOBBIES:
Travel, men's choral singing, recreational cycling, historic circus and draft horses

EMPLOYMENT HISTORY:
1992 to present: Witt/Kieffer, Ford, Hadelman & Lloyd
1973 to 1992: President, Witt Associates Inc.
1970 to 1972: Associate, A.T. Kearney
1968 to 1969: Administrative Extern, New Jersey Hospital Association and Methodist Hospital

WHAT I LOOK FOR IN GENERAL IN A CANDIDATE:

I search for candidates who comprehend the complexities of one of the U.S.A.'s largest industries—that being health care. Our industry is in great transition, with increasing interest in identifying outstanding physician executives. Candidates must understand the insurance industry, as well as the medical care industry, to be successful. Both internationally and domestically, people want better health services and health and medical products.

Successful candidates must have displayed leadership traits since their youngest years. Candidates must be intelligent and show interest in continuing to pursue personal education. The successful candidate must be able to formulate and clearly express his or her ideas on corporate mission, goals, and objectives. A sense of humor is absolute. A balance must exist between bottom-line focus and people-motivational skills. Candidates must understand the practices of total quality management and continuous quality improvement as they can be applied in the health care industry. The person must be able to manage turmoil and change.

GEOGRAPHIC SCOPE OF RECRUITING ACTIVITIES:
Serve clients nationwide and in Europe and Asia

TOTAL YEARS OF RETAINER-TYPE RECRUITING EXPERIENCE:
22 years

HELGA LONG
President
H.M. Long International, Ltd.
237 Park Avenue, 21st Floor
New York, NY 10017
Telephone: (212) 725-5150

Date of birth: August 22, 1943

Ernst Lurker

SPECIAL INTERESTS AND HOBBIES:
> International affairs, nonprofit board activity, bicycling, snorkeling, and
> aerobics

EMPLOYMENT HISTORY:
> 1974 to present: H.M. Long International, Ltd.
> 1973 to 1974: Recruiter, Judd-Falk
> 1973: Marketing Manager, Clevepak Corp.
> 1964 to 1973: Manager, Legal and New Product Services, Mattel Inc.

WHAT I LOOK FOR IN GENERAL IN A CANDIDATE:

After twenty years of successful global search work, I have found that each client is different and every search is unique, even within the same organization. Therefore, what I look for in a candidate is specifically tailored to the client's needs and specifications.

However, the qualities and personal characteristics that I uniformly seek worldwide are sincerity, honesty, loyalty, and commitment to producing results.

GEOGRAPHIC SCOPE OF RECRUITING ACTIVITIES:
> Serve clients nationwide and in North America, South America, Europe, and
> Pacific Rim

TOTAL YEARS OF RETAINER-TYPE RECRUITING EXPERIENCE:
> 20 years

MARK LORENZETTI
Partner
Roberts Ryan & Bentley, Inc.
420 Silas Court
Spring Hill, FL 34609
Telephone: (904) 686-3610

Date of birth: June 14, 1950

Roberts Ryan & Bentley, Inc.

EDUCATION:
Towson State University
B.S., psychology, 1972

SPECIAL INTERESTS AND HOBBIES:
Investing, running, psychology

EMPLOYMENT HISTORY:
1979 to present: Roberts Ryan & Bentley, Inc.
1978 to 1979: Manager, Travel Whirl
1974 to 1978: Assistant Vice President, Sun Life Insurance Company of
America
1972 to 1974: Program Director, American Cancer Society

WHAT I LOOK FOR IN GENERAL IN A CANDIDATE:

Besides exceeding the minimum requirements established by my clients, I expect candidates to present themselves professionally during our interview. Normally, I require a prerequisite writing sample not only to evaluate thought formulation and written communication skills but also to test interest and organizational ability. Despite the additional "burden" imposed, most candidates who are genuine have little problem meeting this demand. I present other, similar hurdles throughout the screening and evaluating process that serve to measure the commitment of candidates. In fact, the operational definition of a candidate is one who meets or exceeds the technical requirements of the position, the nontechnical (personality/chemistry) requirements, and is movable (prepared to change companies) and relocatable. If any of these criteria are not met, the prospect is not considered. Because of my educational background in psychology and my belief that successful searches are 75 percent based on the chemistry between the client and the candidate, I spend an inordinate amount of time measuring and evaluating personality characteristics of candidates.

GEOGRAPHIC SCOPE OF RECRUITING ACTIVITIES:
Serve clients nationwide and Canada

TOTAL YEARS OF RETAINER-TYPE RECRUITING EXPERIENCE:
15 years

JOHN LUCHT
President
The John Lucht Consultancy Inc.
The Olympic Tower
641 Fifth Avenue
New York, NY 10022
Telephone: (212) 935-4660

Waring Abbott

HONOREE: 1990, 1992, 1994

Date of birth: June 1, 1933

EDUCATION:
> University of Wisconsin
>> B.S., 1955
> University of Wisconsin Law School
>> LL.B., 1960

SPECIAL INTERESTS AND HOBBIES:
> Writing, lecturing, and pro bono seminars, author of the best-seller *Rites of Passage at $100,000+ . . . The Insider's Guide to Executive Job Changing* (four editions since 1988, latest, 1993); also *Executive Job-Changing Workbook* (1994).

EMPLOYMENT HISTORY:
> 1977 to present: The John Lucht Consultancy Inc.
> 1971 to 1977: Vice President, Heidrick & Struggles, Inc.
> 1970 to 1971: General Manager–Tetley Tea Division, Squibb BeechNut Inc.
> 1969 to 1970: Director of Marketing, W.A. Sheaffer Pen Co.
> 1964 to 1969: Director of New Product Marketing, Bristol-Myers Co.
> 1960 to 1964: Account Executive, J. Walter Thompson Co.
> 1959 to 1960: Instructor, University of Wisconsin Law School

WHAT I LOOK FOR IN GENERAL IN A CANDIDATE:

For almost every high-level position in any industry, a rare few executives stand out. Their leadership, creativity, expertise, and fine personal characteristics produce an outstanding performance and reputation that's observable both inside and outside the organization.

Practicing independently, I make it a point to serve only one company in each industry. That way, none of my client's competitors is "off-limits" as I do the search. There's a single, simple criterion: Who's the best person in America (or worldwide) for the position?

Usually that means someone who's making a key contribution to a competitor's success. Always it's the one person my client is most strengthened to gain. And often it's someone a competitor is weakened by losing. If so, all the better! Quality of management is every company's number one asset. And shifting the balance of management power in an industry—modestly or dramatically—is what my client and I both try to do in every search we undertake.

GEOGRAPHIC SCOPE OF RECRUITING ACTIVITIES:
> Serve clients nationwide and internationally

TOTAL YEARS OF RETAINER-TYPE RECRUITING EXPERIENCE:
> 22 years

THEODORE E. (TED) LUSK
Partner
Nadzam, Lusk & Associates, Inc.
3211 Scott Boulevard, Suite 205
Santa Clara, CA 95054-3091
Telephone: (408) 727-6601

HONOREE: 1992, 1994

Date of birth: September 4, 1932

Nadzam, Lusk & Associates, Inc.

EDUCATION:
San Jose State College
B.A., industrial relations, 1957

MILITARY:
Sergeant, United States Marine Corps, 1951 to 1954

SPECIAL INTERESTS AND HOBBIES:
Presbyterian Church elder; family, travel, gardening, dining

EMPLOYMENT HISTORY:
1976 to present: Nadzam, Lusk & Associates, Inc.
1970 to 1976: Director–Employee Relations, Singer Business Machines
1966 to 1970: Manager–Industrial Relations, Singer Link
1965 to 1966: Corporate Director–Staffing, Utah Construction & Mining
1964 to 1965: Director–Personnel, Soule Steel
1957 to 1964: Various positions in industrial relations, Aerojet-General

WHAT I LOOK FOR IN GENERAL IN A CANDIDATE:

Track record, track record, and track record. Leadership and managerial skills. Integrity, sense of ethics, and a good dose of common sense. Image and intelligence. Self-confident but not arrogant. Verbal and writing skills. Strategic and tactical abilities.

GEOGRAPHIC SCOPE OF RECRUITING ACTIVITIES:
Serve clients nationwide and in Canada, Europe, and Asia

TOTAL YEARS OF RETAINER-TYPE RECRUITING EXPERIENCE:
18 years

WILLIAM T. MANGUM
President
Thomas Mangum Company
500 E. Del Mar Blvd., Suite 19
Pasadena, CA 91101
Telephone: (818) 577-2070

Date of birth: December 7, 1931

Thomas Mangum Company

EDUCATION:
> University of Southern California
>> B.S., 1952 to 1954

SPECIAL INTERESTS AND HOBBIES:
> Writing. Author of *99 Minutes to the Ideal Job.* Community affairs.

EMPLOYMENT HISTORY:
> 1960 to present: Thomas Mangum Company
> 1956 to 1959: Human Resources Manager/Operations Manager, Fairchild
>> Controls Corporation
> 1954 to 1956: Employee Relations Specialist, Beckman Instruments, Inc.

WHAT I LOOK FOR IN GENERAL IN A CANDIDATE:

In all assignments the basic qualifications and experience are a must and a given factor for serious client candidate consideration. Each candidate thereafter is assessed on some twelve to fifteen general factors as itemized below to establish a match to client suitability. Since each assignment is different, the individual factors evaluated and weighed and the combination of factors required/desired will vary as to the unique nature of the client's needs.

General factors weighed:

- Leadership/management skills
- Interpersonal skills
- Unique skills (visionary, risk, etc.)
- Personal traits
- Intellectual capability
- Professional capability
- Personal style and interest
- Proven track record
- Winning positive attitude
- Values
- Communication skills (verbal, written, personal and listening skill)
- Judgment/decisiveness and problem-solving ability

GEOGRAPHIC SCOPE OF RECRUITING ACTIVITIES:
> Serve clients nationwide and internationally

TOTAL YEARS OF RETAINER-TYPE RECRUITING EXPERIENCE:
> 30 years

NANCY A. MARTIN
Partner
Educational Management Network
8 Williams Lane, P.O. Box 792
Nantucket, MA 02554
Telephone: (508) 228-6700

Date of Birth: June 26, 1944

Educational Management Network'

EDUCATION:
Mount Holyoke College
A.B., 1966
New York University
M.A., 1972

SPECIAL INTERESTS AND HOBBIES:
Study classical voice; needlework; sailing and swimming; reading; most important interest is raising my young son.

EMPLOYMENT HISTORY:
1985 to present: Educational Management Network
1983 to 1985: Senior Consultant, Academy for Educational Development
1978 to 1983: Manager, Peat Marwick & Main
1975 to 1978: Principal, Archer & Wood
1975: Consultant, K.M. Harrison Associates
1970 to 1975: Graduate work and work in professional theater
1966 to 1970: Teacher of English, Oldfields School District

WHAT I LOOK FOR IN GENERAL IN A CANDIDATE:

I look at qualities of character, first and foremost a person's values, how someone cares for others, and how he or she demonstrates those values and care for and of others in his/her professional and personal lives. I look for honesty and the capacity to see clearly one's strengths and weaknesses. Finally, I look for good judgment, tact, and the ability to look beyond day-to-day responsibilities, to keep an eye toward the future. It is then that I look at technical or managerial competencies.

GEOGRAPHIC SCOPE OF RECRUITING ACTIVITIES:
Serve clients nationwide and in France

TOTAL YEARS OF RETAINER-TYPE RECRUITING EXPERIENCE:
18 years

THEODORE B. MARTIN, JR.
Managing Partner
Nordeman Grimm, Inc.
150 N. Michigan Avenue, Suite 3610
Chicago, IL 60601
Telephone: (312) 332-0088

Date of birth: January 1, 1958

Nordeman Grimm, Inc.

EDUCATION:
Washington & Lee University
B.A., French, 1980
Northwestern University, Kellogg Graduate School of Management
Master's in management, 1983

SPECIAL INTERESTS AND HOBBIES:
Participation in sports, international travel, community charity work, W.I.P.E.
(Weekend Infant Program Emcee)

EMPLOYMENT HISTORY:
1985 to present: Nordeman Grimm, Inc.
1984 to 1985: Associate Brand Manager, Kraft, Inc.
1983 to 1984: Marketing Manager, Wilson Sporting Goods

WHAT I LOOK FOR IN GENERAL IN A CANDIDATE:

In general I look for (1) performance excellence, (2) leadership, and (3) references that support what I see. I believe performance excellence characteristics include a high level of applicable intelligence, an unquestionable integrity level, and a serious commitment to working hard. I sense business intelligence facilitates leadership and enhances the ability to have vision, think "outside the box," manage change, improve shareholder value, serve the customer, identify and solve key problems, etc. I look for leaders who are driven and work hard because they are inspired to achieve their goals, compete, and put in the hours required to excel. I believe strong leaders are good developers and motivators of people, with integrity being a key ingredient to their success and respect. I look for candidates with broad interpersonal skills to maximize their leadership potential, including superb communication skills, an excellent listening capability, and a sense of humor. I seek a good objective reference from someone who has no incentive to slant comments about the candidate.

GEOGRAPHIC SCOPE OF RECRUITING ACTIVITIES:
Serve clients nationwide and Europe, Far East

TOTAL YEARS OF RETAINER-TYPE RECRUITING EXPERIENCE:
9 years

WILLIAM H. (MO) MARUMOTO
Chairman of the Board and CEO
The Interface Group, Ltd./Boyden
1025 Thomas Jefferson Street, N.W.
Suite 410, East Lobby
Washington, DC 20007
Telephone: (202) 342-7200

HONOREE: 1992, 1994

Date of birth: December 16, 1934

Boyden

EDUCATION:
    Whittier College
        B.A., 1957

SPECIAL INTERESTS AND HOBBIES:
    Fishing, gardening, contemporary art, classical and country music, collector of Americana antiques

EMPLOYMENT HISTORY:
    1973 to present: The Interface Group, Ltd./Boyden
    1970 to 1973: Special Assistant to the President, The White House
    1969 to 1970: Assistant to the Secretary, U.S. Dept. of Health, Education and Welfare
    1969: Senior Consultant, Peat, Marwick & Mitchell Company
    1968 to 1969: Vice President/Planning and Development, California Institute of the Arts
    1965 to 1968: Associate Director of Development and Alumni Relations, University of California at Los Angeles
    1958 to 1965: Director of Alumni Relations, Whittier College

WHAT I LOOK FOR IN GENERAL IN A CANDIDATE:

Individuals with a strong corporate presence and bearing with exceptional interpersonal skills. Highly aggressive and motivated with strong managerial and leadership skills. Exceptional oral and written communication skills. Highly intelligent, creative, and innovative with sound strategic and analytical skills. Have a high degree of integrity and ethical standards. Has demonstrated record of achievements. Is focused and has a mental toughness and a sense of humor. Ability to be flexible and adjust to a new culture and environment.

GEOGRAPHIC SCOPE OF RECRUITING ACTIVITIES:
    Serve clients nationwide and occasionally Japan, Latin America, and Europe

TOTAL YEARS OF RETAINER-TYPE RECRUITING EXPERIENCE:
    25 years

JAMES P. MASCIARELLI
Managing Partner
Fenwick Partners
57 Bedford Street, Suite 101
Lexington, MA 02173
Telephone: (617) 862-3370

HONOREE: 1992, 1994

Date of birth: November 14, 1948

Fenwick Partners

EDUCATION:
Holy Cross College
A.B., psychology, 1970
Babson College
M.B.A., organizational behavior, 1978

SPECIAL INTERESTS AND HOBBIES:
Music, guitar, travel, reading, chess, hiking, boating

EMPLOYMENT HISTORY:
1983 to present: Fenwick Partners
1981 to 1983: President, The Churchill Group
1979 to 1981: Vice President, Winter, Wyman & Company
1974 to 1979: North American Human Resources Manager, Data General
Corporation
1973 to 1974: Human Resources Manager, Cramer Electronics
1970 to 1973: Executive Director, Community Health Education Council

WHAT I LOOK FOR IN GENERAL IN A CANDIDATE:

I seek the optimum combination of personal factors, resume factors, and motivations for the specific search performed. My background and orientation allow me to evaluate motivational and attitudinal factors that are key to critical success elements for the assignment. Self-knowledge, creativity, and active listening skills are highly valued in my mind. I introduce *only* candidates with strong belief, value, and attitudinal systems that can inspire or at least provide professional modeling behavior for their organizations. The search for leadership maturity and the self-esteem and self-awareness that it implies are foremost on my mind.

GEOGRAPHIC SCOPE OF RECRUITING ACTIVITIES:
Serve clients nationwide and Canada

TOTAL YEARS OF RETAINER-TYPE RECRUITING EXPERIENCE:
13 years

NEAL L. MASLAN
Managing Director
Ward Howell International, Inc.
16255 Ventura Blvd., Suite 400
Encino, CA 91436
Telephone: (818) 905-6010

HONOREE: 1992, 1994

Date of birth: September 22, 1940

Ward Howell International, Inc.

EDUCATION:
> University of Virginia
>> B.A., psychology, 1962
> Yale University
>> M.P.H., health care administration, 1964

MILITARY:
> First Lieutenant, United States Army, 1964 to 1966

SPECIAL INTERESTS AND HOBBIES:
> Tennis, art and antique collecting, children and grandchildren, civic/volunteer boards

EMPLOYMENT HISTORY:
> 1988 to present: Ward Howell International, Inc.
> 1986 to 1988: Vice President, Paul R. Ray & Company
> 1982 to 1986: Senior Vice President, American Medical International
> 1972 to 1982: Executive Vice President, Hyatt Corporation (Hyatt Medical Enterprises)
> 1970 to 1972: Executive Vice President/General Manager, CENCO Corporation (CENCO Hospital and Convalescent Homes)
> 1968 to 1970: Vice President–Administration, Progressive Care Corporation
> 1966 to 1968: Administrator, Terrace Hill Nursing Homes

WHAT I LOOK FOR IN GENERAL IN A CANDIDATE:

> *Intellectual ability.*
> *Integrity and courage of convictions.*
> *Maturity.*
> *Interpersonal skills.*
> *Results orientation/initiative.*
> *Risk taker.*
> *Team orientation.*
> *Business acumen/experience.*
> *Impact.*
> *Planning and organizing.*
> *Management style.*
> *Leadership.*

GEOGRAPHIC SCOPE OF RECRUITING ACTIVITIES:
> Serve clients nationwide and in the United Kingdom and Germany

TOTAL YEARS OF RETAINER-TYPE RECRUITING EXPERIENCE:
> 8 years

LAURENCE RAYMOND MASSE
Managing Director, and Chairman–International
Ward Howell International, Inc.
1300 Grove Avenue, Suite 100
Barrington, IL 60010
Telephone: (708) 382-2206

HONOREE: 1992, 1994

Date of birth: July 27, 1926

Ward Howell International, Inc.

EDUCATION:
Hope College
B.A., English, speech, journalism,
1946 to 1950

MILITARY:
Pharmacist's Mate Third Class, United States Navy, 1944 to 1946

SPECIAL INTERESTS AND HOBBIES:
Family, home, active in two amateur theater groups, reading, gardening, travel, international affairs

EMPLOYMENT HISTORY:
1975 to present: Ward Howell International, Inc.
1973 to 1975: Managing Director, TASA, Inc.
1969 to 1972: Vice President, Industrial Relations, REA Express, Inc.
1968 to 1969: Senior Associate, Heidrick & Struggles, Inc.
1966 to 1968: Director, Personnel and Administration, Europe, Middle East, and Africa, ITT
1956 to 1966: Director, Personnel–International and Director–Personnel, Jell-O Division, General Foods Corporation
1953 to 1956: Project Manager, General Motors Corporation

WHAT I LOOK FOR IN GENERAL IN A CANDIDATE:

In general, I look for candidates who best fill my client's needs and who will best fit in the client's organization and environment. Naturally, I look for all the obvious characteristics of intelligence, integrity, leadership skills, interpersonal skills, motivation, etc., but those alone won't suffice. Also needed is the "fit" or chemistry that will increase the odds for success and reduce the risk of failure. An important part of that component is the candidate's view of him- or herself, philosophy of life, values, and priorities. A good sense of humor and willingness to laugh at oneself are very important. Whenever possible, I take informal "soundings" prior to presenting the candidate with people who have worked with him or her, to reinforce my conclusions or make me probe further.

GEOGRAPHIC SCOPE OF RECRUITING ACTIVITIES:
Serve clients nationally and in Europe, Latin America, and Asia Pacific. Specific countries include: Mexico, Brazil, United Kingdom, France, Germany, Australia, etc.

TOTAL YEARS OF RETAINER-TYPE RECRUITING EXPERIENCE:
22 years

R. BRUCE MASSEY
President
Bruce Massey & Partners Inc.
330 Bay Street, Suite 1104
Toronto, Ontario M5H 2S8 Canada
Telephone: (416) 861-0077

Date of birth: March 8, 1933

Bruce Massey & Partners Inc.

MILITARY:
Major, Canadian Army Infantry (Militia), 1965 to 1975

SPECIAL INTERESTS AND HOBBIES:
Sailboat racing, squash, fly-fishing

EMPLOYMENT HISTORY:
1975 to present: Bruce Massey & Partners Inc. (formerly Massey Charboneau)
1966 to 1975: President, Lab-Volt Ltd.
1957 to 1966: Sales Representative, Standard Electric Time Co.

WHAT I LOOK FOR IN GENERAL IN A CANDIDATE:

Generally, at the levels that I work, candidates have relevant experience and obviously transferable skills applicable to my clients' requirements. I look very hard at their record of achievement and try to determine how much of that is owned by the individual or by others that were part of the person's group or team. I examine closely their leadership potential, energy, versatility, tenacity, and mental toughness. How they have faced adversity and what they have done to overcome it. I try to assess not only their cognitive capabilities for the position at issue but what their potential might represent for the future.

I look for evidence of their integrity and that they have some balance in their work and personal lives. That they have a sense of humor and an ability to deal with ambiguity. Finally, will they "fit" with the client and the organization?

GEOGRAPHIC SCOPE OF RECRUITING ACTIVITIES:
Serve clients nationwide and England, France, and Germany

TOTAL YEARS OF RETAINER-TYPE RECRUITING EXPERIENCE:
20 years

DAVID B. MAZZA
President
Mazza & Riley, Inc.
45 William Street, Suite 270
Wellesley Hills, MA 02181
Telephone: (617) 235-7724

Date of birth: August 22, 1952

EDUCATION:
Brown University
B.A., sociology, 1974
Harvard Business School
M.B.A., 1977

SPECIAL INTERESTS AND HOBBIES:
Tennis, golf, basketball, private investing

Robert Ruscansky

EMPLOYMENT HISTORY:
1990 to present: Mazza & Riley, Inc.
1984 to 1990: Partner, Bartholdi & Mazza, Inc./Bartholdi, Dromeshauser & Mazza
1982 to 1983: Partner, Silva, Burke & Mazza
1982: Vice President, Haley Associates
1978 to 1981: Various positions, Russell Reynolds Associates, Inc.
1977 to 1978: Assistant Product Manager, General Foods Corporation

WHAT I LOOK FOR IN GENERAL IN A CANDIDATE:

While each search is unique, with job descriptions based on the functional, industry, and cultural needs of an individual client, the characteristics that I look for are:

- *Solid career progression and the ability to consistently achieve successful results:* Whether it is returns to investors for a venture capitalist or profitable corporate growth for a CEO, I am interested in tangible, positive results and how they were achieved.
- *Entrepreneurial skills:* Proven ability to function in small or middle-market environments with little structure and limited resources. A high energy level, vision, drive, and a passion for success.
- *Leadership ability:* Someone who can build and motivate a team in highly stressful, growth, or turnaround situations.
- *Strong communications and interpersonal skills:* An open and direct communicator with no hidden agenda. Someone who has a sense of humor and does not take themselves too seriously.
- *Creativity:* The ability to creatively solve difficult problems where no obvious solutions exist.
- *Intelligence:* Not just academic credentials but a "street smart" individual who can think strategically.
- *Maturity:* A self-confident individual with a controlled ego and knowledge of his or her strengths or weaknesses.
- *Honesty and Integrity.*

GEOGRAPHIC SCOPE OF RECRUITING ACTIVITIES:
Serve clients nationwide and internationally

TOTAL YEARS OF RETAINER-TYPE RECRUITING EXPERIENCE:
16 years

JONATHAN E. McBRIDE
President
McBride Associates, Inc.
1511 K Street, NW
Washington, DC 20005
Telephone: (202) 638-1150

HONOREE: 1990, 1992, 1994

Date of birth: June 16, 1942

McBride Associates, Inc.

EDUCATION:
> Yale University
>> B.A., American studies, 1964

MILITARY:
> Lieutenant, United States Naval Reserve, 1964 to 1968

EMPLOYMENT HISTORY:
> 1979 to present: McBride Associates, Inc.
> 1976 to 1979: Vice President, Simmons Associates, Inc.
> 1972 to 1976: Vice President, Lionel D. Edie & Co.
> 1968 to 1972: Account Executive, Merrill, Lynch, Pierce, Fenner & Smith, Inc.

WHAT I LOOK FOR IN GENERAL IN A CANDIDATE:

It seems to me a hiring manager working with a corporate "headhunter" will be more successful by hunting for hearts, not just heads. Same goes for the head-hunter, or perhaps better said, the "heart-hunter."

I see myself as a heart-hunter. I seek personal as well as professional commit-ment—a synthesis of emotional and rational considerations—in favor of my clients' needs. I also seek integrity—not just "honesty," but a sense of "wholeness"—in those candidates I elect to pursue for clients.

Circumstances will arise in a job that neither client nor candidate can antici-pate while still in the recruiting process. A candidate who accepts and takes on a new job because it is a natural expression of who she or he *is*, is much more likely to meet the challenges successfully than is one who changes jobs because it "looks good" or just "makes sense."

GEOGRAPHIC SCOPE OF RECRUITING ACTIVITIES:
> Serve clients nationwide

TOTAL YEARS OF RETAINER-TYPE RECRUITING EXPERIENCE:
> 18 years

RICHARD A. McCALLISTER
Managing Director
Boyden
180 N. Stetson, Suite 5050
Chicago, IL 60601
Telephone: (312) 565-1300

Date of birth: April 10, 1937

Peggy Zarneck Photography, Inc.

EDUCATION:
University of North Carolina, 1958
Illinois State University, 1960
B.S., psychology

SPECIAL INTERESTS AND HOBBIES:
Fitness, running, golf; special interest in economics/history

EMPLOYMENT HISTORY:
1989 to present: Boyden
1975 to 1989: President, William H. Clark Associates, Inc.
1968 to 1975: Director, Price Waterhouse
1966 to 1968: Vice President, Management Psychologists, Inc.
1965 to 1966: Industrial Consultant, Science Research Associates–IBM Subsidiary

WHAT I LOOK FOR IN GENERAL IN A CANDIDATE:

Interviews are dynamic by definition. While the basic issues are fundamental, each search and, in turn, each candidate requires a tailored in-depth approach to evaluation. Our responsibility is to evaluate particular characteristics as they relate to our client's requirements. The importance of performance, chemistry, and integrity, to mention a few, are critical to our client's success in hiring senior management. Our challenge is to be on target on behalf of our clients and to make sure that we have not introduced an individual to a situation that would interrupt a successful career. I believe in behavioral analysis as the most predictive aspect of future success. I apply this evaluation to each candidate we present.

GEOGRAPHIC SCOPE OF RECRUITING ACTIVITIES:
Serve clients nationwide and in the United Kingdom, Europe, Asia

TOTAL YEARS OF RETAINER-TYPE RECRUITING EXPERIENCE:
26 years

HORACIO J. McCOY
President, Mexico/Latin America Region
Korn/Ferry International, Inc.
Montes Urales No. 641
Mexico, D.F. 11000
Telephone: (525) 202-5654

HONOREE: 1992, 1994

Date of birth: January 4, 1939

EDUCATION:
University of Southern California
B.S., business administration, 1961

MILITARY:
Reserves (nonactive), Mexican Army,
1956 to 1957

Korn/Ferry International, Inc.

SPECIAL INTERESTS AND HOBBIES:
Christian bible reading and meditation, golf, opera

EMPLOYMENT HISTORY:
1977 to present: Korn/Ferry International, Inc.
1975 to 1977: Vice President, Hazzard & Associates
1972 to 1975: Operations Director, Super Mercados, S.A.
1971 to 1972: Senior Associate, McKinsey & Company, Inc.
1967 to 1971: Assistant General Manager, Bristol-Myers Company
1965 to 1967: National Sales Manager, Del Monte Foods
1963 to 1965: Account Executive, McCann-Erickson
1961 to 1963: Brand Manager, Procter & Gamble Company

WHAT I LOOK FOR IN GENERAL IN A CANDIDATE:

The relative weight of the following elements depends on the specific position, industry, and function involved:

- Communication skills, articulation, eye contact.
- Key accomplishments, problem-solving skills, decision-making process.
- Intellectual integrity, professional standards and ethics.
- Interpersonal skills, drive level, dependability.
- Strengths and weaknesses as a manager.
- Ability to focus on specific solutions to business problems.
- Motivation level, energy, dynamism, and results orientation.
- Overall business vision and strategic focus.
- Intellectual skills based on past experience.
- Leadership skills and style.
- Cultural fit with client and chemistry match.
- Future management potential.
- Potential presence and appearance.

GEOGRAPHIC SCOPE OF RECRUITING ACTIVITIES:
Serve clients nationwide and throughout Mexico, Latin America, and selectively in the United States

TOTAL YEARS OF RETAINER-TYPE RECRUITING EXPERIENCE:
18 years

MILLINGTON F. McCOY
Managing Director
Gould & McCoy
300 Park Avenue, 20th Floor
New York, NY 10022
Telephone: (212) 688-8671

Bachrach

HONOREE: 1990, 1992, 1994

Date of birth: January 22, 1941

EDUCATION:
University of Missouri
B.A., 1962
Harvard-Radcliffe Program in
Business Administration
Certificate, 1963

SPECIAL INTERESTS AND HOBBIES:
Dressage, psychology, skiing, Committee of 200 (founding member), gardening, study of the Enneagram

EMPLOYMENT HISTORY:
1977 to present: Gould & McCoy
1966 to 1977: Vice President, Handy Associates
1965 to 1966: Advertising and Marketing Research Analyst, Gardner Advertising Agency
1964 to 1965: Field Market Researcher, The Procter & Gamble Company

WHAT I LOOK FOR IN GENERAL IN A CANDIDATE:

Gaining an understanding of the client culture and its requirements for success is the first step in determining what I look for in a candidate. My key to the successful search assignment is the right cultural fit.

After determining cultural fit, the most important part of the assessment process is to figure out whether the candidate is on a positive, upward trend in his or her life and career. I have found that the best way to predict future success is to look for a solid and consistent record of past success, going back to the person's early formative years. Critical qualities I seek in an individual are warmth, a good sense of humor, integrity, strong values, and a high learning-curve style of career. I always look for self-knowledge and awareness, including personal strategy and direction.

Relative to the client organization and its needs, the other things I look for in a candidate include the requisite level of intelligence, emotional maturity, drive, vision, risk-orientation, personality type, and skill fit with the position requirements.

It takes an assessor who is self-aware, mature, and seasoned. Like the best candidates, those of us who learn by our experiences are the ones who get ahead.

GEOGRAPHIC SCOPE OF RECRUITING ACTIVITIES:
Serve clients nationwide and in Europe and Japan

TOTAL YEARS OF RETAINER-TYPE RECRUITING EXPERIENCE:
28 years

RICHARD M. McFARLAND
Principal
Brissenden, McFarland, Fuccella and
  Reynolds, Inc.
712 Route 202-206
Bridgewater, NJ 08807
Telephone: (203) 227-4977

HONOREE: 1990, 1992, 1994

Date of birth: September 10, 1923

Ing-John Studio

EDUCATION:
  Rensselaer Polytechnic Institute
    Bachelor of Chemical Engineering,
    1944

MILITARY:
  Lieutenant Commander, United States Navy Reserve, 1943 to 1945 and 1953
  to 1955

SPECIAL INTERESTS AND HOBBIES:
  Sailing, history (American and ancient), archaeology, natural sciences

EMPLOYMENT HISTORY:
  1981 to present: Brissenden, McFarland, Fuccella and Reynolds, Inc.
  1969 to 1981: Senior Vice President, Heidrick & Struggles, Inc.
  1967 to 1969: Vice President and General Manager, Inorganic Division, Wyandotte Chemical Co.
  1960 to 1967: President, Cumberland Chemical Corp.
  1959 to 1960: Manager–Market Development, Texas Butadiene and Chemical Co.
  1955 to 1959: Product Manager–Plastics, FMC Corporation, Chemical and Plastics Division

WHAT I LOOK FOR IN GENERAL IN A CANDIDATE:

Before a prospect becomes a candidate, he or she is screened by telephone. At this time pertinent facts are obtained directed toward the requirements of the job and the specification developed with the client. Having passed that screen, next comes the face-to-face, in-depth interview, at which time the highly critical first impressions are observed—physical appearance, speech, bearing, credibility, humor, enthusiasm, charisma. Next comes a detailed questioning of early background, education, service time, if any, family, and professional career. Each job is explored as to responsibilities, reporting relationships, accomplishments, and how these were achieved. Emphasis here is on style, managerial skill, leadership, and knowledge. All during this phase, I test for accuracy, truthfulness, communicating skills, and personal stimulus value. At the conclusion of two and a half to three hours of conversation, I decide if the candidate has the requisite knowledge, the desired potential for growth, the right personal chemistry to fit the client's environment.

GEOGRAPHIC SCOPE OF RECRUITING ACTIVITIES:
  Serve clients nationwide

TOTAL YEARS OF RETAINER-TYPE RECRUITING EXPERIENCE:
  25 years

CLARENCE E. McFEELY
Partner
McFeely Wackerle Shulman
20 N. Wacker Drive, Suite 3110
Chicago, IL 60606
Telephone: (312) 641-2977

HONOREE: 1990, 1992, 1994

Date of birth: May 12, 1929

Stuart-Rodgers-Reilly Photography

EDUCATION:
Bradley University, Illinois
B.S., 1951

MILITARY:
First Lieutenant, United States Marine Corps, 1951 to 1953

SPECIAL INTERESTS AND HOBBIES:
Golf, classical music, theater, travel

EMPLOYMENT HISTORY:
1969 to present: McFeely Wackerle Shulman
1969: Managing Partner, William H. Clark & Associates
1960 to 1969: Principal, A.T. Kearney & Company
1959 to 1960: Representative, Dansk Designs, Inc.
1955 to 1959: Employee Relations, The Budd Company
1953 to 1955: Personnel Supervisor, Campbell Soup Company

WHAT I LOOK FOR IN GENERAL IN A CANDIDATE:

- A high level of personal and professional value standards; integrity and ethics.
- Perception, intuitiveness, and insight to understanding people.
- Ability to lead and motivate others.
- Decisiveness and courage to solve difficult problems.
- Ability to plan, organize, and set priorities.
- A high energy level and commitment to excel.
- Good intellectual, educational, and cultural background.
- Healthy balance between personal and professional life.
- Community commitment and social awareness.
- Can handle both success and adversity.
- Good health, fitness, and grooming.

GEOGRAPHIC SCOPE OF RECRUITING ACTIVITIES:
Serve clients nationwide

TOTAL YEARS OF RETAINER-TYPE RECRUITING EXPERIENCE:
34 years

CHARLES M. MENG
Chairman and President
Meng, Finseth & Associates
3858 Carson Street, Suite 202
Torrance, CA 90503
Telephone: (310) 316-0706

HONOREE: 1992, 1994

Date of birth: October 13, 1937

Meng, Finseth & Associates

EDUCATION:
El Camino College
A.A.S., 1960
Long Beach State University
B.A., political science, 1963

MILITARY:
Sergeant, United States Army (Army Security Agency), 1956 to 1963

SPECIAL INTERESTS AND HOBBIES:
Tennis, jogging, reading, pleasure travel

EMPLOYMENT HISTORY:
1985 to present: Meng, Finseth & Associates
1971 to 1985: Chairman and President, Houck, Meng & Company
1967 to 1971: Consultant, KPMG Peat, Marwick

WHAT I LOOK FOR IN GENERAL IN A CANDIDATE:

In recruiting prospective candidates at all levels of senior management, it is imperative to match experience, aptitude, and personality with the client's exacting specification. Leadership, management style, business acumen, and innovation are key factors considered in the evaluation process. In senior management posts, demonstrated illustrations of successful past performance in complex and/or difficult situations are essential. Excellent communicative skills are indispensable for conversing with the organization's management, staff, and their external publics. The individual's track record of professional growth and development are a key factor in determining candidate suitability. Enough cannot be said about personal and professional ethics; candidates must be above reproach with verifiable past histories.

In today's marketplace those individuals with proven records of imagination, achievement, and mastery are positioned to become leading candidates.

Finally, the "art" of our profession is the ability to understand the chemistry of the client and present candidates who will flourish in that environment.

GEOGRAPHIC SCOPE OF RECRUITING ACTIVITIES:
Serve clients nationally and internationally

TOTAL YEARS OF RETAINER-TYPE RECRUITING EXPERIENCE:
25 years

CARL W. MENK
Chairman
Canny, Bowen Inc.
200 Park Avenue
New York, NY 10166
Telephone: (212) 949-6111

HONOREE: 1990, 1992, 1994

Date of birth: October 19, 1921

Canny, Bowen Inc.

EDUCATION:
> Seton Hall University
> > B.S., business administration, 1943
> Columbia University
> > M.A., 1950

MILITARY:
> Second Lieutenant–Pilot, United States Air Force, 1943 to 1946

SPECIAL INTERESTS AND HOBBIES:
> Golf, swimming, oil painting

EMPLOYMENT HISTORY:
> 1984 to present: Canny, Bowen Inc.
> 1969 to 1984: President, Boyden Associates, Inc.
> 1946 to 1969: Senior Vice President, P. Ballantine & Sons

WHAT I LOOK FOR IN GENERAL IN A CANDIDATE:

During my twenty-five years' experience in executive search, I have experienced executive search becoming an accepted and necessary management resource, the increased attention given to search by the media, the rise of the "shoot-out" and its mitigating effect on long-standing close client relationships, a more comprehensive identification of candidates with computerized data banks, and the increased marketing and public relations efforts by firms rather than relying only on performance.

However, the values learned when I first entered the profession have not changed. Search firms should be structured to meet clients' staffing needs by being able to present candidates of integrity who are intelligent, committed motivators, and leaders who will enhance the quality of management of the client company.

GEOGRAPHIC SCOPE OF RECRUITING ACTIVITIES:
> Serve clients nationwide

TOTAL YEARS OF RETAINER-TYPE RECRUITING EXPERIENCE:
> 25 years

JOHN T. MESTEPEY
Vice President/Managing Director
A.T. Kearney Executive Search
201 South Biscayne Blvd., Suite 3180
Miami, FL 33131
Telephone: (305) 577-0046

Date of birth: March 15, 1943

A.T. Kearney Executive Search

EDUCATION:
> Loyola University of Los Angeles
> > B.S., psychology, 1964

MILITARY:
> First Lieutenant, United States Marine Corps, 1968 to 1971

SPECIAL INTERESTS AND HOBBIES:
> Golf, fishing

EMPLOYMENT HISTORY:
> 1987 to present: A.T. Kearney Executive Search
> 1978 to 1987: Managing Partner, Fleming Associates
> 1976 to 1978: Director of Market Development, Hy-Gain Electronics
> 1975 to 1976: Director of Program Development, Lincoln National
> > Life–Career Development Corp.
> 1972 to 1975: National Director of Recruiting, Aetna Life & Casualty

WHAT I LOOK FOR IN GENERAL IN A CANDIDATE:

To be a candidate for a search, a person must first fit the specifications that have been developed for the position by my client and me. This includes, of course, relevant educational background and work experience. In addition, a person must demonstrate individual qualities and characteristics such as personality, values, energy, drive, and intelligence, which suggest the possibility of some compatibility with the culture of the client company. Last, I like candidates with good senses of humor who enjoy being part of the search process and who are honest and forthright with me throughout the process.

GEOGRAPHIC SCOPE OF RECRUITING ACTIVITIES:
> Serve clients nationwide and in Latin America, Europe, Asia/Pacific

TOTAL YEARS OF RETAINER-TYPE RECRUITING EXPERIENCE:
> 17 years

HERBERT T. MINES
President and CEO
Herbert Mines Associates, Inc.
399 Park Avenue
New York, NY 10022
Telephone: (212) 355-0909

Herbert Mines Associates, Inc.

HONOREE: 1990, 1992, 1994

Date of birth: January 30, 1929

EDUCATION:
> Babson College
>> B.S., economics, 1949
> Cornell University
>> M.I.L.R., 1954

SPECIAL INTERESTS AND HOBBIES:
> Intergroup relations, education, tennis, art

EMPLOYMENT HISTORY:
> 1981 to present: Herbert Mines Associates, Inc.
> 1972 to 1981: Chairman–Search Division, Wells Management Corp.
> 1970 to 1972: Vice President–Human Resources, Revlon
> 1966 to 1970: Senior Vice President–Human Resources, Neiman-Marcus
> 1954 to 1966: Administrator–Training and Organizational Development, Macy's
> 1949 to 1952: Various positions, G. Fox & Company

WHAT I LOOK FOR IN GENERAL IN A CANDIDATE:

- General appearance, dress, manner, stature, and verbal presentation.
- The ability to express themselves clearly and concisely and know when they have completed their thoughts.
- The willingness to discuss subjects which are embarrassing or failures in their career and to deal with them in a practical, understandable way without blaming others. Self-knowledge and a sense of self-worth, which makes it possible to discuss their strengths and weaknesses dispassionately.
- An understanding of their own personal psychological profile so they can relate their experiences realistically, particularly where these involve other personalities with whom they were uncomfortable or work situations which did not fit.
- Energy, a sense of humor, consistency, and clarity in their descriptions of past activities and future objectives.
- The understanding of why they made mistakes in the past and how they can be avoided in the future. The perception of how to avoid situations where they are likely to fail and to seek those where their strengths can be best utilized.
- The ability to formulate a clear response to the position being discussed and if both sides are interested, to pursue the project with consistency, but without being overly aggressive.

GEOGRAPHIC SCOPE OF RECRUITING ACTIVITIES:
> Serve clients nationwide and the United Kingdom, France, Italy, Spain, Germany, Canada, and Hong Kong

TOTAL YEARS OF RETAINER-TYPE RECRUITING EXPERIENCE:
> 22 years

P. JOHN MIRTZ
Partner
Mirtz Morice, Inc.
One Dock Street
Stamford, CT 06902
Telephone: (203) 964-9266

HONOREE: 1992, 1994

Date of birth: February 22, 1940

Mirtz Morice, Inc.

EDUCATION:
Miami University, Oxford, Ohio
B.A., psychology, 1958 to 1962

MILITARY:
Captain, United States Marine Corps, 1962 to 1966

SPECIAL INTERESTS AND HOBBIES:
Reading, athletics

EMPLOYMENT HISTORY:
1982 to present: Mirtz Morice, Inc.
1980 to 1982: Vice President and Partner, William H. Clark Associates
1971 to 1980: Senior Vice President and Office Manager, Billington, Fox &
Ellis Inc.
1966 to 1971: Personnel Manager, Celanese Corporation

WHAT I LOOK FOR IN GENERAL IN A CANDIDATE:

Evaluating those candidate qualities required by our diverse client group has
been a challenging and stimulating process over the last twenty years. Each client
has its own culture, professional standards, and unique problems. Finding the correct qualities in candidates requires an understanding of all of those issues combined with integrity, highly professional evaluation skills, and doggedness that
keeps the process going until the right person is found.

The personalities and skills of our candidates are as varied as our client
requirements. However, there are certain personal qualities that have been important to me. Integrity, solid values, high work ethic, and leadership ability top the
list. On the professional side, I have always been impressed by those (rare) individuals who have the capacity to build a business, products, and so on by anticipating future requirements. While pure intellectual horsepower must be coupled
with a balanced personality, the "visionary" will require an even greater multinational perspective.

GEOGRAPHIC SCOPE OF RECRUITING ACTIVITIES:
Serve clients nationwide

TOTAL YEARS OF RETAINER-TYPE RECRUITING EXPERIENCE:
23 years

NORMAN F. MITCHELL
Vice President, Southeastern Region
A. T. Kearney, Inc.
1100 Abernathy Road, Suite 900
Atlanta, GA 30328
Telephone: (404) 393-9900

A.T. Kearney Executive Search

Date of birth: March 26, 1940

EDUCATION:
>University of Dayton
>>B.S., business administration, 1962
>Indiana University
>>M.B.A., personnel and organizational behavior, 1964

SPECIAL INTERESTS AND HOBBIES:
>Family, professional and civic volunteer. AESC Board of Directors (1988–1991) serving second term on AESC board (1994–1996); 1988, Chair, Ethics and Professional Practices; 1989, Chair, Regional Affairs; 1994, Chair, International Conference; 1995, Chair, Regional Affairs. Golf, reading, avid collector of wooden ducks and decoys, past president of Indian Hills Civic Association, and twice president of Indian Hills Country Club

EMPLOYMENT HISTORY:
>1987 to present: A.T. Kearney, Inc.
>1974 to 1987: Executive Vice President, Fleming Associates
>1969 to 1974: Vice President, Administration, Bendix Home Systems
>1965 to 1969: Division Labor Relations Manager, Mead Corporation
>1964 to 1965: Assistant to President, Precision Rubber Products

WHAT I LOOK FOR IN GENERAL IN A CANDIDATE:

The client requirements dictate what I look for in a candidate. Search assignments vary in complexity and scope. The client need and requirement is the measure against which candidates should be evaluated. It is critically important that they share the client's value system, the work ethic, and the overall corporate culture. An effective search is a real blend of "art and science." Technology is rapidly changing the nature of our business, but the "soft side" issues are critical in evaluating candidates.

Some clients need more, some clients need less, but candidates must "fit" what the client wants. Large, multinational *Fortune* 100 companies require something very different than entrepreneurial-driven, high-tech, or service-oriented organizations. Objectivity is the key. Grit, determination, self-motivation, interpersonal skills, a sense of team, leadership versus management, commitment, integrity, and vision are the general requirements that are common to providing an effective solution for clients.

GEOGRAPHIC SCOPE OF RECRUITING ACTIVITIES:
>Serve clients nationwide and rely heavily on international partners who have strong understanding of cultural differences, market needs, and the important cultural factors that determine ultimate candidate success

TOTAL YEARS OF RETAINER-TYPE RECRUITING EXPERIENCE:
>20 years

JAMES M. MONTGOMERY
President
Houze, Shourds & Montgomery, Inc.
Greater Los Angeles World Trade Center
One World Trade, Suite 1840
Long Beach, CA 90831
Telephone: (310) 495-6495

HONOREE: 1990, 1992, 1994

Date of birth: May 5, 1939

Houze, Shourds & Montgomery, Inc.

MILITARY:
Private First Class, United States Marine Corps, 1957 to 1960

SPECIAL INTERESTS AND HOBBIES:
Golf, sailing, biking, collecting Native art, chair business support group for the opera, serve on civic boards

EMPLOYMENT HISTORY:
1978 to present: Houze, Shourds & Montgomery, Inc.
1973 to 1978: Director–Industrial Relations, Rohr Industries
1962 to 1973: Director–Corporate Personnel, Rockwell International

WHAT I LOOK FOR IN GENERAL IN A CANDIDATE:

Baseline requirements are candor, the appearance of substance (or more appropriately, the absence of superficiality), intellectual capacity, self-confidence, effective communications skills (the ability to articulate answers to unplanned questions and the ability to be a sensitive and active listener), flexibility, and integrity.

In addition to the baseline requirements, I'm interested in whether or not the candidate has strategic vision, integration and/or implementation skills, potential for higher (or broader) responsibilities, a sense of humor, and enough ego to lead and enough humility to follow.

And finally, experience! The track record! The "ideal" or "perfect" track record doesn't exist, but when all is said and done—the interview assessment formalized, the reference checks completed—the most reliable predictor of future performance is past performance. Therefore, I am keenly interested in whether or not a candidate can articulate and substantiate a rich and balanced overview of his or her experience. A candidate who is clearly "packaging" his or her background and omits important events is a candidate who raises my anxiety level about his or her suitability.

GEOGRAPHIC SCOPE OF RECRUITING ACTIVITIES:
Serve clients nationwide and in conjunction with Penrhyn International in London, Brussels, Stockholm, Tokyo, Melbourne, Toronto, Montreal, Johannesburg, Zurich

TOTAL YEARS OF RETAINER-TYPE RECRUITING EXPERIENCE:
17 years

JAMES L. MORICE
Partner
Mirtz Morice, Inc.
One Dock Street
Stamford, CT 06902
Telephone: (203) 964-9266

Mirtz Morice, Inc.

HONOREE: 1992, 1994

Date of birth: September 25, 1937

EDUCATION:
Keystone Junior College
A.A.S., engineering, 1958
New York University
B.S., personnel and labor relations, 1964

MILITARY:
Specialist Fourth Class, United States Army, 1958 to 1960

SPECIAL INTERESTS AND HOBBIES:
Travel (U.S. and international), reading, gardening, athletics, flying (private pilot)

EMPLOYMENT HISTORY:
1982 to present; Mirtz Morice, Inc.
1980 to 1982: Vice President and Partner, William H. Clark Associates
1976 to 1980: Vice President and Principal, SpencerStuart & Associates
1972 to 1975: Vice President and Partner, Billington Fox & Ellis, Inc.
1969 to 1972: Manager, Staff Recruitment, McKinsey & Company, Inc.
1964 to 1969: Various positions, Equitable Life Assurance Society of the U.S.
1962 to 1964: Training Assistant, Chemical Bank
1960 to 1962: Copy boy and news assistant, New York Times Company

WHAT I LOOK FOR IN GENERAL IN A CANDIDATE:

In general, style and competence as a manager, skill as a leader, expertise in a functional and/or technical field, effectiveness as a communicator, interpersonal skills, strength of conviction, personal confidence, vigor, and the all-important grouping of honesty, forthrightness, and integrity are at the heart of forming opinions about candidates. The "fit" or balance of chemistry and expertise between the successful candidate and key members of the client organization is mostly what determines the success of the recruitment exercise. The process includes satisfying not only the tangibles of the job to be done but also the intangibles of the broader role to be played in the corporation.

Executive search is, or should be, an extension of a business problem-solving exercise with clients, not just a hiring exercise. It is relatively simple to systematically identify and attract the attention of prospective candidates to any search. The value added to clients is objective advice and counsel leading to the best, sometimes unique (innovative responsibility, organizational, or work relationship alignments), recruitment solutions that help clients meet competitive challenges and establish and maintain leadership in their industries.

Success in our business/profession is not necessarily a quantitative measure. It is, rather, a result of consistently doing good work—bringing about constructive resolutions in a timely way.

GEOGRAPHIC SCOPE OF RECRUITING ACTIVITIES:
Serve clients nationwide and in the United Kingdom, Europe, and Southeast Asia

TOTAL YEARS OF RETAINER-TYPE RECRUITING EXPERIENCE:
22 years

EDWIN S. MRUK
Senior Partner
Mruk & Partners
675 Third Avenue, Suite 1805
New York, NY 10017
Telephone: (212) 983-7676

Date of birth: November 29, 1932

Mruk & Partners

EDUCATION:
The Johns Hopkins University
B.S., 1954

SPECIAL INTERESTS AND HOBBIES:
Opera, gourmet cooking, antiques, future of health care

EMPLOYMENT HISTORY:
1987 to present: Mruk & Partners
1985 to 1987: Group Senior Vice President, American Ultramar Ltd.
1960 to 1985: Senior Partner, Ernst & Young
1957 to 1960: Vice President, Jerome Barnum Associates
1954 to 1957: Consultant, Mruk Sheehan Associates

WHAT I LOOK FOR IN GENERAL IN A CANDIDATE:

We first look for proficiency and successful experience in the functional and/or industrial sector required by our client. From that starting point we assess an individual's personal qualifications, which include honesty and integrity, and the ability to communicate laterally as well as up and down the organization chart.

For senior management and executive positions, we also look for evidence of leadership skills and capability. Finally, we assess the candidate's ability and agreement to achieve the client organizational goals and objectives.

GEOGRAPHIC SCOPE OF RECRUITING ACTIVITIES:
Serve clients nationwide and globally

TOTAL YEARS OF RETAINER-TYPE RECRUITING EXPERIENCE:
34 years

FERDINAND NADHERNY
Senior Managing Director
Russell Reynolds Associates, Inc.
200 S. Wacker Drive
Chicago, IL 60606
Telephone: (312) 993-9696

HONOREE: 1990, 1992, 1994

Date of birth: December 12, 1926

Russell Reynolds Associates, Inc.

EDUCATION:
> Yale University
> > A.B., economics, 1950
> Harvard Business School
> > M.B.A., 1952

MILITARY:
> S2/C, United States Navy, 1945 to 1946

SPECIAL INTERESTS AND HOBBIES:
> Family, reading, politics, golf, education

EMPLOYMENT HISTORY:
> 1974 to present: Russell Reynolds Associates, Inc.
> 1972 to 1974: Associate, Boyden Associates
> 1969 to 1972: Executive Vice President, Combine Motivation Education Systems
> 1966 to 1969: Assistant to President, Science Research Association (IBM)
> 1964 to 1966: Executive Secretary, Office of Economic Opportunity
> 1952 to 1962: General Manager, Cabot Corporation

WHAT I LOOK FOR IN GENERAL IN A CANDIDATE:

In general, what I look for in a candidate is someone who has had an extremely successful career and has reached a point where it is timely to make a job change. I look for people who are bright and have high energy levels. Good people skills are also extremely important. Candidates must also be good communicators. Integrity and honesty are a must. Attempting to make sure that an individual candidate would fit well into a company's culture, share a similar business philosophy, and especially have a good chemistry with the board of directors or person to whom one is reporting is also important. I personally like to present candidates who have interests outside of business and are happily married.

GEOGRAPHIC SCOPE OF RECRUITING ACTIVITIES:
> Serve clients nationwide

TOTAL YEARS OF RETAINER-TYPE RECRUITING EXPERIENCE:
> 22 years

RICHARD J. (DICK) NADZAM
Partner
Nadzam, Lusk & Associates, Inc.
3211 Scott Boulevard, Suite 205
Santa Clara, CA 95054-3091
Telephone: (408) 727-6601

Date of birth: November 14, 1935

Nadzam, Lusk & Associates, Inc.

EDUCATION:
> Penn Technical Institute
>> Associate Specialized Technology (AST), 1960

MILITARY:
> Sergeant, United States Marine Corps, 1954 to 1957

SPECIAL INTERESTS AND HOBBIES:
> Photography, wine tasting/making, travel

EMPLOYMENT HISTORY:
> 1976 to present: Nadzam, Lusk & Associates, Inc.
> 1972 to 1976: Partner, Nadzam, Davidson Associates
> 1970 to 1972: Director, Industrial Relations, Singer Link
> 1967 to 1970: Manager, Employment, Singer Link
> 1966 to 1967: Technical Recruiter, Link Group/General Precision
> 1964 to 1966: Bids and Proposals Writer, Link Group/General Precision
> 1962 to 1964: Technical Writer, General Electric Co.
> 1960 to 1962: Electronics Technician, General Electric Co.

WHAT I LOOK FOR IN GENERAL IN A CANDIDATE:

I look for a successful track record, for specific accomplishments, for leadership, verbal and written communications, and common sense.

I also look to ensure that candidates fit the cultural and management style of the client.

GEOGRAPHIC SCOPE OF RECRUITING ACTIVITIES:
> Serve clients nationwide and Canada, Europe, and Asia

TOTAL YEARS OF RETAINER-TYPE RECRUITING EXPERIENCE:
> 22 years

CAROLINE W. NAHAS
Managing Vice President
Korn/Ferry International
1800 Century Park East, Suite 900
Los Angeles, CA 90067
Telephone: (310) 843-4142

Date of birth: June 21, 1948

Foto-Look Intl.

EDUCATION:
   University of California at Los Angeles
      B.A., 1970

EMPLOYMENT HISTORY:
   1977 to present: Korn/Ferry International
   1970 to 1977: International Account Officer, Head of Management Recruit-
      ment–Southern California, Bank of America

WHAT I LOOK FOR IN GENERAL IN A CANDIDATE:

   Key and constant criteria sought in candidates are: leadership, proven track
record, pattern of success, ability to grow a business and manage through adverse
circumstances. Team builder—a leader who has made a difference.

GEOGRAPHIC SCOPE OF RECRUITING ACTIVITIES:
   Serve clients nationwide

TOTAL YEARS OF RETAINER-TYPE RECRUITING EXPERIENCE:
   17 years

THOMAS J. NEFF
President
SpencerStuart
55 East 52nd Street
New York, NY 10055
Telephone: (212) 407-0200

HONOREE: 1990, 1992, 1994

Date of birth: October 2, 1937

SpencerStuart

EDUCATION:
Lafayette College, Pennsylvania
B.S., industrial engineering, 1959
Lehigh University, Pennsylvania
M.B.A., marketing and finance, 1961

MILITARY:
First Lieutenant, United States Army, 1961 to 1963

SPECIAL INTERESTS AND HOBBIES:
Tennis, golf, jogging

EMPLOYMENT HISTORY:
1976 to present: SpencerStuart
1974 to 1976: Principal, Booz, Allen & Hamilton, Inc.
1969 to 1974: President, Hospital Data Sciences, Inc.
1966 to 1969: Director of Marketing Planning, TWA, Inc.
1963 to 1966: Associate, McKinsey & Company

WHAT I LOOK FOR IN GENERAL IN A CANDIDATE:

Each client and each assignment is unique, and it is essential to understand this to ensure that we are recruiting a tailor-made executive and not a generic solution. Generally, clients emphasize leadership more than management, with a balance at senior levels of strategic and operating skills, team building, decisiveness, and global perspective.

GEOGRAPHIC SCOPE OF RECRUITING ACTIVITIES:
Serve clients nationally and internationally

TOTAL YEARS OF RETAINER-TYPE RECRUITING EXPERIENCE:
20 years

LAWRENCE F. NEIN
Managing Partner
Lamalie Amrop International
123 N. Wacker Drive, Suite 950
Chicago, IL 60606-1700
Telephone: (312) 782-3113

HONOREE: 1990, 1992, 1994

Date of birth: April 2, 1936

Nordeman Grimm, Inc.

EDUCATION:
   Miami University of Ohio
      B.S., 1958
   Wharton School, University of Pennsylvania
      M.B.A., 1963

MILITARY:
   Lieutenant Junior Grade, United States Navy, 1958 to 1962

SPECIAL INTERESTS AND HOBBIES:
   Real estate investment, golf

EMPLOYMENT HISTORY:
   1994 to present: Lamalie Amrop International
   1984 to 1993: Managing Partner, Nordeman Grimm, Inc.
   1982 to 1984: President, Education & Information Systems, Inc.
   1976 to 1982: President, Sargent-Welch Scientific Company
   1973 to 1976: President, Hartmarx Corporation–Gleneagles Division
   1970 to 1973: President, The House Stores, Inc.
   1963 to 1970: Management Consultant, McKinsey & Company, Inc.

WHAT I LOOK FOR IN GENERAL IN A CANDIDATE:

   I look at all candidates with a few key thoughts in mind.
   First, what are his or her achievements versus the critical needs of the position I am recruiting for? That is, how does this person's accomplishments match up against the (two or three) things that need to be done really well in the position to get exceptional results?
   The second thing I look for is cultural fit. Some organizations and positions call for dashing, aggressive, flamboyant, risk-taking personalities. In others, such a person would fall flat on his face.
   In all cases, I look for fervor, energy, and leadership in the sense of letting others shine and not having to take all the credit personally. These are key elements in a true leader at any level, I believe, and are "must haves" in my personal screen.

GEOGRAPHIC SCOPE OF RECRUITING ACTIVITIES:
   Serve clients nationwide and in Europe

TOTAL YEARS OF RETAINER-TYPE RECRUITING EXPERIENCE:
   9 years

BARBARA NELSON
Partner
Herman Smith Executive Initiatives Inc.
P.O. Box 629, 161 Bay Street,
Canada Trust Tower
BCE Place
Toronto, Ontario M5J 2S1 Canada
Telephone: (416) 862-8830

Date of birth: April 14, 1950

EDUCATION:
>   Keuka College, 1968 to 1970
>   Colgate University
>>   B.A., English and fine art, 1974

Herman Smith Executive Initiatives Inc.

SPECIAL INTERESTS AND HOBBIES:
>   Food and wine, art and design, warm weather

EMPLOYMENT HISTORY:
>   1989 to present: Herman Smith Executive Initiatives Inc.
>   1987 to 1989: Principal, BNI Ventures
>   1981 to 1987: Vice President/Marketing Manager, St. Clair Videotex Design, Sherwood Communications
>   1978 to 1981: Director, Image Creation Operations, Hemton Corporation
>   1974 to 1978: Account Coordinator, Robert Scott Advertising Group

WHAT I LOOK FOR IN GENERAL IN A CANDIDATE:

>   Cultural fit with the company and client's needs
>   Common sense, intelligence
>   Sense of humor
>   Energy and passion
>   Resiliency in times of change and diversity
>   Candid, open sense of oneself
>   Trust and predictability
>   A certain level of wisdom learned from experience and mistakes
>   Ability to learn and keep on learning, to teach and keep on teaching
>   Creativity

>>   "A good executive is multi-faceted like a diamond—the larger the number of facets, the more brilliantly it shines. Some facets are larger, some smaller and not all diamonds have the same number. But all facets are part of a whole diamond which ultimately focuses the light passing through the facets to a single integrating point. Further, few diamonds are without flaws."
>>   —Harry Levinson, *HBR*, 1990

GEOGRAPHIC SCOPE OF RECRUITING ACTIVITIES:
>   Serve clients nationwide and in the United States and Canada

TOTAL YEARS OF RETAINER-TYPE RECRUITING EXPERIENCE:
>   5 years

ROBERT NESBIT
Vice President and Partner
Korn/Ferry International
237 Park Avenue, 11th Floor
New York, NY 10017
Telephone: (212) 687-1834

Date of birth: February 8, 1932

Korn/Ferry International

EDUCATION:
> University of Scranton
> New York University
> > M.S., retailing

MILITARY:
> United States Army Infantry Officer

EMPLOYMENT HISTORY:
> 1979 to present: Korn/Ferry International
> Previous:
> Director of Corporate Marketing, Genesco, Inc. Divisional Merchandising
> > Manager, Associated Merchandising Corp.
> Product Development and Specification Buying positions, J.C. Penney
> Faculty Member, New York University, Graduate School of Retailing

WHAT I LOOK FOR IN GENERAL IN A CANDIDATE:

Other than a track record of solid management advancement in area(s) that coincide with the client's needs, I seek a personality that has the predictable potential of meshing successfully with the culture of their firm and/or the individual to whom this person will report.

GEOGRAPHIC SCOPE OF RECRUITING ACTIVITIES:
> Serve clients nationally and internationally

TOTAL YEARS OF RETAINER-TYPE RECRUITING EXPERIENCE:
> 15 years

ARTHUR NEWMAN
Senior Partner, Practice Leader–Energy &
**   Natural Resources**
Lamalie Amrop International
1301 McKinney Street, Suite 3520
Houston, TX 77010
Telephone: (713) 739-8602

Date of birth: April 20, 1938

Lamalie Amrop International

EDUCATION:
Columbia University
    B.A., liberal arts, 1959
    B.S., industrial engineering and management sciences, 1960
    M.S., industrial engineering and management sciences, 1965

MILITARY:
Lieutenant, United States Navy, 1960 to 1965

SPECIAL INTERESTS AND HOBBIES:
Reading, music, tennis, running, photography, travel

EMPLOYMENT HISTORY:
1990 to present: Lamalie Amrop International
1974 to 1990: President, Arthur Newman Associates, Inc.
1966 to 1974: Information Systems Manager, Lever Brothers Company
1962 to 1966: Planning Engineer, Development Engineer, Western Electric

WHAT I LOOK FOR IN GENERAL IN A CANDIDATE:

Briefly, I am interested in candidates with the following characteristics: upper-level intellect, an understanding of the strategic context of both the company and the industry, a record of performance that indicates a probability of success in the new company, strength of character, and the ability to motivate people to achieve. Leadership and problem-solving skills displaying creativity and foresight are also important. Underlying all this is the requirement that the individual must be compatible with the organization as it will likely evolve.

GEOGRAPHIC SCOPE OF RECRUITING ACTIVITIES:
Serve clients worldwide

TOTAL YEARS OF RETAINER-TYPE RECRUITING EXPERIENCE:
20 years

JACQUES C. NORDEMAN
Chairman
Nordeman Grimm, Inc.
717 Fifth Avenue
New York, NY 10022
Telephone: (212) 935-1000

HONOREE: 1990, 1992, 1994

Date of birth: March 24, 1937

Nordeman Grimm, Inc.

EDUCATION:
> Colgate University
> > B.A., fine arts, 1958
> Harvard University
> > M.B.A., 1964

MILITARY:
> Lieutenant Junior Grade, United States Navy, 1959 to 1962

SPECIAL INTERESTS AND HOBBIES:
> Golf, skiing, Dixieland musician (drummer), photography, theater, travel

EMPLOYMENT HISTORY:
> 1969 to present: Nordeman Grimm, Inc.
> 1968 to 1969: Partner, Parker Nordeman
> 1964 to 1968: Account Management, Benton & Bowles

WHAT I LOOK FOR IN GENERAL IN A CANDIDATE:

As to the basic qualities that separate the extraordinary individuals from the ordinary, I look for:

- People who are real. They are down-to-earth and without pretension. Individuals with the highest personal standards of honesty, integrity, and trust. Genuine people with solid values.
- "Smarts." I am intrigued with a person's intelligence and thought processes and am attracted to (1) individuals who are quick and able to cut through to the heart of an issue; and (2) individuals who demonstrate the use of sound judgment.
- A strong sense of self, combined with a sensitivity to others. I am attracted to individuals with an understated confidence and humility.
- A sense of balance—between family, professional life, and outside interests.
- A strong sense of purpose, combined with creativity, energy, and often a flare or passion for whatever they do.
- Good communicators who express ideas in a logical, forthright, and direct manner.
- A sense of humor; able to keep things in perspective.
- Leadership—usually evident throughout every stage of an exceptional career.

GEOGRAPHIC SCOPE OF RECRUITING ACTIVITIES:
> Serve clients nationally and internationally

TOTAL YEARS OF RETAINER-TYPE RECRUITING EXPERIENCE:
> 25 years

DAYTON OGDEN
Chief Executive Officer
SpencerStuart
695 East Main Street
Stamford, CT 06901
Telephone: (203) 326-3715

HONOREE: 1990, 1992, 1994

Date of birth: January 11, 1945

SpencerStuart

EDUCATION:
> Yale University
>> B.A., American studies, 1967

MILITARY:
> Lieutenant Junior Grade, United States Navy, 1968 to 1971

EMPLOYMENT HISTORY:
> 1979 to present: SpencerStuart
> 1975 to 1979: Vice President, Simmons Associates
> 1973 to 1975: Director of Human Resources, Dunham and Smith Agencies
> 1967 to 1973: Special Assistant to Personnel Director, Port Authority of New
>> York and New Jersey

WHAT I LOOK FOR IN GENERAL IN A CANDIDATE:

When assessing a candidate, the most important determinant to look at is the individual's pattern of achievement. Most successful people typically begin early on in their lives to establish the bedrock for their future success. Experiences such as summer jobs, athletics, academic history, and military performance—although seemingly unrelated to specific business careers—are important indicators of a person's capabilities and desire to win. These early achievements prefigure the individual's progress toward a successful business life.

Second, I make it a point to determine what a candidate has actually accomplished on his or her own, as distinct from having been merely a part of the process. Success has many claimants, but only one true author.

Finally, I assess a candidate for the emotional balance and sense of humor required to provide leadership. Qualities such as empathy, flexibility, tolerance for ambiguity, and courage of conviction rank very high with me. Obviously, all these traits are weighed within the context of the specification and key selection criteria we develop with the client.

GEOGRAPHIC SCOPE OF RECRUITING ACTIVITIES:
> Serve clients nationwide and in Europe, Asia, and South America

TOTAL YEARS OF RETAINER-TYPE RECRUITING EXPERIENCE:
> 19 years

THOMAS H. OGDON
President
The Ogdon Partnership
375 Park Avenue
New York, NY 10152-0175
Telephone: (212) 308-1600

HONOREE: 1990, 1992, 1994

Date of birth: April 16, 1935

The Ogdon Partnership

EDUCATION:
Amherst College
B.A., English, 1957

SPECIAL INTERESTS AND HOBBIES:
Fishing, tennis, squash, gardening, golf

EMPLOYMENT HISTORY:
1987 to present: The Ogdon Partnership
1980 to 1987: Executive Vice President/Chief Operating Officer, Haley Associates
1979: Vice President, Russell Reynolds Associates, Inc.
1975 to 1978: Senior Vice President, Needham Harper & Steers
1961 to 1975: Senior Vice President, Management Supervisor, Benton & Bowles
1959 to 1961: Copywriter, Grey Advertising
1958: Trainee, Ted Bates Advertising

WHAT I LOOK FOR IN GENERAL IN A CANDIDATE:

The first thing I look for is the degree to which a candidate is truly comfortable with him or herself. It's a kissing cousin to self-confidence—but different. Other things we all look for—leadership abilities, a sense of humor, the ability to move all the way to an important decision, and handling difficult interpersonal situations—all come naturally to someone with this sense of self. That a person has the proper technical qualifications for the position is of course a given.

GEOGRAPHIC SCOPE OF RECRUITING ACTIVITIES:
Serve clients nationwide and Canada, France, England, Germany, Australia

TOTAL YEARS OF RETAINER-TYPE RECRUITING EXPERIENCE:
15 years

JOSEPH E. (JOE) ONSTOTT
Managing Director
The Onstott Group, Inc.
60 William Street
Wellesley, MA 02181
Telephone: (617) 235-3050

Date of birth: November 2, 1949

EDUCATION:
Midland College
B.A., journalism, 1972
Harvard Business School
Owner/President Program (OPM),
1990

Westwood Studios

MILITARY:
Staff Sergeant, United States Army, 1972 to 1974

SPECIAL INTERESTS AND HOBBIES:
Golf, skiing, travel, family activities

EMPLOYMENT HISTORY:
1987 to present: The Onstott Group, Inc.
1986 to 1987: Vice President, Boyden International
1983 to 1986: Chief Operating Officer, Sherman Howe Computer Centers
1981 to 1983: Vice President–Sales and Marketing, Hendrix Technologies
1980 to 1981: Director of Marketing, Dest Corporation
1974 to 1980: Marketing Manager, IBM

WHAT I LOOK FOR IN GENERAL IN A CANDIDATE:

Determining the technical fit for the qualifications of the position is only the tip of the iceberg. That is the science of search. The art of the profession is the *selection* process—determining who will be successful in the context of the company's corporate culture, philosophy, and strategic goals.

In general, these are the qualities I look for in a candidate:

- A high degree of personal and professional integrity.
- Sustained and verifiable track record of accomplishment.
- Strong leadership, communication, and motivational skills.
- Strategic vision and results-oriented follow-through.
- Creativity and innovation.
- The ability to build and manage effective teams.
- Energy and enthusiasm.
- Native intelligence coupled with intuition ("street smarts").
- Balance between professional and personal life.
- A personal standard of excellence.

GEOGRAPHIC SCOPE OF RECRUITING ACTIVITIES:
Serve clients nationwide

TOTAL YEARS OF RETAINER-TYPE RECRUITING EXPERIENCE:
8 years

GEORGE W. OTT
President and Chief Executive Officer
Ott & Hansen, Inc.
136 S. Oak Knoll, Suite 300
Pasadena, CA 91101
Telephone: (818) 578-0551

Elson-Alexandre

HONOREE: 1992, 1994

Date of birth: May 5, 1932

EDUCATION:
> University of Southern California
>> B.S., business administration, 1954
>> M.B.A., industrial management, 1960
> Certified Public Accountant, 1967

MILITARY:
> Lieutenant Junior Grade, United States Navy (Reserve), 1954 to 1956

SPECIAL INTERESTS AND HOBBIES:
> Active in community affairs; Board Member and President, Career Encores; Board Member and Executive Vice President, Salvation Army Los Angeles Metro Board; Board Member and Executive Vice President, Los Angeles Chapter, National Association of Corporate Directors; golf and model railroading

EMPLOYMENT HISTORY:
> 1976 to present: Ott & Hansen, Inc.
> 1971 to 1976: Vice President and member of Executive Committee, Korn/Ferry International
> 1963 to 1971: Partner, Peat Marwick Mitchell & Company
> 1961 to 1963: Company Administrator, Plasmadyne Corporation
> 1959 to 1961: Administrative Engineer, Lear Corporation
> 1956 to 1959: Engineering Planner, Douglas Aircraft Company, El Segundo Division

WHAT I LOOK FOR IN GENERAL IN A CANDIDATE:

Evaluating candidates first depends upon the position requirements and the type and size of the company. Company size, style, and industry need to be taken into account.

Evaluating a candidate starts with determining the individual's biographical background—positions held and companies worked for—to determine if that matches the hiring company's needs. In the process, I attempt to uncover the candidate's growth pattern, strengths, weaknesses, etc.

In evaluating a candidate's biographical pattern, I also attempt to evaluate integrity, work ethic, leadership ability, flexibility, adaptability, and intelligence.

The "art form" is to take this subjective evaluation of both client and candidate and engineer the placement by a good fit that works for both parties.

GEOGRAPHIC SCOPE OF RECRUITING ACTIVITIES:
> Serve clients nationwide

TOTAL YEARS OF RETAINER-TYPE RECRUITING EXPERIENCE:
> 31 years

FRANK PALMA
Executive Vice President
The Goodrich & Sherwood Company
6 Century Drive
Parsippany, NJ 07054
Telephone: (201) 455-7100

Date of birth: July 10, 1937

The Goodrich & Sherwood Company

EDUCATION:
City College of New York
B.A., economics, 1962

MILITARY:
Sergeant, United States Army Reserve, 1962 to 1968

SPECIAL INTERESTS AND HOBBIES:
Golf, oil painting, collecting baseball memorabilia (have the largest Brooklyn
Dodgers collection in existence)

EMPLOYMENT HISTORY:
1985 to present: The Goodrich & Sherwood Company
1979 to 1985: Principal, Martin Bauman Associates
1972 to 1979: Regional Vice President of Human Resources, RCA
1968 to 1972: Director of O.D., Sun Chemical Corporation
1965 to 1968: Director of Recruiting, American Broadcasting Company

WHAT I LOOK FOR IN GENERAL IN A CANDIDATE:

I look for a successful pattern of consistent achievement within the candidate's field of expertise. I am particularly interested in the individual's management style and core competencies and how well they match up to both the environment and specifications of my client.

Interpersonal skills and the ability to effectively communicate are always essential factors to be considered. Most of my clients want a candidate who has intelligence, integrity, good judgment, and long-term potential beyond the entry-level position.

I am always particularly interested in how well candidates have managed their business careers, as well as certain aspects of their personal lives.

GEOGRAPHIC SCOPE OF RECRUITING ACTIVITIES:
Serve clients nationwide and in Canada, Mexico, United Kingdom, and Latin
America

TOTAL YEARS OF RETAINER-TYPE RECRUITING EXPERIENCE:
15 years

DAVID W. PALMLUND III
Senior Partner
Lamalie Amrop International
4246 Thanksgiving Tower
Dallas, TX 75201
Telephone: (214) 754-0019

Date of birth: April 12, 1942

Lamalie Amrop International

EDUCATION:
Syracuse University
B.S., accounting, 1964; M.B.A.,
management accounting, 1968

MILITARY:
Captain, United States Army Ordnance
Corps, 1965 to 1967

SPECIAL INTERESTS AND HOBBIES:
Skiing, big-game fishing, art, antique and Netsuke collecting, real estate
investing

EMPLOYMENT HISTORY:
1981 to present: Lamalie Amrop International
1977 to 1981: Executive Vice President and President, Financing Subsidiary,
American Home Shield
1972 to 1977: Various positions, Merrill Lynch–Realty Operations
1971 to 1972: Senior Vice President–Finance, Vice President–Controller,
American Home Shield
1968 to 1971: Financial Analyst, American Cyanamid
1964 to 1968: Cost Engineer, Eastman Kodak Company

WHAT I LOOK FOR IN GENERAL IN A CANDIDATE:

When evaluating candidates, I first look for the following:
- Physical presence, intellectual and communications capabilities, and the
  ability to influence.
- Reasoning and organization skills, the ability to justify a career, and
  street smarts.
- Leadership capabilities—a willingness to take charge and drive programs
  through to solve problems.
- Creative abilities—to have the courage to be a risk taker and think outside of normal parameters and be a visionary.
- People skills—ability to relate up, down, and sideways with warmth and
  humor.
- Self-awareness—personal life, work ethic, integrity, stability, and aggressiveness.

I then match what I have found against my client's requirements and ensure
that I have a candidate who goes beyond the personnel specifications and can
provide an added dimension to my client. I continue into a detailed analysis of
the candidate's career.

GEOGRAPHIC SCOPE OF RECRUITING ACTIVITIES:
Serve clients nationwide and work separately in all continents and in conjunction with our forty-seven overseas offices

TOTAL YEARS OF RETAINER-TYPE RECRUITING EXPERIENCE:
14 years

MANUEL PAPAYANOPULOS
Vice President
Korn/Ferry International (Mexico City Office)
Monte Urales 641
Lomas de Chapultepec
11000 Mexico, D.F.
Telephone: (525) 202-6020 and 202-0385

HONOREE: 1992, 1994

Date of birth: February 21, 1945

Korn/Ferry International

SPECIAL INTERESTS AND HOBBIES:
Chess, water skiing, tennis, reading

EMPLOYMENT HISTORY:
1982 to present: Korn/Ferry International
1979 to 1982: Partner, Tasa
1975 to 1978: Managing Partner/Middle Management, Tasa
1975: Deputy Director–Human Resources, Cajas Corrugadas de Mexico
1973 to 1975: Personnel Manager, American Express Company de Mexico
1969 to 1972: Personnel Assistant, Cyanamid de Mexico

WHAT I LOOK FOR IN GENERAL IN A CANDIDATE:

Honesty and intellect are basic essential factors involved in all my candidates' evaluations. In-depth interviewing is conducted in accordance with the requirements of a given client, and, in general terms, my assessment includes the evaluation of the following elements:

- A proven track record of accomplishments. Delivery is a very important issue for most clients.
- Leadership capabilities, a successful team player.
- Ambition, initiative, aggressiveness, motivation.
- Presence, executive stature.
- Communication skills, articulation.
- Computer, high-tech skills, orientation.
- Internationalization, global management skills, languages.
- Scholastic background, cultural, social.

GEOGRAPHIC SCOPE OF RECRUITING ACTIVITIES:
Serve clients nationwide

TOTAL YEARS OF RETAINER-TYPE RECRUITING EXPERIENCE:
19 years

DAVID R. PEASBACK
Vice Chairman and Chief Executive Officer
Canny, Bowen Inc.
200 Park Avenue
New York, NY 10166
Telephone: (212) 949-6611

Canny, Bowen Inc.

HONOREE: 1990, 1992, 1994

Date of birth: March 15, 1933

EDUCATION:
> Colgate University
>> B.A., economics, 1955
> University of Virginia Law School
>> LL.B., 1961

MILITARY:
> Sergeant, United States Marine Corps, 1956 to 1958

SPECIAL INTERESTS AND HOBBIES:
> Skiing, tennis, paddle tennis, swimming

EMPLOYMENT HISTORY:
> 1988 to present: Canny, Bowen Inc.
> 1972 to 1987: Partner to President and Chief Executive Officer, Heidrick & Struggles, Inc.
> 1968 to 1972: Vice President of Subsidiary, Bangor Punta Corp.
> 1965 to 1968: Litigation attorney, Litton Industries Inc.
> 1961 to 1964: Associate, Covington & Burling Law Firm
> 1955 to 1956: Salesman–Case Soap, Procter & Gamble

WHAT I LOOK FOR IN GENERAL IN A CANDIDATE:

It is a mistake to evaluate a candidate in a vacuum. The executive must be evaluated on how he or she could be expected to perform for a specific client. Accordingly, once it is determined that the candidate has the requisite function and industry experience, *personal impact* becomes a pivotal issue. I define this as a combination of personality, appearance, and management style, which forms the cornerstone for building acceptance in the new environment. Every organization has a unique culture, and the candidate must be comfortable with it and vice versa. The absence of the "fit" explains why an executive with an unblemished record of success sometimes fails when he changes jobs. Personal chemistry, though it is an overworked expression, also must be considered. Although it is related to what I labeled personal impact, personal chemistry is more individualized; for example, will the new Chief Financial Officer or Senior Vice President–Human Resources get along with the CEO?

GEOGRAPHIC SCOPE OF RECRUITING ACTIVITIES:
> Serve clients nationwide and in Europe and Canada

TOTAL YEARS OF RETAINER-TYPE RECRUITING EXPERIENCE:
> 21 years

STEVEN G. PEZIM
President
The Bedford Consulting Group Inc.
The Bedford House, 60 Bedford Road
Toronto, Ontario M5R 2K2 Canada
Telephone: (416) 963-9000

Date of birth: August 13, 1955

The Bedford Consulting Group, Inc.

SPECIAL INTERESTS AND HOBBIES:
Golf, tennis, skiing, reading

EMPLOYMENT HISTORY:
1979 to present: The Bedford Consulting Group Inc.

WHAT I LOOK FOR IN GENERAL IN A CANDIDATE:

Each organization and assignment have their unique qualities and challenges. My assessment is relatively straightforward and falls into two parts—career and personal.

On the career side, skills, experience, and academics are relatively easy to verify and match. I look for progression of responsibilities from quality organizations and examine the situations surrounding the candidate's accomplishments and failures, probe for what the candidate has learned from each, and find out what their drives and ambitions are.

I see the personal side as the value-added component and generally look for positive attributes that include leadership, development of people, integrity, decisiveness, communication skills, presence, self-confidence, values, overall balance, high energy, passion, humility, and a sense of humor.

GEOGRAPHIC SCOPE OF RECRUITING ACTIVITIES:
Serve clients in Argentina, Australia, Austria, Brazil, Canada, China, Czech Republic, Denmark, France, Germany, Holland, Hong Kong, Hungary, India, Italy, Kuwait, Norway, Philippines, Poland, Portugal, Spain, Sweden, Switzerland, United Kingdom, and the United States.

TOTAL YEARS OF RETAINER-TYPE RECRUITING EXPERIENCE:
15 years

NICK J. PIERCE
Partner
Paul Ray Berndtson, Inc.
10 S. Riverside Plaza, Suite 720
Chicago, IL 60606
Telephone: (312) 876-0730

Date of birth: May 3, 1951

EDUCATION:
> University of Illinois
> > B.S., marketing, 1973

EMPLOYMENT HISTORY:
> 1989 to present: Paul Ray Berndtson, Inc.
> 1987 to 1989: Vice President, Paul Stafford
> > Associates

Paul Ray Berndston, Inc.

> 1982 to 1987: Vice President, Managing Director, Kleinstein Associates
> 1977 to 1982: Partner, Pierce-James Associates
> 1973 to 1977: Managing Director, Consultants to Executive Management LTD.
> 1973: Business Analyst, The Dun & Bradstreet Corporation

WHAT I LOOK FOR IN GENERAL IN A CANDIDATE:

Interviewing is an art and must first establish an environment in which the interviewee feels comfortable and willing to confide full information for the benefit of all parties concerned.

I dissect an interview into two evaluative components:
Tangible Characteristics:

1. Measurable results in direct comparison to the unique parameters of the search being undertaken.
2. Demonstrated history of properly evaluating problems and issues while developing successful action plans.

Intangible Characteristics:

1. Cultural fit with client.
2. Listening skills.
3. Ability to SUCCINCTLY articulate FOCUSED logical reasoning regarding complex concepts.
4. Sense of urgency; bias for action; decisiveness.
5. Experience influencing others to one's point of view; professional presence.
6. Tenacity and determination; history of overcoming challenges and disappointments, personally or professionally, which led to past success.
7. Independence in thinking; ability to think for oneself and not necessarily follow popular opinion; self-confidence.
8. Preparedness.
9. Willingness to accept criticism and direction; ego under control.
10. Enthusiastic and pleasant personality; honesty; team player.

GEOGRAPHIC SCOPE OF RECRUITING ACTIVITIES:
Serve clients nationwide, Pan-European and Caribbean

TOTAL YEARS OF RETAINER-TYPE RECRUITING EXPERIENCE:
20+ years

RENE PLESSNER
President
Rene Plessner Associates, Inc.
375 Park Avenue, Suite 3508
New York, NY 10152
Telephone: (212) 421-3490

Date of birth: June 28, 1938

Rene Plessner Associates, Inc.

EDUCATION:
Columbia University
B.A., political science, 1960

SPECIAL INTERESTS AND HOBBIES:
Sports, fitness, reading

EMPLOYMENT HISTORY:
1972 to present: Rene Plessner Associates, Inc.
1969 to 1972: President, Spectrum Cosmetics, Inc.
1967 to 1969: Brand Manager, Revlon, Inc.
1964 to 1966: Lehn & Fink
1961 to 1963: Helena Rubinstein

WHAT I LOOK FOR IN GENERAL IN A CANDIDATE:

The ability to manage and motivate people
Good administrative skills
Good work ethic
Honesty
Smart
Flexibility of personality
Appropriate experience

GEOGRAPHIC SCOPE OF RECRUITING ACTIVITIES:
Serve clients nationwide and Germany, France, England

TOTAL YEARS OF RETAINER-TYPE RECRUITING EXPERIENCE:
22 years

JOHN PLUMMER
President
Plummer & Associates, Inc.
30 Myano Lane, Suite 36
Stamford, CT 06902
Telephone: (203) 965-7878

Date of birth: April 21, 1944

EDUCATION:
  University of Southern California
    B.A., economics, letters, arts and
    sciences, 1966
    M.B.A., statistics/industrial relations,
    1968

Plummer & Associates, Inc.

SPECIAL INTERESTS AND HOBBIES:
  Sailing, boating, gardening, children with special needs

EMPLOYMENT HISTORY:
  1989 to present: Plummer & Associates, Inc.
  1987 to 1989: Partner, Ward Howell International, Inc.
  1983 to 1987: Partner, Korn/Ferry International
  1981 to 1982: Senior Vice President–Human Resources, FedMart
  1978 to 1981: Vice President–Personnel, Abraham & Straus–Division of Federated Department Stores
  1976 to 1978: Director–Personnel and Employee Relations, Mervyn's
  1967 to 1976: Assistant to the Vice President–Personnel, Bullock's Department Stores–Division of Federated Department Stores

WHAT I LOOK FOR IN GENERAL IN A CANDIDATE:

Our clients require a unique blend of skills, experience, technical knowledge, education, and cultural fit. Start-up, high-growth, turnaround, and maintenance environments also require differing personal characteristics. Generally, our firm is known for identifying individuals with:

  High Intellect: Enormous capacity with well-developed strategic and analytical thinking abilities.
  Vision: Capable of assessing situations from all viewpoints before developing tactics and strategies. Able to translate a business concept into a vision understandable by all.
  Organization: Highly organized, able to balance short-term and long-term issues and juggle a large number of conflicting priorities.
  Strength of Character: A healthy understanding of capabilities, knowledge of shortfalls, ability to learn from mistakes, and good values.
  Management/Leadership: Understands that success is best achieved by working through people, has respect for others, and knows that effective leadership is based upon earned respect.

GEOGRAPHIC SCOPE OF RECRUITING ACTIVITIES:
  Serve clients nationwide and the United Kingdom, Europe, Asia, Caribbean, and Latin America

TOTAL YEARS OF RETAINER-TYPE RECRUITING EXPERIENCE:
  11 years

ROLAND L. POIRIER
Partner
Poirier, Hoevel & Co.
12400 Wilshire Blvd., #1250
Los Angeles, CA 90025
Telephone: (310) 207-3427

Date of birth: July 28, 1941

Westside Studio

EDUCATION:
    Georgetown University
        B.A., 1963

MILITARY:
    United States Coast Guard Reserves, 1963 to 1969

SPECIAL INTERESTS AND HOBBIES:
    Worldwide travel, new technologies, physical fitness, world history and religions, languages

EMPLOYMENT HISTORY:
    1975 to present: Poirier, Hoevel & Co.
    1971 to 1975: Executive Search Consultant, Peat, Marwick, Main & Co.
    1964 to 1970: Data Processing Marketing Rep (H.R.), IBM Corporation

WHAT I LOOK FOR IN GENERAL IN A CANDIDATE:

An individual capable of successfully duplicating a proven history of success from a similar environment. A professional yet engaging demeanor. Demonstrated leadership and management capabilities. An innovative thinker who is well attuned to new technologies and their role in the current and business of the future. Additionally, a well-rounded individual with broad outside interests.

GEOGRAPHIC SCOPE OF RECRUITING ACTIVITIES:
    Serve clients nationwide and in Europe, South America, Asia, and Canada

TOTAL YEARS OF RETAINER-TYPE RECRUITING EXPERIENCE:
    22 years

CHARLES A. POLACHI, JR.
Managing Partner
Fenwick Partners
57 Bedford Street, Suite 101
Lexington, MA 02173
Telephone: (617) 862-3370

Date of birth: July 18, 1953

Fenwick Partners

EDUCATION:
College of the Holy Cross
B.A., biology, 1975
Boston College
M.B.A., 1981

SPECIAL INTERESTS AND HOBBIES:
Family, farming, personal computers, volunteer with civic/church/arts
groups

EMPLOYMENT HISTORY:
1983 to present: Fenwick Partners
1980 to 1983: Vice President, PAR Associates
1978 to 1980: Senior Consultant, Bartholdi & Company
1975 to 1978: Manager University Relations, Data General Corporation

WHAT I LOOK FOR IN GENERAL IN A CANDIDATE:

1. Vision
2. Ability to communicate that vision
3. Clear, consistent management style
4. Humility
5. Persistence, will "stay the course"
6. Listening skills
7. Achievement orientation
8. Team builder and leader
9. Demonstrated track record of success
10. Ethics

GEOGRAPHIC SCOPE OF RECRUITING ACTIVITIES:
Serve clients nationwide and in Europe

TOTAL YEARS OF RETAINER-TYPE RECRUITING EXPERIENCE:
16 years

GARY J. POSNER
Partner
Educational Management Network
5143 N. Stanford Drive
Nashville, TN 37215
Telephone: (615) 665-3388

HONOREE: 1992, 1994

Date of birth: December 31, 1946

Educational Management Network

EDUCATION:
Michigan State University
B.A., business, 1968
M.A., administration–higher education, 1971

EMPLOYMENT HISTORY:
1993 to present: Educational Management Network
1988 to 1993: Vice President, Kaludis Consulting Group
1986 to 1988: President, University Search Consultants
1984 to 1986: Vice President for Administration, University of Pennsylvania
1982 to 1984: Vice President for Human Resources, University of Pennsylvania
1978 to 1982: Director, University Personnel Services, Cornell University
1968 to 1978: Director, Employee Relations and Chief Negotiator, Michigan State University

WHAT I LOOK FOR IN GENERAL IN A CANDIDATE:

Institutions of higher education are facing unprecedented pressures to work smarter, think strategically, and utilize technology effectively within a limited resource base. Key qualities that I look for in candidates pursuing senior administrative positions in the college and university sector include:

1. A solid understanding of the academic and political environment and pressures of today's colleges and universities.
2. An ability to assume a leadership role that transcends a specialty area of expertise.
3. Self-confidence tempered with a sensitivity to listen to diverse viewpoints.
4. An ability to thrive in a culturally diverse environment.

Higher education often utilizes search committees to evaluate and refine candidate pools. While adding some time to the search process, candidates should welcome committee involvement as a way for both the institution to get to know them and to determine if the position, the culture, and the environment "fit" their needs. A successful search marriage occurs when the institution offers the position ring and the qualified candidate says "I do."

GEOGRAPHIC SCOPE OF RECRUITING ACTIVITIES:
Serve clients nationwide and internationally

TOTAL YEARS OF RETAINER-TYPE RECRUITING EXPERIENCE:
9 years

DAVID L. POWELL, SR.
Chief Executive Officer
David Powell, Inc.
2995 Woodside Road, Suite 150
Woodside, CA 94062
Telephone: (415) 851-6000

HONOREE: 1992, 1994

Date of birth: February 6, 1937

David Powell, Inc.

EDUCATION:
St. Lawrence University
B.A., 1959

MILITARY:
Captain, United States Marine Corps, 1959 to 1964

SPECIAL INTERESTS AND HOBBIES:
Fly-fishing, golf, carving totem poles, family

EMPLOYMENT HISTORY:
1976 to present: David Powell, Inc.
1972 to 1976: President, Western Division, Staub Warmbold & Associates
1971 to 1972: Director, Administration, ElectroPrint, Inc.
1968 to 1971: Director, Human Resources, National Semiconductor
1966 to 1968: Personnel Manager, Fairchild Semiconductor
1964 to 1966: Labor Relations Manager, Del Monte

WHAT I LOOK FOR IN GENERAL IN A CANDIDATE:

Since our firm primarily seeks CEOs for high-technology clients, there are usually technical and specific product or market requirements. So, the initial strategy must be very focused and the research and networking precise. We need, therefore, a very clear, well-developed picture from the client, not always easy to obtain from a board search committee.

The ideal candidate is *employed* in a respected successful organization, where sound business practices, product innovation, and profitable growth are a way of life. The person is street smart, intelligent, and communicates in all directions with ease and effectiveness. This person stimulates ideas, teamwork, spirit, and confidence in customers and employees. Energy and honesty are always sought.

GEOGRAPHIC SCOPE OF RECRUITING ACTIVITIES:
Serve clients nationwide and internationally

TOTAL YEARS OF RETAINER-TYPE RECRUITING EXPERIENCE:
23 years

P. ANTHONY PRICE
Managing Director
Russell Reynolds Associates, Inc.
101 California Street, Suite 3140
San Francisco, CA 94111
Telephone: (415) 392-3130

HONOREE: 1990, 1994

Date of birth: January 5, 1941

Russell Reynolds Associates, Inc.

EDUCATION:
University of California at Berkeley
B.S., mechanical engineering, 1963
Harvard University
M.B.A., 1965

SPECIAL INTERESTS AND HOBBIES:
Piano, tennis, fly-fishing, skiing

EMPLOYMENT HISTORY:
1978 to present: Russell Reynolds Associates, Inc.
1974 to 1978: Executive Vice President and Chief Operating Officer,
MacLean-Fogg Company
1965 to 1974: Director–Corporate Development, FMC Corp.

WHAT I LOOK FOR IN GENERAL IN A CANDIDATE:

Assuming relevant background, I then judge motivation for them to potentially move and whether this specific move is in their (and family's) best interests.
Next is style fit (with client) and interpersonal/organizational skills. I look more
at reasons for accomplishments than the results, per se, and for consistency/
trends/patterns of behavior. Finally, I usually try to judge a candidate's sense of
self and balance in assessing own strengths and weaknesses.

GEOGRAPHIC SCOPE OF RECRUITING ACTIVITIES:
Clients nationwide and in Asia Pacific, Japan, Europe, and United Kingdom

TOTAL YEARS OF RETAINER-TYPE RECRUITING EXPERIENCE:
15+ years

WINDLE B. PRIEM
Managing Director
Korn/Ferry International
237 Park Avenue
New York, NY 10017
Telephone: (212) 687-1834

HONOREE: 1990, 1992, 1994

Date of birth: October 17, 1937

EDUCATION:
>   Worcester Polytechnic Institute
>   B.S., mechanical engineering, 1959
>   Babson College
>   M.B.A., finance, 1964

MILITARY:
>   Lieutenant Junior Grade, United States Navy, 1959 to 1962

EMPLOYMENT HISTORY:
>   1976 to present: Korn/Ferry International
>   1972 to 1976: Regional Director, U.S. Small Business Administration
>   1964 to 1972: Vice President, Marine Midland Bank

WHAT I LOOK FOR IN GENERAL IN A CANDIDATE:

As a financial service specialist, I take a businessman's approach to search, meaning that I always have my eye on what impact the individual will have on the bottom line. This is true whether I am recruiting a Chief Executive Officer for a major financial institution or looking for an individual contributor, such as a mergers and acquisitions professional. Whatever the position, I ask myself, "Will this candidate make a difference? Will this individual bring added value to the company? Will corporate governance be served properly?" I am always looking for people who can take the business to the next level of maturity. I want people who are more than their resumes.

GEOGRAPHIC SCOPE OF RECRUITING ACTIVITIES:
>   Serve clients nationwide and in Europe

TOTAL YEARS OF RETAINER-TYPE RECRUITING EXPERIENCE:
>   19 years

BARBARA L. PROVUS
Principal and Founder
Shepherd Bueschel &
    Provus, Inc.
One S. Wacker Drive, Suite 2740
Chicago, IL 60606
Telephone: (312) 372-1142

HONOREE: 1990, 1992, 1994

Date of birth: November 20, 1949

John Reilly Photography

EDUCATION:
> Russell Sage College, New York
>> B.A., sociology, 1971
> Loyola University
>> M.S., industrial relations, 1978

SPECIAL INTERESTS AND HOBBIES:
> The Anti-cruelty Society of Chicago (board member); The Chicago Network; Human Resources Management Association of Chicago (board member); baseball, modern art, gardening

EMPLOYMENT HISTORY:
> 1992 to present: Shepherd Bueschel & Provus, Inc.
> 1986 to 1991: Principal and Founder, Sweeney Shepherd Bueschel Provus Harbert & Mummert Inc.
> 1982 to 1986: Vice President, Lamalie Associates
> 1980 to 1982: Manager, Management Development, Federated Department Stores
> 1973 to 1980: Secretary to Consultant–Executive Search, Booz, Allen & Hamilton, Inc.

WHAT I LOOK FOR IN GENERAL IN A CANDIDATE:

In addition to the predefined requirements of the position, i.e., education, industry experience, functional skills, management ability, and so on, I believe there are several additional traits the successful candidate should have:

- The ability to "stretch" and challenge the organization. Will this candidate simply fill a functional void—or will he or she bring additional value to the situation? Can he or she be a catalyst to drive the organization beyond the status quo, but in a positive, productive manner?
- Also, the candidate must be recruitable—and for the "right"reasons. If there's no "acceptable" reason for the candidate to leave his or her current job, you may be going after the wrong candidate. However, part of my role is to *help the candidate assess his or her current situation and try to find a "reason" he or she should be attracted to my client's opportunity, short and/or long term.*
- *Third, I look for "humanness." What kind of person is he or she—and will he or she, in some small way, be able to bring to my client good values and a "caring" that goes beyond the bottom line.*

Finally, I require ethics and integrity, not only in candidates, but in my client's and my own actions.

GEOGRAPHIC SCOPE OF RECRUITING ACTIVITIES:
> Serve clients nationwide and internationally if candidates are domiciled in the U.S.A.

TOTAL YEARS OF RETAINER-TYPE RECRUITING EXPERIENCE:
> 15 years

CONRAD E. PRUSAK
Managing Partner
Ethos Consulting Inc.
100 Pine Street, Suite 2250
San Francisco, CA 94111-5208
Telephone: (415) 397-2211

Date of birth: December 2, 1952

Ethos Consulting Inc.

EDUCATION:
> University of Notre Dame
> B.A., history, 1974
> Stanford University
> M.B.A., 1980

SPECIAL INTERESTS AND HOBBIES:
> Travel and swimming

EMPLOYMENT HISTORY:
> 1992 to present: Ethos Consulting Inc.
> 1986 to 1992: Managing Partner, Heidrick & Struggles, Inc.
> 1982 to 1986: Managing Director, Arthur Young Executive Resource Consultants
> 1980 to 1982: Associate, Booz-Allen & Hamilton, Inc.
> 1975 to 1978: Associate, First Boston Corporation

WHAT I LOOK FOR IN GENERAL IN A CANDIDATE:

Important overall candidate characteristics include leadership, excellent listening skills, successful team building, a bias for action, a results orientation, disciplined thinking, cross-functional appreciation, a positive attitude, substance over form, and a true desire to make a constructive impact on an organization. The candidate will have done some homework on my client company before my interview and will come prepared to not only answer but also ask tough questions. The quiet self-confidence of a candidate whose ego is in check but who also has a healthy sense of ambition is important. The candidate will be candid and forthright about his or her accomplishments and setbacks. An overall impression of balance, both professionally and personally, will be clear. In summary, I will have a thorough understanding of what the candidate has to offer so that I can make a clear determination of fit vis-à-vis the needs of my client.

GEOGRAPHIC SCOPE OF RECRUITING ACTIVITIES:
> Serve clients nationwide and in Europe and Asia

TOTAL YEARS OF RETAINER-TYPE RECRUITING EXPERIENCE:
> 12 years

STEVE A. RABEN
Partner
Barton Raben, Inc.
Three Riverway, Suite 910
Houston, TX 77056
Telephone: (713) 961-9111

Date of birth: August 20, 1940

Woodallen Photography

EDUCATION:
Southwestern University
B.B.A., economics, 1963
University of Texas
Graduate study in economics, 1965

MILITARY:
United States Army Intelligence, 1966 to 1969; Active Reserve, 1972 to 1982

SPECIAL INTERESTS AND HOBBIES:
Director, T.D. Rowe Corporation; Trustee, The Episcopal High School; Advisor, Cambridge Energy Research Associates; skeet and sporting clay shooting, hunting, running, reading

EMPLOYMENT HISTORY:
1982 to present: Barton Raben, Inc.
1972 to 1982: Managing Vice President, National Energy Practice, Korn/Ferry International
1970 to 1972: Marketing Representative, The New England
1969 to 1970: Account Executive, Thompson McKinnon Archinschloss

WHAT I LOOK FOR IN GENERAL IN A CANDIDATE:

Leadership exemplified in ongoing openness to new business challenges, organization focus, and new thought development.
Practiced high business ethics and values.
One who stimulates new, different, or unconventional thinking toward problem solving.
Market and financial acumen.
Openness in discussing personal weaknesses.
A history of attracting and growing high-quality future leaders.
Recognition of subordinate and/or peer contributions.

GEOGRAPHIC SCOPE OF RECRUITING ACTIVITIES:
Serve clients nationwide and in Europe, North and West Africa, and the Pacific Rim

TOTAL YEARS OF RETAINER-TYPE RECRUITING EXPERIENCE:
22 years

CHARLES C. RATIGAN
Partner and Director
Heidrick & Struggles, Inc.
125 South Wacker Drive, Suite 2800
Chicago, IL 60606
Telephone: (312) 781-3786

Date of birth: April 17, 1945

Bachrach

EDUCATION:
> Fresno State College
>> B.A., economics, 1968
> Loyola University of Chicago
>> M.B.A., marketing, 1978

MILITARY:
> Lieutenant, United States Navy, 1968 to 1970

SPECIAL INTERESTS AND HOBBIES:
> Golf, flying, and horses

EMPLOYMENT HISTORY:
> 1981 to present: Heidrick & Struggles, Inc.
> 1970 to 1981: Various positions, Pfizer, Inc.

WHAT I LOOK FOR IN GENERAL IN A CANDIDATE:

A background appropriate to the search, a record of success, the desire to succeed, adaptability, brightness, decisiveness, leadership, flexibility, sound judgment, the ability to compromise, good communication skills, and a customer orientation. Should possess a passion for their work, the desire and willingness to work hard, and a team spirit. Must have a clear vision, impeccable ethics, and the potential to deliver more over the longer term. If the candidate has had a failure somewhere along the way, I look for a pattern of successful recovery, learning from the failure, and a desire to pick up and carry on, bettered by the experience.

GEOGRAPHIC SCOPE OF RECRUITING ACTIVITIES:
> Serve clients nationwide and in Europe

TOTAL YEARS OF RETAINER-TYPE RECRUITING EXPERIENCE:
> 13 years

PAUL R. RAY, JR.
President and Chief Executive
Officer
Paul Ray Berndtson
301 Commerce Street, Suite 2300
Fort Worth, TX 76102
Telephone: (817) 334-0500

HONOREE: 1990, 1992, 1994

Date of birth: November 6, 1943

Paul Ray Berndtson

EDUCATION:
>University of Arkansas
>>B.S., business administration, 1966
>University of Texas
>>J.D., 1970

SPECIAL INTERESTS AND HOBBIES:
>Community activities specifically related to education, health care, and substance abuse; running, hunting, fishing

EMPLOYMENT HISTORY:
>1978 to present: Paul Ray Berndtson
>1969 to 1978: Various Marketing and Management positions, R.J. Reynolds Tobacco Co.

WHAT I LOOK FOR IN GENERAL IN A CANDIDATE:

Depending upon the search, the qualities most important are strategic vision, leadership skills, and an international overview with a results orientation. In today's business climate, a comfort with empowering people to make decisions is important, as is a consensus/team approach to managing.

GEOGRAPHIC SCOPE OF RECRUITING ACTIVITIES:
>Serve clients in Europe, Pacific Rim, and North America

TOTAL YEARS OF RETAINER-TYPE RECRUITING EXPERIENCE:
>16 years

PAUL R. RAY, SR.
Chairman
Paul Ray Berndtson
301 Commerce Street, Suite 2300
Ft. Worth, TX 76102
Telephone: (817) 334-0500

HONOREE: 1990, 1992, 1994

Date of birth: April 27, 1918

Paul Ray Berndtson

MILITARY:
>   Major, United States Army, 1941 to 1945

SPECIAL INTERESTS AND HOBBIES:
>   Knights of Malta, Knights of the Holy Sepulchre; golf—member United
>   States Seniors' Golf Association

EMPLOYMENT HISTORY:
>   1965 to present: Paul Ray Berndtson
>   1962 to 1965: Vice President, Boyden Associates
>   1959 to 1962: Vice President, Chickasha Cotton Oil Company
>   1953 to 1959: Vice President and General Manager, Burrus Mills
>   1950 to 1953: General Manager–Soybean Division, A.E. Staley
>   Manufacturing Co.
>   1946 to 1950 and 1939 to 1941: Vice President and General Manager,
>   Doughboy Industries
>   1936 to 1939: Finance Department Trainee, Cargill, Inc.

WHAT I LOOK FOR IN GENERAL IN A CANDIDATE:

>   Potential to move well beyond current position
>   Ability to concisely articulate a point of view
>   Strong leadership qualities
>   Candor, honesty, and straightforwardness in all situations
>   A builder rather than a caretaker
>   Must fit client culture
>   Consistent record of achievement
>   Drive and enthusiasm
>   A focused individual

GEOGRAPHIC SCOPE OF RECRUITING ACTIVITIES:
>   Serve clients nationwide and on most international assignments we will work
>   with our foreign offices. We have twenty-one offices located in Europe,
>   Asia, Canada, Mexico, and Australia.

TOTAL YEARS OF RETAINER-TYPE RECRUITING EXPERIENCE:
>   32 years

MICHAEL S. REEDER
Senior Partner
Lamalie Amrop International
191 Peachtree Street, N.E., Suite 800
Atlanta, GA 30303
Telephone: (404) 688-0800

Date of birth: May 4, 1950

Lamalie Amrop International

EDUCATION:
University of Florida
B.A., business administration, 1972
University of Tampa
M.B.A., 1977

SPECIAL INTERESTS AND HOBBIES:
Tennis, family

EMPLOYMENT HISTORY:
1983 to present: Lamalie Amrop International
1980 to 1983: Vice President, MSL International Consultants Ltd. (Hay Group)
1973 to 1980: Manager of Employment Services, Florida Power Corporation
1972 to 1973: Assistant Personnel Manager, Florida Mental Health Institute

WHAT I LOOK FOR IN GENERAL IN A CANDIDATE:

In today's changing marketplace relative to managed care/health care, I generally seek an individual who shows and has shown the capability of adapting to change. In addition, "leadership" qualities are highly sought. Within that framework, the person's ability to motivate, build, and create a team-oriented environment is critical to the success of the senior executive's workplace.

GEOGRAPHIC SCOPE OF RECRUITING ACTIVITIES:
Serve clients nationwide and the United Kingdom and Finland

TOTAL YEARS OF RETAINER-TYPE RECRUITING EXPERIENCE:
14 years

HERBERT L. REGEHLY
President
IMC Group of Companies
14 East 60th Street, Suite 1200
New York, NY 10022
Telephone: (212) 838-9535

Date of birth: February 16, 1938

Innkeeper's Management Corporation

EDUCATION:
Hotel School in Germany
Matriculated, 1954 to 1957
Gutenberg Real Gymnasium in Wiesbaden, Germany
Matriculated in Humanistic Studies, 1954

SPECIAL INTERESTS AND HOBBIES:
Classical music, literature, numismatics

EMPLOYMENT HISTORY:
1964 to present: IMC Group of Companies
1962 to 1964: Associate, Brody Corporation
1960 to 1962: Associate, Restaurant Associates
1957 to 1960: Various training operating and administrative positions, hotels
and restaurants in Europe

WHAT I LOOK FOR IN GENERAL IN A CANDIDATE:

At the level in which we work, operational experience, functional knowledge,
and technical competence are usually a given. Beyond the above-mentioned parameters, we look for candidates who will add value to the client company, who will
enhance profitability, who will bring an added dimension to the organization.

We look for evidence of competitiveness, integrity, self-confidence, common
sense, humility, and a sense of humor.

We evaluate—among other things—a candidate's leadership abilities, moral
compass, management skills, and his or her ability to articulate both the mission
and vision.

We assess his or her composure, presence, cultural and social values, involvement in community affairs, and whether or not a supportive home environment
exists.

We ascertain that the candidate's style, personality, principles, and philosophy "fit" the client organization's corporate culture.

In every case, we search for candidates who exceed our client's expectations.

GEOGRAPHIC SCOPE OF RECRUITING ACTIVITIES:
Serve clients nationwide and in Europe, Africa, Asia Pacific, and Latin America

TOTAL YEARS OF RETAINER-TYPE RECRUITING EXPERIENCE:
30 years

KEN RICH
Partner
Paul Ray Berndtson, Inc.
101 Park Avenue, 41st Floor
New York, NY 10178
Telephone: (212) 371-1316

Paul Ray Berndston

Date of birth: August 17, 1946

EDUCATION:
LaFayette College
A.B., chemistry, 1967
University of Chicago
M.B.A., finance and marketing, 1969

SPECIAL INTERESTS AND HOBBIES:
My children and their pursuits, community involvement, alma mater, fund-raising, cross-training, reading, theater, music, tennis, politics, and spectator sports

EMPLOYMENT HISTORY:
1983 to present: Partner, Paul Ray Berndtson, Inc.
1981 to 1983: Manager, Operational Planning and Business Development, General Electric Credit Corporation
1978 to 1981: Manager, Marketing, Executive Office, Peat, Marwick, Mitchell & Co.
1975 to 1978: Resident Vice President, International Banking Group, Citibank, N.A.
1973 to 1974: Special Assistant to Assistant Secretary–Policy, Development & Research, U.S. Department of Housing & Urban Development
1969 to 1973: Associate, Corporate Finance Department, Kuhn, Loeb & Co.

WHAT I LOOK FOR IN GENERAL IN A CANDIDATE:
Assuming that the candidate exhibits the technical competency we seek, fits the corporate culture, and has compatible chemistry with the hiring manager, I look for the following characteristics in general: aggressiveness and enthusiasm (commitment, high energy, self-confidence, drive, and ambition); effective communication skills; record of success; rational thought process (ability to be a critical thinker); maturity (stature and leadership skills); planning and organizational skills (self-sufficiency, willingness to take ownership for actions); and reaction to pressure (ability to translate pressure into positive energy). I seek candidates who have impeccable integrity and who are sincere and forthright, innovative, self-motivated, entrepreneurial, team-oriented, bright, resilient, patient but uncompromising, and who have a sense of humor, a strong value system, a strong work ethic, and a winning attitude. These individuals are strategists with vision and the ability to develop and implement a tactical plan. They can also attract and retain top-quality team members.

GEOGRAPHIC SCOPE OF RECRUITING ACTIVITIES:
Serve clients nationwide and Europe, Pacific Rim, and Canada

TOTAL YEARS OF RETAINER-TYPE RECRUITING EXPERIENCE:
11 years

NORMAN C. ROBERTS
President
Norman Roberts & Associates, Inc.
1800 Century Park East, Suite 430
Los Angeles, CA 90067-1507
Telephone: (310) 552-1112

HONOREE: 1992, 1994

Date of birth: March 28, 1941

Norman Roberts & Associates, Inc.

EDUCATION:
University of California at Los Angeles
B.A., political science, 1962
University of Southern California
M.S., public administration, 1967

SPECIAL INTERESTS AND HOBBIES:
Sports and reading

EMPLOYMENT HISTORY:
1988 to present: Norman Roberts & Associates, Inc.
1976 to 1988: Senior Vice President, Korn/Ferry International
1971 to 1976: Principal Consultant, Arthur D. Little, Inc.
1969 to 1971: Senior Consultant, Peat, Marwick, Mitchell and Company
1966 to 1969: Supervisor of Contracts and Management Services, Economic and Youth Opportunities Agency
1965 to 1966: Assistant City Administrator, City of Lomita, California
1962 to 1965: Administrative Assistant/Board of Public Works, City of Los Angeles

WHAT I LOOK FOR IN GENERAL IN A CANDIDATE:

I first look for appropriate training and competency, as demonstrated by the education and experience of the candidate. Thereafter, I focus on personal attributes and management style/abilities. Typically, these include good communication skills, a professional presence, self-confidence, honesty and integrity, and the ability to listen. The accuracy and completeness of information provided to me is indicative of the individual's integrity, and I view this as critical. I am also generally interested in the candidate's enthusiasm, the compatibility of the person's long-term goals with the position we are trying to fill, the appropriateness of his or her compensation requirements, and ways of overcoming barriers for accepting a job offer (for example, housing, family commitments, and so on). Finally, the quality of the references obtained is a key indicator, as is the content of the background checks.

GEOGRAPHIC SCOPE OF RECRUITING ACTIVITIES:
Serve clients nationwide

TOTAL YEARS OF RETAINER-TYPE RECRUITING EXPERIENCE:
25 years

JOHN H. ROBISON
Chairman
Robison & McAulay
1350 First Citizens Plaza
128 S. Tryon Street
Charlotte, NC 28202
Telephone: (704) 376-0059

HONOREE: 1990, 1992, 1994

Date of birth: September 25, 1930

Robison & McAulay

EDUCATION:
> University of North Carolina, Chapel Hill
> > B.S., business administration, 1952
> Stonier Graduate School of Banking
> > Certificate of completion, 1964

MILITARY:
> Captain, United States Army, 1952 to 1955

EMPLOYMENT HISTORY:
> 1979 to present: Robison & McAulay
> 1975 to 1979: President, Locke & Robison
> 1973 to 1975: Principal, Woodward, Harris, Robison & Associates
> 1967 to 1973: Executive Vice President, Bankers Trust of South Carolina
> 1952 to 1967: Senior Vice President, North Carolina National Bank

WHAT I LOOK FOR IN GENERAL IN A CANDIDATE:

Some years ago, a now forgotten corporation used the slogan, "We sell to sell again." We have found that premise to be a critical element in the development and maintenance of our search practice. The image of our firm by a client five years later is going to rely on the successful performance of the candidate we recruited for that client.

Every corporate culture we serve and every search we do is different from every other one. Our selection of candidates, therefore, must rely on our comprehensive understanding of our individual client's needs and culture. The broad categories of characteristics that we look for in candidates are character, technical competence, and personal traits. The subcategories of the above can be numerous and may have as many variable definitions as we have diversity of clients. Our mission is to ascertain that those candidates selected possess those particular qualifications that will enable them to render the greatest contribution to our client and, in doing so, to their own career enhancement.

GEOGRAPHIC SCOPE OF RECRUITING ACTIVITIES:
> Serve clients nationwide and in North America, from our Charlotte, North Carolina, office; and in Europe, from Robison & McAulay GmbH in Aachen, Germany

TOTAL YEARS OF RETAINER-TYPE RECRUITING EXPERIENCE:
> 21 years

NANCY R. ROBLIN
Vice President
Paul-Tittle Associates, Inc.
1485 Chain Bridge Road, Suite 304
McLean, VA 22101
Telephone: (703) 442-0500

Date of birth: June 25, 1944

Paul-Tittle Associates, Inc.

EDUCATION:
>   Vassar College
>>   B.A., English literature, 1966
>   University of California at San Diego
>>   Contemporary music, 1971
>   Boston University, School of Fine Arts
>>   Master's, music, organ performance/choral studies, 1976

SPECIAL INTERESTS AND HOBBIES:
>   Choral conducting, keyboard performance, singing, reading, animal behavior, sailing, cooking, gardening, medicine and medical research, history, archaeology

EMPLOYMENT HISTORY:
>   1990 to present: Paul-Tittle Associates, Inc.
>   1986 to 1990: Executive Recruiter, COMSAT Corporation
>   1984 to 1986: Senior Staffing Consultant, Planning Research Corporation
>   1983 to 1984: Director, A.G. Fishkin and Associates
>   1979 to 1983: Associate, Management Recruiters
>   1976 to present: Founder/Artistic Director, The Frederick Chorale

WHAT I LOOK FOR IN GENERAL IN A CANDIDATE:

Our clients retain us to secure exceptional talent at all levels in the high-tech community, particularly telecom/datacom, interactive multimedia, wireless communications, international ventures, and emerging technologies.

I seek individuals with multiple skills, diverse career experience, and a proven record of significant accomplishments. I especially focus on executive-level women and men with multidisciplinary backgrounds in marketing, sales, finance, and technology. They are proven leaders, highly attuned to their markets and customers. Importantly, in today's ever-changing, competitive global economy, they must be highly flexible agents of change. They are frequently deal-makers with an established contact base and the skill to put together profitable ventures.

Additionally, I frequently seek out fast-track but less experienced candidates with exceptional growth potential. They are generally well educated, bright, ambitious, and excellent communicators. I invest considerable efforts in career counseling for these future leaders.

GEOGRAPHIC SCOPE OF RECRUITING ACTIVITIES:
>   Serve clients nationwide and internationally

TOTAL YEARS OF RETAINER-TYPE RECRUITING EXPERIENCE:
>   4 years

GERARD R. ROCHE
Chairman
Heidrick & Struggles, Inc.
245 Park Avenue
New York, NY 10167-0152
Telephone: (212) 867-9876

HONOREE: 1990, 1992, 1994

Date of birth: July 27, 1931

Bachrach

EDUCATION:
University of Scranton
B.S., accounting, 1953
New York University
M.B.A., 1958
University of Scranton
Honorary Doctor of Laws, 1982

MILITARY:
Lieutenant Junior Grade, United States Navy, Mediterranean, 1953 to 1955

SPECIAL INTERESTS AND HOBBIES:
Golf, tennis, reading

EMPLOYMENT HISTORY:
1964 to present: Heidrick & Struggles, Inc.
1959 to 1963: Marketing Director–Kordite, Mobil Oil Company
1956 to 1958: Account Executive, American Broadcasting Company
1955 to 1956: Management Trainee, American Telephone and Telegraph

WHAT I LOOK FOR IN GENERAL IN A CANDIDATE:
- Vision, drive and demonstrated leadership abilities
- Track record of success
- Global business perspective
- Intelligence and honesty
- Unquestionable integrity and ethics
- Solid interpersonal and communication skills
- Solid personal characteristics and values
- Chemistry with the client—perhaps the most important aspect of all

GEOGRAPHIC SCOPE OF RECRUITING ACTIVITIES:
Serve clients nationwide and internationally

TOTAL YEARS OF RETAINER-TYPE RECRUITING EXPERIENCE:
30 years

CARLOS A. ROJAS-MAGNON
Managing Partner
Amrop International
Amberes No. 4, 2nd Floor
Colonia Juarez, 06600 Mexico, D.F.
Telephone: 011-52-5-208-3977

Date of birth: January 11, 1941

RZL Y Asociados, S.C.

EDUCATION:

Universidad Nacional Autonoma de Mexico
Chemical engineer, 1959 to 1964

SPECIAL INTERESTS AND HOBBIES:

Scuba diving, sailing, reading, classical music, traveling, underwater photography

EMPLOYMENT HISTORY:

1985 to present: Amrop International
1984 to 1990: Partner, Founder, and President, Delano, Magnon & Associates
1977 to 1984: Partner and Executive Vice President, Korn/Ferry Hazzard International
1971 to 1977: Partner and Executive Vice President, Hazzard & Associates
1966 to 1970: Senior Staff Member, Arthur D. Little, Inc., Mexico
1965 to 1966: General Manager, Aervalv, S.A.

WHAT I LOOK FOR IN GENERAL IN A CANDIDATE:

What I look for in a candidate is first of all a high level of integrity. Second, I want to see a high level of intelligence and a good education. Finally, I look for a good deal of experience. Other matters of great importance to me include professionalism, the ability to lead others, a high level of ability to communicate orally and in writing, excellent language skills, and the ability to work in a team.

GEOGRAPHIC SCOPE OF RECRUITING ACTIVITIES:

Serve clients nationwide and in North, Central, and South America

TOTAL YEARS OF RETAINER-TYPE RECRUITING EXPERIENCE:

25 years

ROBERT S. ROLLO
Managing Partner
R. Rollo Associates
777 South Figueroa Street, 38th Floor
Los Angeles, CA 90017
Telephone: (213) 892-7845

Date of birth: April 4, 1947

R. Rollo Associates

EDUCATION:
   University of Southern California
      B.S., 1969
      M.B.A., 1970

MILITARY:
   Lieutenant Junior Grade, United States Navy, 1970 to 1973

SPECIAL INTERESTS AND HOBBIES:
   Boating, scuba diving, running, golf; trustee, The Archeology Fund
      (Oman/Yemen emphasis)

EMPLOYMENT HISTORY:
   1992 to present: R. Rollo Associates
   1981 to 1992: Managing Partner, Korn/Ferry International
   1979 to 1981: Vice President, Marketing, A.M. Jacquard
   1978 to 1979: Director, Strategic Planning, AM International
   1973 to 1978, Vice President, Union Bank

WHAT I LOOK FOR IN GENERAL IN A CANDIDATE:

Of greatest importance is the "fit" a potential candidate has with the client. Will the candidate "fit" the need and "fit" the company? Each search has its own peculiarities, and that is what makes executive recruiting so fascinating.

In general, however, I am continually looking for the following attributes in candidates as the foundation for their ultimate "fit" with the client:

- Intelligent, honest, straightforward personal presentation.
- Established skill sets that are easily verifiable.
- Record of success in managing an operation out of difficulties.
- Good at time management.
- Subordinates who have been promoted and/or recruited to outstanding positions.
- Demonstrated strategic sense and the ability to successfully implement a defined plan.
- Excellent communication ability.
- An international perspective; looks at the world in a broad sense.
- A genuine sense of humor.

GEOGRAPHIC SCOPE OF RECRUITING ACTIVITIES:
   Serve clients nationwide and in Latin America

TOTAL YEARS OF RETAINER-TYPE RECRUITING EXPERIENCE:
   13 years

GEORGE A. ROSSI
Managing Director
Heidrick & Struggles, Inc.
One Post Office Square
Boston, MA 02109
Telephone: (617) 423-1140

Date of birth: May 21, 1941

Heidrick & Struggles, Inc.

EDUCATION:
Northeastern University
B.S./B.A., 1965
M.B.A., finance, 1967

SPECIAL INTERESTS AND HOBBIES:
Professional ski instructor, motorcyclist, private pilot

EMPLOYMENT HISTORY:
1983 to present: Heidrick & Struggles, Inc.
1981 to 1983: President–Boston Office, Gilbert & Tweed
1980 to 1982: Human Resources Director, Data General Corporation
1970 to 1979: Worldwide Staffing Placement Manager, Digital Equipment
Corporation
1969 to 1970: Employee Relations Director, Honeywell Information Systems
1968 to 1969: Quality Assurance Director, Diamond Crystal Salt Company
1967 to 1969: Staffing Representative, Honeywell Information Systems

WHAT I LOOK FOR IN GENERAL IN A CANDIDATE:

Generally speaking, I look for the following:

- The major long-term changes the candidate has had in each of his or her major positions.
- The ability to deal with conflict.
- Individual's philosophy towards employees, shareholders, and supervisors.
- Individual's ability to work with others (process skills).
- Management styles that he or she is most comfortable with.
- Candidate's ability to adapt to difficult environments.
- Overall ethics, honesty, and competitiveness.
- Track record in developing subordinates.

GEOGRAPHIC SCOPE OF RECRUITING ACTIVITIES:
Serve clients nationwide and in Europe, Pacific Rim, Latin America

TOTAL YEARS OF RETAINER-TYPE RECRUITING EXPERIENCE:
12 years

BRENDA L. RUELLO
Partner and Member of Executive Committee
Heidrick & Struggles, Inc.
245 Park Avenue
New York, NY 10167
Telephone: (212) 867-9876

HONOREE: 1990, 1992, 1994

Date of birth: December 22, 1937

Heidrick & Struggles, Inc.

EDUCATION:
> Syracuse University
> > B.A., fine arts, 1959

SPECIAL INTERESTS AND HOBBIES:
> Photography, gardening, landscaping

EMPLOYMENT HISTORY:
> 1977 to present: Heidrick & Struggles, Inc.
> 1975 to 1977: Manager–Executive Search, Peat, Marwick, Mitchell & Co.
> 1970 to 1975: Consultant/Recruiter, Booz, Allen & Hamilton, Inc.
> 1964 to 1966: Consultant–Executive Search, Kiernan & Company
> 1959 to 1964: Personnel Training, Bloomingdale's

WHAT I LOOK FOR IN GENERAL IN A CANDIDATE:

A leader who manages a business rather than a career—ability to manage change—"fire in the belly"—global vision, with the ability to execute against that vision.

Commitment to developing a strong motivated team, with the ability to achieve a marketplace leadership role with either the company's products or services. Entrepreneurial instincts combined with respect for total quality objectives. Someone who is inspired to reach out for "hidden" star talent. A thinking implementer who is forthright and unpretentious with an easy self-confidence, a good sense of humor, and the energy and tenacity to exert every effort necessary to solve business problems. Someone who responds to crisis situations with immediacy, emotional control, clear thinking, and solid judgment.

GEOGRAPHIC SCOPE OF RECRUITING ACTIVITIES:
> Serve clients nationwide and in France, England, Holland, and Australia

TOTAL YEARS OF RETAINER-TYPE RECRUITING EXPERIENCE:
> 17 years

NORMAN D. SANDERS
Managing Director
Norm Sanders Associates, Inc.
2 Village Court
Hazlet, NJ 07730
Telephone: (908) 264-3700

Date of birth: November 26, 1937

Norm Sanders Associates, Inc.

EDUCATION:
> Ohio University
>> B.F.A., communications, 1959

MILITARY:
> Staff Sergeant, United States Air Force, 1960 to 1966

EMPLOYMENT HISTORY:
> 1991 to present: Norm Sanders Associates, Inc.
> 1989 to 1991: Managing Director, Russell Reynolds Associates, Inc.
> 1977 to 1989: Senior Consultant, Handy Associates
> 1972 to 1977: Vice President, Sales, CBS, Inc.

WHAT I LOOK FOR IN GENERAL IN A CANDIDATE:

Since technology is the basis of our practice, we search for senior executive candidates who have the demonstrated ability to apply technology to leverage points of a business. A track record of visionary initiatives; working as a change agent; and a successful history of implementation attainment. All must be contained in a package that passes our view of the client's "chemistry test."

GEOGRAPHIC SCOPE OF RECRUITING ACTIVITIES:
Serve clients nationwide and in Canada, Mexico, Europe, and Asia

TOTAL YEARS OF RETAINER-TYPE RECRUITING EXPERIENCE:
> 17 years

PATRICIA L. SAWYER
Partner
Smith & Sawyer, Inc.
230 Park Avenue, 33rd Floor
New York, NY 10169
Telephone: (212) 490-4390

Harry Heleotis

Date of birth: July 1, 1950

EDUCATION:
Mary Washington College of the
        University of Virginia
        B.A., mathematics and economics, 1971
George Washington University
        M.S., computer science, 1979
Harvard Graduate School of Business
        M.B.A., 1982

SPECIAL INTERESTS AND HOBBIES:
Women's issues, scuba diving, soaring, textile art, nature adventures

EMPLOYMENT HISTORY:
1990 to present: Smith & Sawyer, Inc.
1988 to 1990: Vice President, Strategic Initiatives, American Express, Travel
        Related Services
1986 to 1988: Vice President, Advanced Technology, Equitable Life Assurance
        Society
1982 to 1986: Senior Associate, Booz, Allen & Hamilton, Inc.
1974 to 1980: Computer Scientist, NASA/Langley Research Center
1973 to 1974: Systems Analyst, LTV Aerospace
1972 to 1973: Cost Analyst, Newport News Shipbuilding & Drydock Company

WHAT I LOOK FOR IN GENERAL IN A CANDIDATE:
It is always important to work with the client in defining the critical industry and
functional knowledge that will assure early success in a senior-level position. These
are the "necessary but not sufficient" credentials that I look for first in a candidate.
In addition, I look for the following personal qualities:

- Intellectual horsepower to grapple with complex business problems and
  suggest options and potential solutions that are more sound or creative
  than those of his or her counterparts in competitor companies.
- Leadership potential in the context of the client's culture.
- Self-knowledge, and sufficient self-confidence to share personal weak-
  nesses with complementary strengths on his or her team.
- Good business judgment, an apparent understanding of consequences.
- Energy, focus, and persistence.
- Communication skills, including listening, and an open, inquisitive mind.
- A healthy respect for competition and an interest in winning.
- Strong personal values, and a flawless record of ethics and professionalism.

GEOGRAPHIC SCOPE OF RECRUITING ACTIVITIES:
Serve clients nationwide and in conjunction with our partners in Penrhyn
        International all European/Scandinavian countries, Middle East, Africa,
        United Kingdom, Australia, Canada, Hong Kong, Japan

TOTAL YEARS OF RETAINER-TYPE RECRUITING EXPERIENCE:
5 years

RICHARD D. SBARBARO
President
Lauer, Sbarbaro Associates, Inc.
30 N. LaSalle Street
Chicago, IL 60602
Telephone: (312) 372-7050

HONOREE: 1990, 1992, 1994

Date of birth: December 16, 1946

John Reilly Photography

EDUCATION:
> DePaul University
> > B.S.C., marketing, 1967
> > M.B.A., marketing, 1971

SPECIAL INTERESTS AND HOBBIES:
> Running, cycling, water sports, golf; DePaul University Athletic Board, Management Advisory Board and Adjunct Professor, Graduate School of Business; Director, EMA Partners International

EMPLOYMENT HISTORY:
> 1979 to present: Lauer, Sbarbaro Associates, Inc.
> 1978 to 1979: Principal, Booz, Allen & Hamilton
> 1971 to 1978: Senior Vice President, Midwest Stock Exchange
> 1969 to 1971: Senior Consultant, Fry Consultants
> 1967 to 1969: Sales Manager, Illinois Bell Telephone Company

WHAT I LOOK FOR IN GENERAL IN A CANDIDATE:

Once the technical competence to successfully meet the client's requirements is established, the softer skills become paramount. They include:

> Leadership—a successful track record with increasing success.
> Integrity—no matter what the level, this is a *must*.
> Common sense—essential for balance both on and off the job.
> Intelligence—this will have been established early on in his or her career.
> Willingness to learn—every manager can benefit from expanded knowledge.
> Sense of humor—genuine and natural.
> People skills—a strong motivator, must truly enjoy people and accept and recognize strengths and weaknesses.
> Vision and balance—management that can set the course with lofty objectives yet recognize reality.
> Energy—very high, but maintainable.
> Compassion—recognition of employees as assets and human beings, not just expense.

GEOGRAPHIC SCOPE OF RECRUITING ACTIVITIES:
> Serve clients nationwide and through EMA Partners International in the Netherlands, Belgium, Venezuela, Argentina, Uruguay, Australia, England, Mexico, Italy, Russia, Spain, Switzerland, Singapore, Austria, Czech Republic, Poland, Hungary, Slovenia, Croatia, Germany, France, Canada, and Pacific Rim

TOTAL YEARS OF RETAINER-TYPE RECRUITING EXPERIENCE:
> 15 years

PETER R. SCHMIDT
President (BCC)/Director
(Boyden World Corp.)
Boyden Consulting Corporation
55 Madison Avenue
Morristown, NJ 07960
Telephone: (201) 267-0890
375 Park Avenue
New York, NY 10152
Telephone: (212) 980-6480

Date of birth: December 11, 1934

Dalia Photo: Video

EDUCATION:
    Duke University
        B.A., 1956

MILITARY:
    Captain, United States Navy; active, 1956 to 1960, reserve, 1960 to 1985

SPECIAL INTERESTS AND HOBBIES:
    Chairman: Duke University, Northern New Jersey Development Council;
        Board of University of Denver, MBA School; naval history, golf, sailing,
        reading

EMPLOYMENT HISTORY:
    1969 to present: President, Boyden Consulting, and Director, Boyden World
        Corp.
    1961 to 1969: Various positions, Bell Laboratories

WHAT I LOOK FOR IN GENERAL IN A CANDIDATE:

Today's global manager has a far more difficult task in today's marketplace
than his predecessors. He or she must not only be familiar with many different
international cultures but must also have great flexibility to operate in them on a
profitable basis. Quick of mind, intuitive with excellent strategic skills, today's
manager more than ever must have excellent people skills. In general, we would
look for candidates with a solid energy level, enthusiastic, but with some humility,
who have a great deal of self-confidence. Additionally, the remainder of the 90s
will require managers to be able to do more with less. Therefore, they must be
creative, able to bring out the best in their people, and provide the leadership
and "team skills" with intelligence, compassion, and yet with a positive goal orientation.

GEOGRAPHIC SCOPE OF RECRUITING ACTIVITIES:
    Serve clients worldwide

TOTAL YEARS OF RETAINER-TYPE RECRUITING EXPERIENCE:
    25 years

LAMBERT SCHUYLER, JR.
Partner
Schuyler, Frye & Baker, Inc.
1100 Abernathy Road, NE Suite 1825
Atlanta, GA 30328
Telephone: (404) 804-1996

Date of birth: August 4, 1938

EDUCATION:

> Albright College, 1962
> Babson College
> B.S., business administration, 1964

Schuyler, Frye & Baker, Inc.

SPECIAL INTERESTS AND HOBBIES:

> Volunteer—1996 Summer Olympic Games Organizing Committee and Habitat for Humanity; golf, bicycling, reading

EMPLOYMENT HISTORY:

> 1982 to present: Partner and Founder, Schuyler, Frye & Baker, Inc.
> 1979 to 1982: Vice President, Lamalie Associates, Inc.
> 1973 to 1979: Vice President, Billington, Fox & Ellis, Inc.
> 1970 to 1973: Senior Management Consultant, Gilbert/Commonwealth Companies, Inc.
> 1969 to 1970: Division Controller, Whittaker Corporation
> 1966 to 1969: Senior Consultant, Arthur Andersen & Co.
> 1964 to 1966: Management Trainee, Reading Trust Company

WHAT I LOOK FOR IN GENERAL IN A CANDIDATE:

Here are the general characteristics that I look for in candidates:

- In-depth understanding of the industries and organizations where they have worked.
- Real, comprehensive, general management skills and experience, including successful turnarounds of troubled organizations.
- Genuine leadership ability, supported by a record of successfully building or changing organizations to pursue new opportunities.
- Innate entrepreneurial ability and vision, together with the drive and enthusiasm to sell new ideas and strategies.
- Above-average intelligence, a continuing thirst for knowledge, and the ability to bring an international perspective to their work.
- Excellent communication and interpersonal skills marked by personal warmth, trust, and a good sense of humor.
- A person who understands his or her strengths and weaknesses.

GEOGRAPHIC SCOPE OF RECRUITING ACTIVITIES:

> Serve clients nationwide and in Europe, Canada, Mexico, Far East, and Australia

TOTAL YEARS OF RETAINER-TYPE RECRUITING EXPERIENCE:

> 21 years

LEE J. SCHWEICHLER
President
Schweichler Associates, Inc.
200 Tamal Vista, Bldg. 200, Suite 100
Corte Madera, CA 94925
Telephone: (415) 924-7200

Date of birth: July 28, 1945

Schweichler Associates, Inc.

EDUCATION:
> State University of New York at Buffalo
> > B.S., business administration, 1967
> University of California at Berkeley
> > M.B.A., industrial relations/
> > organizational behavior, 1972

MILITARY:
> Sergeant, United States Army Reserves, 1968 to 1974

SPECIAL INTERESTS AND HOBBIES:
> Skiing, sailing; school board member, Sterne School, San Francisco, CA
> > (school for children with learning disabilities)

EMPLOYMENT HISTORY:
> 1978 to present: Schweichler Associates, Inc.
> 1975 to 1978: Vice President, The Thomas Tucker Co.
> 1971 to 1975: Manager, Arthur Young & Co.
> 1969 to 1971: Senior Consultant, Ernst & Ernst

WHAT I LOOK FOR IN GENERAL IN A CANDIDATE:

Candidate evaluation takes place on multiple levels. Critical to the process is the appropriate definition of the role, objectives, organizational environment, and the management style of the key decision maker. On the candidate side we look at:

1. The specifics of an individual's background:
   Experience
   Accomplishments
   Organizations where she/he "grew up," and the environments of those companies
2. The orientation/focus of the individual and relationship to the need. For example operations/internal focus versus marketing/external focus.
3. Most important, the intellectual ability and personal manner needed to work with the board and/or key decision maker, and the management depth to respond to the key objectives.

GEOGRAPHIC SCOPE OF RECRUITING ACTIVITIES:
> Serve clients nationwide

TOTAL YEARS OF RETAINER-TYPE RECRUITING EXPERIENCE:
> 24 years

STEVEN A. SEIDEN
President
Seiden Associates, Inc.
375 Park Avenue, Suite 3201
New York, NY 10472
Telephone: (212) 688-8383

HONOREE: 1992, 1994

Date of birth: February 18, 1936

Bachrach

EDUCATION:
   Yale University
      A.B., art history, 1958

MILITARY:
   Specialist Fourth Class, United States Army, 1961 to 1962

SPECIAL INTERESTS AND HOBBIES:
   Management science, foreign travel, golf, fly-fishing

EMPLOYMENT HISTORY:
   1984 to present: Seiden Associates, Inc.
   1966 to 1984: Copresident, Herzfeld & Stern, Members, New York Stock
      Exchange
   1964 to 1966: Vice President, Irving L. Straus Associates
   1962 to 1964: Vice President, Louis Sherry, Inc.
   1958 to 1962: Vice President, Seiden Holding Co., Inc.

WHAT I LOOK FOR IN GENERAL IN A CANDIDATE:

Leadership, chemistry, and track record.

Leadership becomes apparent after meeting an executive for just a short while. Robert Browning wrote, "A man's reach should exceed his grasp." A leader embodies that ideal.

The "chemistry" between client and candidate is critical. However, we don't view "chemistry" as a separate issue. Chemistry is the product of mutual respect and esteem which two successful executives—client and candidate—instinctively develop for one another.

A measurable track record is imperative. I maintain an attitude of healthy skepticism in which both references and financial records serve as evidence to corroborate a candidate's past results.

GEOGRAPHIC SCOPE OF RECRUITING ACTIVITIES:
   Serve clients nationwide and in the United Kingdom

TOTAL YEARS OF RETAINER-TYPE RECRUITING EXPERIENCE:
   10 years

DANIEL M. SHEPHERD
Principal & Founder
Shepherd Bueschel & Provus, Inc.
One South Wacker Drive, Suite 2740
Chicago, IL 60606
Telephone: (312) 372-1142

HONOREE: 1992, 1994

Date of birth: April 8, 1939

EDUCATION:
    University of Kentucky
        B.S., civil engineering, 1962
    Harvard University
        M.B.A., 1964

John Reilly Photography

MILITARY:
    Captain, United States Army Corps of Engineers, 1964 to 1966

SPECIAL INTERESTS AND HOBBIES:
    My children, coin and art collecting, skiing, Chicago Cubs, exceptional food
    and wine

EMPLOYMENT HISTORY:
    1992 to present: Shepherd Bueschel & Provus, Inc.
    1986 to 1991: Principal and Founder, Sweeney Shepherd Bueschel Provus
        Harbert & Mummert, Inc.
    1982 to 1986: Vice President, Lamalie Associates, Inc.
    1978 to 1982: Vice President, Heidrick & Struggles, Inc.
    1976 to 1978: Vice President–Product/Market Management, Masonite Corpo-
        ration
    1973 to 1976: Vice President, General Manager–Thunderbird Boats, Corpo-
        rate Director—Operations, Fuga Industries, Inc.
    1970 to 1973: Various positions, Mattel, Inc.
    1966 to 1970: Various positions, Procter & Gamble Company

WHAT I LOOK FOR IN GENERAL IN A CANDIDATE:

- A value-added twist in matching a candidate's technical skills with the
  client's needs.
- Intellectual efficiency and capacity; mental clarity; common sense and
  street savvy; and the ability to reach high levels of abstraction.
- Self-awareness and emotional maturity and stability.
- People skills/style in relating to superiors, peers, and subordinates.
- The ability to organize and to direct—leadership.
- Presence, balance, luck, sense of humor, work ethic, energy, integrity, skele-
  tons.

GEOGRAPHIC SCOPE OF RECRUITING ACTIVITIES:
    Serve clients nationwide

TOTAL YEARS OF RETAINER-TYPE RECRUITING EXPERIENCE:
    15 years

ANDREW SHERWOOD
Chairman
The Goodrich & Sherwood Company
521 Fifth Avenue
New York, NY 10017
Telephone: (212) 697-4131

HONOREE: 1990, 1992, 1994

Date of birth: January 8, 1942

The Goodrich & Sherwood Company

EDUCATION:
>Nichols College
>>B.B.A., marketing/management, 1964

SPECIAL INTERESTS AND HOBBIES:
>Member National Ski Patrol, tennis, hunting, sporting clays, fishing, restoring vintage race cars, equestrian riding

EMPLOYMENT HISTORY:
>1971 to present: The Goodrich & Sherwood Company
>1967 to 1971: Executive Vice President, Ward Clancy Associates
>1965 to 1967: Director, Gilbert Lane

WHAT I LOOK FOR IN GENERAL IN A CANDIDATE:

When interviewing a top-level candidate, I look for balance and ability to communicate appropriately to the situation. The better senior executives I have known and recruited are balanced individuals who can manage diversified problems, opportunities, and people simultaneously with skill and diplomacy. With balance and effective communication style and less emotion, volatility, disruption, and extremism, the greater a likelihood for a smooth-running organization, clearly defined objectives, respect, control, and ultimate success. Qualities I look for:

- Integrity, strength of character, a good role model.
- Results-oriented. What has the person accomplished? Against what objectives?
- Sense of humor. Do people enjoy interacting with this person? Have they in the past?
- Presence. Will this person represent the company well, both inside and outside the corporation?
- Energy. A sense of urgency, enough to do the job and motivate others without intimidating.
- Vision. Will this person build for the future or just maintain?
- Stamina. Enough to handle tough decisions without getting bogged down, sick, or exhausted.
- Communicator. Leads by communicating and encouraging.
- Loyalty to the company, staff, customers, stockholders, and family.
- Well-organized. Does the individual organize thoughts and work well?
- Leadership. A person others seek out and follow willingly.
- High frustration level. Able to manage without flying off the handle.
- Open to new ideas that others sponsor.
- Secure with superiors, subordinates alike.

GEOGRAPHIC SCOPE OF RECRUITING ACTIVITIES:
>Serve clients nationwide and in Europe

TOTAL YEARS OF RETAINER-TYPE RECRUITING EXPERIENCE:
>27 years

MARY E. SHOURDS
Executive Vice President
Houze, Shourds & Montgomery, Inc.
Greater Los Angeles World Trade Center
One World Trade, Suite 1840
Long Beach, CA 90831-1840
Telephone: (310) 495-6495

HONOREE: 1990, 1992, 1994

Date of birth: November 7, 1942

McDonald Photography

EDUCATION:
> Pepperdine University
> > B.S., 1974
> UCLA
> > M.B.A., 1983

SPECIAL INTERESTS AND HOBBIES:
> The sciences, cooking, reading, golf, collecting Southwestern American and African art, serve on the Executive Committee for the Long Beach Community Partnership

EMPLOYMENT HISTORY:
> 1977 to present: Houze, Shourds & Montgomery, Inc.
> 1975 to 1977: Vice President, Hergenrather & Company
> 1964 to 1975: Rockwell International, various Human Resources positions to Director–Human Resources Information Systems Organization and Corporate Offices

WHAT I LOOK FOR IN GENERAL IN A CANDIDATE:

Complex markets and organizations vary dramatically and move rapidly. Thus, candidates must be capable of diagnosing the particular market and culture in which they operate and then applying the sensitivity and flexibility—and inspiring the vision and commitment—required to respond rapidly and initiate change within that structure.

I also look for candidates who evidence strong interest in the development of others, who listen with skill and empathy, who build learning organizations, who consistently attract stars, and who establish lean, flexible, open systems in the businesses they lead.

On the personal side, I look for candidates capable of rigorous self-assessment, who evidence a well-tested value system, who have moral courage, a balanced lifestyle and interests, a good sense of humor, and intellectual integrity.

GEOGRAPHIC SCOPE OF RECRUITING ACTIVITIES:
> Serve clients nationwide and internationally individually and in conjunction with Penrhyn International in London, Brussels, Stockholm, Tokyo, Melbourne, Toronto, Montreal, Johannesburg, and Zurich

TOTAL YEARS OF RETAINER-TYPE RECRUITING EXPERIENCE:
> 18 years

MEL SHULMAN
Partner
McFeely Wackerle Shulman
425 California Street, Suite 2502
San Francisco, CA 94104
Telephone: (415) 398-3488

Date of birth: March 22, 1937

McFeely Wackerle Shulman

EDUCATION:
>   Syracuse University
>   B.A., business administration
>   (marketing finance), 1958
>   Cornell University Law School
>   J.D., 1962
>   New York University
>   LL.M., taxation, 1963

SPECIAL INTERESTS AND HOBBIES:
>   Golf, tennis, collecting art

EMPLOYMENT HISTORY:
>   1991 to present: McFeely Wackerle Shulman
>   1989 to 1991: Partner, Shulman & Cameron
>   1985 to 1989: Managing Partner, Ward Howell International, Inc.
>   1979 to 1985: Vice President, David Powell, Inc.
>   1978 to 1979: Director, Administration, Itel Corporation
>   1976 to 1978: Vice President, Administration, Fibreboard Corporation
>   1970 to 1976: Director, Human Resources, Chemetron Corporation
>   1967 to 1970: Labor Relations Administrator, National Broadcasting Company
>   1963 to 1967: Attorney, Whitman Ransom & Coulson, Esqs.

WHAT I LOOK FOR IN GENERAL IN A CANDIDATE:

Passion, emotion, commitment, and enthusiasm are key personal traits I look for in all candidates. An "edge of the seat" candidate explaining his job successes and failures typically gives more insight into how he or she reacts in certain situations. Many of my venture capital clients believe these traits are the basis for quality entrepreneurship. I believe they offer a background for success whether the company is large or small.

Additionally, I attempt to determine how a candidate thinks—processes information, evaluates alternatives, and presents conclusions. Too much equivocation raises questions.

Finally, the rationale for potentially leaving the current employer and the perceived rationale for joining my client is important.

GEOGRAPHIC SCOPE OF RECRUITING ACTIVITIES:
>   Serve clients nationwide

TOTAL YEARS OF RETAINER-TYPE RECRUITING EXPERIENCE:
>   15 years

FRED SIEGEL
President
CONEX Incorporated
919 Third Avenue, 18th Floor
New York, NY 10022
Telephone: (212) 371-3737

HONOREE: 1992, 1994

Date of birth: April 17, 1941

Armand D'Arienzo

EDUCATION:
New York City Technical College
A.A.S., accounting, 1966
Long Island University
B.S., accounting, 1969

MILITARY:
Airman 2nd Class, United States Air Force, 1961 to 1965

SPECIAL INTERESTS AND HOBBIES:
Politics, a variety of sports

EMPLOYMENT HISTORY:
1988 to present: President, CONEX Incorporated; Board Member, Intersearch Worldwide Ltd.
1980 to 1988: Partner, Consulting Associates
1976 to 1980: Associate Dean, New York University Graduate School of Business
1974 to 1976: Recruitment Manager, Arthur Young & Co.
1970 to 1974: Assistant to the Mayor, New York City Office of the Mayor
1969 to 1970: Auditor, Price Waterhouse & Co.

WHAT I LOOK FOR IN GENERAL IN A CANDIDATE:

Work ethic, fit, relative work experience, and a strong educational background are the key general factors we look for in a candidate. Knowing the candidate and client well enough to ensure success for both sides, we believe, separates the outstanding recruiters from the ordinary.

We look for gaps on resumes and quick turnover of jobs as indicators of potential problems. A good deal of time is spent in determining why candidates leave positions, and we look for patterns. It is important to determine if candidates can deal with pressure, whether or not they are hands-on, and if they have the personality, work habits, demeanor, leadership, and technical skills necessary for the job.

We also seek candidates with a well-developed management style and philosophy, communication skills, depth of P&L responsibility, analytical skills, and, where necessary, technical skills. We also seek candidates with clear progression in their employment history from excellent companies. Since the bulk of our clients are in the international arena, language skills and global business interest, as well as experience, are often make-or-break factors.

GEOGRAPHIC SCOPE OF RECRUITING ACTIVITIES:
Serve clients nationwide and in Europe, Asia, North and South America, Australia

TOTAL YEARS OF RETAINER-TYPE RECRUITING EXPERIENCE:
14 years

J. GERALD SIMMONS
President
Handy HRM Corp.
250 Park Avenue
New York, NY 10177
Telephone: (212) 210-5656

HONOREE: 1990, 1992, 1994

Date of birth: September 17, 1929

Alec Harrison Photography

EDUCATION:
University of Miami
B.S., business administration, 1956
Harvard University
Advanced Management Program

MILITARY:
Special Agent, United States Army Counter Intelligence, 1951 to 1954

SPECIAL INTERESTS AND HOBBIES:
Tennis, squash, golf

EMPLOYMENT HISTORY:
1976 to present: Handy HRM Corp.
1973 to 1976: Vice President–Marketing, Wiltek Inc.
1971 to 1973: General Manager, Department and Specialty Store Division,
Revlon Inc.
1956 to 1971: Director of Marketing Services, Data Processing Division, IBM
Corporation

WHAT I LOOK FOR IN GENERAL IN A CANDIDATE:

1. Track record of success
2. Intelligence/"smarts"/knowledge
3. Good communication skills, oral/written
4. "Stick-to-it-iveness"
5. Someone for whom success is an aphrodisiac

GEOGRAPHIC SCOPE OF RECRUITING ACTIVITIES:
Serve clients nationwide

TOTAL YEARS OF RETAINER-TYPE RECRUITING EXPERIENCE:
18 years

RICHARD C. SLAYTON
President
Slayton International, Inc.
181 W. Madison, Suite 4510
Chicago, IL 60611
Telephone: (312) 456-0080

HONOREE: 1990, 1992, 1994

Date of Birth: April 3, 1937

Stuart-Rodgers Ltd. Photography

EDUCATION:
University of Michigan
B.S. degree, industrial engineering, 1960
M.B.A. degree, 1965
University of Michigan
M.B.A. degree, 1965

MILITARY:
Rated, United States Naval Reserve, 1954 to 1965

SPECIAL INTERESTS AND HOBBIES:
Fly-fishing, skeet, bird hunting, downhill and cross-country skiing

EMPLOYMENT HISTORY:
1985 to present: Slayton International, Inc.
1976 to 1985: Boyden International
1983 to 1985: Senior Vice President and Manager–Midwest Operations
1982 to 1983: Vice President and Manager–Toledo Office
1976 to 1982: Vice President
1970 to 1976: President, Business Technology Associates
1967 to 1970: Associate Director of Consulting, K.W. Tunnell
1960 to 1967: Various positions in manufacturing and marketing, General
Electric Company

WHAT I LOOK FOR IN GENERAL IN A CANDIDATE:

Each professional is endowed at birth with certain qualities common to all, namely, intelligence, energy level, appearance, common sense, and feelings. As a professional develops, other qualities are developed, namely, knowledge in one's chosen field, integrity, aggressiveness, organization, written and verbal skills, decision-making ability, interpersonal relations, personality, and overall executive stature.

All of the above comprise a total composite of a candidate that, with career accomplishments, must be evaluated and matched with the particular requirements of a client.

GEOGRAPHIC SCOPE OF RECRUITING ACTIVITIES:
Serve clients nationwide and in Europe and Far East

TOTAL YEARS OF RETAINER-TYPE RECRUITING EXPERIENCE:
21 years

HERMAN M. SMITH
President
Herman Smith Executive Initiatives Inc.
P.O. Box 629, 161 Bay Street, Suite 3600
Toronto, Ontario M5J 2S1 Canada
Telephone: (416) 862-8830

Date of birth: June 21, 1937

Herman Smith Executive Initiatives Inc.

EDUCATION:
The University of Western Ontario
B.A., 1957

SPECIAL INTERESTS AND HOBBIES:
Jazz piano, sailing and boating

EMPLOYMENT HISTORY:
1974 to present: Herman Smith Executive Initiatives Inc.
1970 to 1974: President, Smith Caldwell Limited
1967 to 1970: Partner, Hickling Johnston Limited
1962 to 1967: Director of Advertising, Harding Caroets Limited
1959 to 1962: Product Manager, The Daymond Company Limited
1957 to 1959: Sales Trainee, The Steel Company of Canada Limited

WHAT I LOOK FOR IN GENERAL IN A CANDIDATE:

Predictable behavior has always been a focus. Track record and the degree of enthusiasm that certain topics engender in discussion give me a snapshot of one's motivation. I look for learners. I look for happy people.

Another area of concentration is an executive's record of successful change in moving from one organization to another. Meeting a senior executive of many, many successful years in one organization makes me want to look at those whose achievements are predictable in varied environments and situations.

Intelligence, energy, passion, and sincerity are qualities I always look for. They fit most situations.

GEOGRAPHIC SCOPE OF RECRUITING ACTIVITIES:
Serve clients in Canada, United Kingdom, England, and the United States

TOTAL YEARS OF RETAINER-TYPE RECRUITING EXPERIENCE:
27 years

JOHN E. SMITH, JR.
President
Smith Search, S.C.
Barranca Del Muerto 472, Col. Alpes
Mexico, D.F. 01010
Telephone: (525) 593-8766

HONOREE: 1992, 1994

Date of birth: December 22, 1933

Fotografía Itami, S.A.

EDUCATION:
Georgetown University, School of Foreign Service
B.S., foreign service, 1967

SPECIAL INTERESTS AND HOBBIES:
Bicycling, skiing, family, work

EMPLOYMENT HISTORY:
1972 to present: Smith Search, S.C.
1964 to 1972: Director, Noble & Associates
1959 to 1964: Vice President, Foote Cone & Belding de Mexico

WHAT I LOOK FOR IN GENERAL IN A CANDIDATE:

The type of executive we will place is most frequently bilingual in Spanish, bicultural (by dint of extended American cultural, corporate, or educational exposure), U.S.-educated (usually at the M.B.A. level), and upscale (not unimportant in what is still a caste society, egalitarian revolution notwithstanding), which means mostly of European descent. He (sometimes she) is usually in the employ of a leadership Mexican industrial or financial group or a multinational corporation. In either case, they are clearly drawn from an intellectual, business, social upper crust geared and galvanized since birth to assume roles of responsibility and leadership within the Mexican infrastructure.

We feel comfortable recruiting Mexicans for American companies operating in Mexico or elsewhere in Latin America. We feel equally comfortable recruiting Mexicans for Mexicans, both always of the leadership stripe/ilk. We also enjoy the challenge of recruiting in the Spanish-speaking market of the United States.

Candidates, irrespective of the search, must be winners, proven problem-solvers, achievers, apt and agile in dealing with the increasingly international and increasingly competitive markets of Latin America, especially Mexico. We place a premium on the candidate who is creative, of high energy level and powerful personality.

GEOGRAPHIC SCOPE OF RECRUITING ACTIVITIES:
Serve clients in Mexico, United States, Central America, and northern South America

TOTAL YEARS OF RETAINER-TYPE RECRUITING EXPERIENCE:
21 years

ROBERT L. SMITH
Partner
Smith & Sawyer, Inc.
230 Park Avenue, 33rd Floor
New York, NY 10169
Telephone: (212) 490-4390

HONOREE: 1992, 1994

Date of birth: July 1, 1938

Harry Heleotis

EDUCATION:
> University of Florida
>> Bachelor of Industrial Engineering, 1961
> Harvard University
>> M.B.A., 1963

SPECIAL INTERESTS AND HOBBIES:
> AESC (various board positions and past chairman), organizational and personal dynamics/behavior, scuba diving, nature adventure travel, gardening

EMPLOYMENT HISTORY:
> 1989 to present: Founder, Smith & Sawyer, Inc.
> 1975 to 1989: President and Founder, Johnson, Smith & Knisely
> 1971 to 1975: Vice President, Nordeman Grimm, Inc.
> 1971: Account Executive, Diebold Group, Inc.
> 1967 to 1971: Large Account Marketing, IBM Corporation
> 1966 to 1967: Sales/Marketing Management, Burlington House
> 1964 to 1966: Sales/Marketing Management, Craftex Mills, Inc.
> 1963 to 1964: Sales Representative, Xerox Corporation

WHAT I LOOK FOR IN GENERAL IN A CANDIDATE:

To be successful, a candidate must have the *"tools"* and the *personal characteristics* necessary to excel in a new and highly risky environment.

The "Tools"

- Does this candidate have the requisite educational foundation (if any is required) on which to build professional skills?
- Has this candidate worked in positions which would build the required functional skills and industry knowledge?
- Has this candidate worked for companies with acknowledged reputations for excellence in selecting, hiring, and training outstanding executives?

Personal Characteristics:

- Will the candidate's management style and personal values be a good fit?
- Will the candidate be able to build good working relationships with the other members of the management team?
- Is this candidate a "Business Athlete" with a broad set of skills and the ability to respond creatively and effectively to rapid and abrupt changes?
- Does this candidate have the charisma, stamina, and personal energy to provide leadership and infuse the organization with a high level of vitality?

GEOGRAPHIC SCOPE OF RECRUITING ACTIVITIES:
> Serve clients nationally and coordinated with partners of Penrhyn International in Europe/Scandinavia, United Kingdom, Middle East, Africa, Canada, Hong Kong, Japan

TOTAL YEARS OF RETAINER-TYPE RECRUITING EXPERIENCE:
> 23 years

CHARLES SPLAINE
President
Splaine & Associates
15951 Los Gatos Boulevard
Los Gatos, CA 95032
Telephone: (408) 354-3664

Date of birth: December 23, 1938

EDUCATION:
College of the Holy Cross
B.S., economics 1960
University of Pennsylvania–The Wharton
School M.B.A., industrial
management, 1965

Triad Photography Group

MILITARY:
Lieutenant, United States Navy, 1960 to 1963

SPECIAL INTERESTS AND HOBBIES:
Family, running, fly-fishing, golf, reading, wine collecting

EMPLOYMENT HISTORY:
1982 to present: Splaine & Associates
1980 to 1982: President, COO, Atalla Corporation
1970 to 1980: President, Field Operations Group, Memorex Corporation
1965 to 1970: Marketing Representative, IBM

WHAT I LOOK FOR IN GENERAL IN A CANDIDATE:

Professionally:
Someone who possesses the majority of the characteristics that the optimal candidate should have. Who has been with few companies, and who seems to be very mature and stable. I look for a demonstrated track record for innovation, motivation, proven management skills, and confirmation that he or she is capable of achieving through others. Specifically, I look for:

- A track record for attracting and retaining key people
- Loyalty (not political)
- High intellect
- Persistence, resiliency
- Demonstrable communication skills
- Risk taker
- Verifiable record of successes
- Capability of aspiring to a larger role

Personal Qualities:
- Integrity
- Good image
- Personal life in order
- Courage
- High energy

GEOGRAPHIC SCOPE OF RECRUITING ACTIVITIES:
Serve clients nationwide and in Singapore, Malaysia, Thailand, Hong Kong, Taiwan/Asia, England, Germany, Europe

TOTAL YEARS OF RETAINER-TYPE RECRUITING EXPERIENCE:
12 years

ROBERT D. SPRIGGS
Chairman
Spriggs & Company, Inc.
1701 Lake Avenue, Suite 265
Glenview, IL 60025-2088
Telephone: (708) 657-7181

HONOREE: 1990, 1992, 1994

Date of birth: September 10, 1929

Spriggs & Company, Inc.

EDUCATION:
University of Illinois
B.S., law, 1955
J.D., 1957

MILITARY:
Communications Technician, Third Class, United States Navy, 1951 to 1954

SPECIAL INTERESTS AND HOBBIES:
Tennis, photography

EMPLOYMENT HISTORY:
1967 to present: Spriggs & Company, Inc.
1964 to 1967: Vice President, Johnson & Associates, Inc.
1963 to 1964: Associate, McKinsey & Company, Inc.
1959 to 1962: Director, Industrial Relations, Robertshaw Corporation
1958 to 1959: Manager, Salaried Employment, Brunswick Corporation
1957 to 1958: Labor Relations Staff Assistant, Caterpillar Tractor Company

WHAT I LOOK FOR IN GENERAL IN A CANDIDATE:

The fundamental building blocks need to be set in place. This means a candidate has to have the requisite industry and professional knowledge coupled with extremely high energy. It is not enough to be a self-starter; one must be a consistent finisher as well. The final element in the package is a very successful track record. Scoring high on these fundamentals will get you into the game. The acid test from here to the finish line is a function of how well the individual is able to cope creatively with the unique problems of the marketplace. The fast pace of change in these arenas seriously demands new ways of solving old problems. These creative schemes and solutions need to produce very substantial levels of success through originality and wholly new approaches in order to generate market edge over competitors.

GEOGRAPHIC SCOPE OF RECRUITING ACTIVITIES:
Serve clients nationwide and in South Africa, Canada, England

TOTAL YEARS OF RETAINER-TYPE RECRUITING EXPERIENCE:
30 years

ROBERT A. STAUB
President
Staub, Warmbold & Associates, Inc.
575 Madison Avenue, 10th Floor
New York, NY 10022
Telephone: (212) 605-0554

HONOREE: 1990, 1994

Date of birth: April 4, 1934

Bachrach

EDUCATION:
University of Miami
B.B.A., economics, 1956

EMPLOYMENT HISTORY:
1962 to present: Staub, Warmbold & Associates, Inc.
1960 to 1962: Associate, Burke & O'Brien
1959 to 1960: Personnel Manager, Allstate Insurance Company
1956 to 1959: Various positions in Sales, Marketing, and Personnel, Ford
Motor Co.

WHAT I LOOK FOR IN GENERAL IN A CANDIDATE:

In general, certain elements are critical in the evaluation of senior management candidates. I look at each prospective candidate in terms of the following:

How strong a businessman is the candidate?
How will the candidate's personality and style fit into the client organization?
How substantial is the candidate's intellect?
How do I rate the candidate's managerial capabilities?
How qualified is the candidate functionally?
How stable is the candidate's family environment?
Will the candidate's family be able to adjust to the location of his or her new
position?

GEOGRAPHIC SCOPE OF RECRUITING ACTIVITIES:
Clients nationwide and in Europe and Asia

TOTAL YEARS OF RETAINER-TYPE RECRUITING EXPERIENCE:
29 years

GILBERT R. (GIL) STENHOLM, JR.
Comanaging Director and Partner–
Consumer Goods North American Practice
SpencerStuart
401 North Michigan Avenue, Suite 3400
Chicago, IL 60611
Telephone: (312) 321-8338

Date of birth: February 21, 1946

SpencerStuart

EDUCATION:
Bob Jones University
B.S., business administration, 1968

MILITARY:
First Lieutenant, United States Army, 1969 to 1972

SPECIAL INTERESTS AND HOBBIES:
Avid golfer (1 handicap), local schools, coach, Hubbard Street Chicago–board member

EMPLOYMENT HISTORY:
1980 to present: SpencerStuart
1976 to 1980: Principal/Associate, Booz, Allen & Hamilton
1975 to 1976: Consultant, Russell Reynolds
1974 to 1975: Consultant, Westcott Associates
1974: Manager–Employment, Masonite
1972 to 1974: Manager–Recruitment, Baxter
1968 to 1969: Sales Manager, General Foods

WHAT I LOOK FOR IN GENERAL IN A CANDIDATE:

- Pleasing personality and ability to relate well to wide variety of audiences.
- Forward thinker, probing mind, thinks beyond obvious, strategic, visionary, problem solver.
- Open-minded, developer of talent, delegates as necessary—good balance between people and business needs.
- Energetic, resourceful, fair, motivational, team-focused—effective leader.
- Honest, forthright, direct, ethical.
- Articulate, down-to-earth, lacks hidden agendas.
- Performance-driven, demanding, winning philosophy and attitude—competitive.
- Functional skilled, with broad business perspectives.
- Global outlook, financially focused.
- Stable personal life, dependable, organized, and efficient.

GEOGRAPHIC SCOPE OF RECRUITING ACTIVITIES
Serve clients nationwide and in Asia Pacific, South America and Europe

TOTAL YEARS OF RETAINER-TYPE RECRUITING EXPERIENCE
19 years

STEPHEN STRAIN
Director, High Technology Practice
SpencerStuart
3000 Sand Hill Road Bldg. 1, Suite 275
Menlo Park, CA 94025
Telephone: (415) 688-1285

Ingersoll Studio

Date of Birth: October 22, 1940

EDUCATION:
Miami University, Ohio
B.A. degree; Political Science, 1964
Little Rock University
B.B.A. degree, 1968
University of California, Los Angeles
MBA degree, 1970

MILITARY:
Captain, United States Air Force, 1964 to 1968

SPECIAL INTERESTS AND HOBBIES:
Sailing, snow skiing

EMPLOYMENT HISTORY:
1991 to present: SpencerStuart
1990 to 1991: Vice President, Corporate Human Resources, Maxtor Corporation
1988 to 1990: Vice President, Human Resources, Western Digital Corporation
1987 to 1988: Vice President, Human Resources, Seagate Technology
1984 to 1987: Director, Human Resources, Advanced Micro Devices, Inc.
1974 to 1984: Various Personnel Positions, Hewlett Packard Company
1972 to 1974: Training Manager, Pacific, Gas & Electric Company
1970 to 1972: Plant Service Center Foreman, Pacific Telephone Company

WHAT I LOOK FOR IN GENERAL IN A CANDIDATE:

I look first for technical and functional competence. Does the individual have in-depth knowledge of the industry and the function of the position he/she is being considered for; does the individual have a track record of accomplishing significant results in this industry and function; and does the individual have the right types of and levels of experience which will make a significant contribution and add value to the position. This becomes the base-line to consider the second criteria, management and leadership. In this area, I evaluate the individual's depth of experience, with an emphasis on the style of leadership and why this has been successful. This includes interpersonal and communication skills, energy level, and the ability to influence others. Third, I then evaluate how the individual fits the client culture, and whether I feel he/she can be effective in this culture. This includes evaluating whether the candidate's and the client's values are in alignment, and whether the personal style of the candidate and the management team would be effective together.

GEOGRAPHIC SCOPE OF RECRUITING ACTIVITIES:
Serve clients nationally and internationally.

TOTAL YEARS OF RETAINER-TYPE RECRUITING EXPERIENCE:
3 years

BRIAN M. SULLIVAN
President
Sullivan & Company
20 Exchange Place, 50th Floor
New York, NY 10005
Telephone: (212) 422-3000

Date of birth: March 13, 1953

Sullivan & Company

EDUCATION:
> Lehigh University
>> B.S., finance, 1975
> Denver University
>> M.B.A., finance, 1976

SPECIAL INTERESTS AND HOBBIES:
> Collecting wine, golf, travel

EMPLOYMENT HISTORY:
> 1988 to present: Sullivan & Company
> 1986 to 1988: Vice President, E.J. Lance Management, Inc.
> 1980 to 1986: Director Asset Management, Revlon, Inc.
> 1976 to 1979: Stockbroker, Kidder Peabody & Co., Inc.

WHAT I LOOK FOR IN GENERAL IN A CANDIDATE:

I. Culture

The cultural fit of a candidate with a client can overwhelmingly determine the success of the placement; therefore, I am acutely aware of culture and style throughout the recruitment period.

II. Technical Knowledge and Leadership

Culture and style will not enable a marginal candidate to excel; therefore, I look for candidates who have built their careers on a firm foundation of technical acumen and can display a track record of taking additional responsibility (not just new responsibility) within their companies. This usually implies the ability to lead by example and create loyalty.

III. Communication Skills and Depth of Knowledge

Spontaneity and the ability to react quickly under pressure are also key traits for executives. Therefore, when I interview candidates, I ask them how they would solve the business issue my client is facing. This shows me a depth of knowledge in handling problems and the ability to react quickly in a pressure situation.

IV. Character

Last, I ask myself if this is the kind of person my client would want around when things are going poorly. It's easy to get along when things are going well, but top executives are those who stay consistent in adverse times.

GEOGRAPHIC SCOPE OF RECRUITING ACTIVITIES:
> Serve clients nationwide and Europe, Latin America, and Asia

TOTAL YEARS OF RETAINER-TYPE RECRUITING EXPERIENCE:
> 6 years

WILLIAM K. SUR
Senior Vice President and Director
Canny, Bowen Inc.
200 Park Avenue
New York, NY 10166
Telephone: (212) 949-6611

HONOREE: 1992, 1994

Date of birth: April 6, 1932

Canny, Bowen Inc.

EDUCATION:
Villanova University
B.S., economics-finance major, 1954

MILITARY:
Lieutenant Junior Grade, United States Navy, 1954 to 1958

SPECIAL INTERESTS AND HOBBIES:
Skiing, golf, antiquing, shooting

EMPLOYMENT HISTORY:
1991 to present: Canny, Bowen Inc.
1989 to 1991: President, Stricker, Sur & Associates
1982 to 1989: President, Sollis, Sur & Associates
1966 to 1982: Senior Vice President and Director, SpencerStuart
1961 to 1966: Senior Financial Analyst, Merck & Co., Inc.
1958 to 1961: Sales Representative, Olin Mathieson Chemical Corp.

WHAT I LOOK FOR IN GENERAL IN A CANDIDATE:

We first help define the need and the environment that exists in the client's company. That provides us with the key parameters to use in evaluating potential candidates. We seek to determine his or her character, principally by the individual's actions in given situations, and by assessing the person's career successes (failures). We are interested in the candidate's accomplishments, how they were achieved, and under what circumstances, with what degree of difficulty. We seek specific and personal examples of creativity and innovativeness which directionally provide evidence of leadership and indications of managerial style. Once these key factors are ascertained, other traits (motivations, aspirations, self-perceptions) and professional skills (business knowledge, industry knowledge, planning ability, profit orientation, etc.) are more readily gauged, again, in light of the client's need and environment.

GEOGRAPHIC SCOPE OF RECRUITING ACTIVITIES:
Serve clients nationwide and in Europe

TOTAL YEARS OF RETAINER-TYPE RECRUITING EXPERIENCE:
28 years

CHARLES W. SWEET
President
A.T. Kearney Executive Search
222 West Adams Street
Chicago, IL 60606
Telephone: (312) 648-0111 or (312) 223-6260

HONOREE: 1992, 1994

Date of birth: June 11, 1943

Terry's Photography

EDUCATION:
Hamilton College
A.B., English, 1965
University of Chicago
M.B.A., 1968

MILITARY:
Officer Candidate, United States Marine Corps, 1966

SPECIAL INTERESTS AND HOBBIES:
Tennis, bridge, reading

EMPLOYMENT HISTORY:
1972 to present: A.T. Kearney, Inc.
1971 to 1972: Manager–Human Resources, Marlennan
1969 to 1971: Human Resources Coordinator, R.R. Donnelley
1968 to 1969: Human Resources Positions, Ford Motor Company
1965 to 1967: Salesman, Procter & Gamble Co.

WHAT I LOOK FOR IN GENERAL IN A CANDIDATE:

The importance of executive search has grown in direct proportion to industry's understanding of the impact that an outstanding individual can have upon
an organization. My job is to understand the client and the client's organization
and to identify and help the client recruit candidates who fall within the client's
parameters. In each case I look for people with a proven record of accomplishment, leadership ability, intelligence, integrity, and communication skills. Two
additional qualities must be explained in detail:

- It is critical to analyze how a candidate has dealt with failure. I believe
  that most people handle success well. Candidates who have gone to the
  right schools and progressed well in their careers without a hitch give no
  indication how they will handle the considerable stress imposed upon
  modern-day key executives. Outstanding people find ways to deal with
  setback, are resilient, and find ways to find solutions to problems when
  none is apparent.
- Interpersonal skills are key to the success of almost every job. I have
  found that if I use my personality as the barometer, I can judge pretty
  accurately if the candidate will get along with the client.

GEOGRAPHIC SCOPE OF RECRUITING ACTIVITIES:
Serve clients nationwide and in Switzerland, Germany, France, Holland, and
the United Kingdom

TOTAL YEARS OF RETAINER-TYPE RECRUITING EXPERIENCE:
21 years

J. ROBERT SWIDLER
Managing Partner for Canada
Egon Zehnder International Inc.
1 Place Ville-Marie, Suite 3310
Montreal, Quebec H3B 3N2 Canada
Telephone: (514) 876-4249

HONOREE: 1992, 1994

Date of birth: September 17, 1946

EDUCATION:
McGill University
Bachelor of Commerce, economics, 1968
Cornell University
M.B.A., finance, 1970

SPECIAL INTERESTS AND HOBBIES:
All sports, reading, nutrition, nature, education, family

EMPLOYMENT HISTORY:
1989 to present: Egon Zehnder International Inc.
1979 to 1989: President, J. Robert Swidler Inc.
1970 to 1979: Partner-in-Charge–Consulting, Management Consulting,
Touche Ross & Company

WHAT I LOOK FOR IN GENERAL IN A CANDIDATE:

Energy level, people skills, international orientation, integrity, loyalty, quality
of mind, hands-on mind, hands-on nature, focus on results, well-balanced lifestyle.

GEOGRAPHIC SCOPE OF RECRUITING ACTIVITIES:
Serve clients throughout North America

TOTAL YEARS OF RETAINER-TYPE RECRUITING EXPERIENCE:
22 years

MICHAEL A. TAPPAN
Vice Chairman–International
Ward Howell International, Inc.
99 Park Avenue
New York, NY 10016
Telephone: (212) 953-5853

Date of birth: January 31, 1939

EDUCATION:
> Yale University
>> B.A., English literature, 1960
> Harvard University
>> M.B.A., finance, 1962

SPECIAL INTERESTS AND HOBBIES:
> Russia and former Soviet Union, international
> business, golf, cross-country skiing, gardening

Wagner International Photos

EMPLOYMENT HISTORY:
> 1987 to present: Ward Howell International, Inc.
> 1982 to 1987: Principal, Interdatum Incorporated
> 1981 to 1982: Senior Vice President, Billington, Fox & Ellis, Inc.
> 1971 to 1981: Senior Vice President, Russell Reynolds Associates, Inc.
> 1962 to 1971: Vice President, Clark, Dodge & Co. Incorporated

WHAT I LOOK FOR IN GENERAL IN A CANDIDATE:
1. Well-documented record of achievement and progress in a particular function and industry, as required by the client.
2. Logical and successful career path progression.
3. Increasing levels of responsibility.
4. Dedication and commitment to employer and career balanced by family life, community spirit, breadth of interests and activities, and focus beyond self.
5. Ability to recognize and learn from failure.
6. Leadership ability and a well-articulated management style and philosophy.
7. Vision, ability to take the long view.
8. Reasonable fit with the client's culture.
9. Personal characteristics appropriate to the demands of the particular position, especially strategic overview, communications skills, personal presence, ability to prioritize and delegate combined with a willingness to focus on detail, self-confidence, political awareness, strength of character and integrity, and a sense of humor.
10. On international assignments, foreign language ability, overseas business experience, and willingness to adapt to different cultures and customs.
11. Professional and personal motivation appropriate to the particular client company and position.

GEOGRAPHIC SCOPE OF RECRUITING ACTIVITIES:
> Serve clients nationwide and as the founder of my firm's offices and search practice in the former Soviet Union, my predominant professional focus has become the recruitment of Western executives to positions in Russia and the other new Independent States. This is now my area of principal specialization and expertise, as opposed to focus on a particular industry or function.

TOTAL YEARS OF RETAINER-TYPE RECRUITING EXPERIENCE:
> 23 years

A. ROBERT TAYLOR
Senior Vice President, Executive Search
A.T. Kearney, Inc.
201 South Biscayne Boulevard, Suite 3180
Miami, FL 33131
Telephone: (305) 577-0046

Date of birth: January 21, 1919

Bachrach

SPECIAL INTERESTS AND HOBBIES:
Hiking, health care, music

EMPLOYMENT HISTORY:
1988 to present: A.T. Kearney, Inc.
1986 to 1988: Chairman, Taylor Mark Stanley, Inc.
1970 to 1985: President and Founder, TASA, Inc. (Mexico and Coral Gables, Florida)
1965 to 1970: Vice President, Latin America, Boyden Associates, Inc.
1963 to 1965: President and Founder, Learning Systems Institute (Paris)
1960 to 1962: Director, Human Resources, ITT Europe (Brussels)
1940 to 1960: Various Engineering and Human Resource positions, as follows:
Trinidad Leaseholds, Trinidad, British West Indies
Mobil Oil, Venezuela
Reaction Motors, Inc., New Jersey
General Mills, Inc., Minneapolis

WHAT I LOOK FOR IN GENERAL IN A CANDIDATE:

As an executive search consultant, I work with the client on developing a thorough description of the position, including the culture, environment of the company, and the executive specifications. In evaluating a prospective candidate, the first consideration is integrity. Next comes "does the background fit the experience requirements," or, if not, "are there redeeming factors"? Suitability for the culture and environment of the client company and attitude toward the client opportunity are evaluated. The most difficult factor to judge is personality and human chemistry in relation to the people with whom the prospective candidate would work—predicting probable behavior and performance in the proposed position. Finally, what are the candidate's ongoing career objectives—would they fit the client's plans and objectives and would this be a successful marriage for both client and candidate?

GEOGRAPHIC SCOPE OF RECRUITING ACTIVITIES:
Serve clients nationwide and in Europe, Latin America, Asia, Pacific

TOTAL YEARS OF RETAINER-TYPE RECRUITING EXPERIENCE:
28 years

WILLIAM E. THOLKE
President
Canny, Bowen Inc.
200 Park Avenue
New York, NY 10166
Telephone: (212) 949-6611

Date of birth: March 25, 1943

EDUCATION:
> University of Illinois
>> B.S., business administration, 1964
>> M.S., industrial relations, 1965

SPECIAL INTERESTS AND HOBBIES:
> Yachting, scuba diving

Mari Kane/Triad Photography Group

EMPLOYMENT HISTORY:
> 1993 to present: Canny, Bowen Inc.
> 1985 to 1993: Senior Vice President and Managing Director, Korn/Ferry International
> 1982 to 1985: Partner, Bacci, Bennett, Tappan & Tholke, Inc.
> 1979 to 1982: Senior Partner and Managing Director–Western Region, SpencerStuart and Associates
> 1972 to 1979: Managing Director–Western Region, Eastman & Beaudine, Inc.
> 1969 to 1972: Consultant: Booz, Allen & Hamilton
> 1966 to 1969: Director–Manpower Planning, Standard Oil of Indiana
> 1965 to 1966: Manager–Recruiting, Esso Research & Engineering

WHAT I LOOK FOR IN GENERAL IN A CANDIDATE:

I look for the following in a candidate:

- Strong record of achievement
- High energy
- High integrity and honesty
- Mentor who can grow people under him or her
- Strong and confident leadership style
- Presence and immediate credibility
- Open and candid personality
- Excellent communicator, both verbally and in writing
- International perspective
- Vision

GEOGRAPHIC SCOPE OF RECRUITING ACTIVITIES:
> Serve clients nationwide and in North America, Latin America, Asia/Pacific, and Europe

TOTAL YEARS OF RETAINER-TYPE RECRUITING EXPERIENCE:
> 24 years

CARLTON W. (TONY) THOMPSON
Senior Director
SpencerStuart
695 East Main Street
Stamford, CT 06904
Telephone: (203) 324-6333

HONOREE: 1990, 1994

Date of birth: November 8, 1933

Bachrach

EDUCATION:
Stanford University
B.A., English, 1955

MILITARY:
First Lieutenant, United States Air Force, 1956 to 1959

SPECIAL INTERESTS AND HOBBIES:
Fitness, tennis, reading

EMPLOYMENT HISTORY:
1983 to present: SpencerStuart
1973 to 1983: Senior Vice President, Russell Reynolds Associates, Inc.
1959 to 1973: Time Inc.
1972 to 1973: Vice President–Marketing, HBO
1970 to 1972: Southern Pacific Publishing Division, Time-Life Books
1969 to 1970: Associate Publisher, *Life En Espanol*
1968 to 1969: Division Manager, Time Inc.
1966 to 1968: Division Manager, Time International
1959 to 1966: Various sales and promotion assignments

WHAT I LOOK FOR IN GENERAL IN A CANDIDATE:

Intelligence
Excellent interpersonal skills
Sense of humor
High energy level
Good communicator
Well groomed

GEOGRAPHIC SCOPE OF RECRUITING ACTIVITIES:
Clients nationwide and in the United Kingdom, Japan, Hong Kong, and
Mexico

TOTAL YEARS OF RETAINER-TYPE RECRUITING EXPERIENCE:
20 years

JOHN T. THOMPSON
Partner and Director
Heidrick & Struggles, Inc.
2740 Sand Hill Road
Menlo Park, CA 94025
Telephone: (415) 854-9300

Date of birth: January 11, 1948

Russ Fischella

EDUCATION:
Virginia Polytechnic Institute and State University
B.A., economics, 1970
M.B.A., 1971

SPECIAL INTERESTS AND HOBBIES:
Golf, home cinema/audio

EMPLOYMENT HISTORY:
1989 to present: Heidrick & Struggles, Inc.
1983 to 1989: Vice President, David Powell, Inc.
1983: Director–Organization Planning & Development, Atari, Inc.
1978 to 1982: Director–Organization Development, The Williams Companies
1972 to 1976: Specialist. College of Business Extension Services, Virginia
Polytechnic Institute and State University
1970 to 1971: Assistant to Director, Alumni Association, Virginia Polytechnic
Institute and State University

WHAT I LOOK FOR IN GENERAL IN A CANDIDATE:
Ultimately I serve as a proxy for my clients in the market. In general, I assess candidates in three basic categories: *know-how, capacity,* and *motive.* With respect to know-how, the candidate's previous track record is the best predictor for future performance. Assessing a candidate's track record through a complete business cycle is quite important. When assessing a candidate's capacity, I evaluate intellectual, interpersonal, and physical capacity. I virtually always seek out an individual who is bright and has the high tolerance for ambiguity required in most executive transitions. With regard to interpersonal capacity, I evaluate an individual's openness, risk profile, and authenticity. With regard to physical capacity, most of today's CEO positions necessitate a high level of resilience to stress, which requires good physical conditioning. In assessing motive, I always want to know a candidate's objectives, and whether a candidate has a passion for the opportunity.

GEOGRAPHIC SCOPE OF RECRUITING ACTIVITIES:
Serve clients nationwide and in Europe, Asia/Pacific

TOTAL YEARS OF RETAINER-TYPE RECRUITING EXPERIENCE:
11 years

JOHN A. TRAVIS
President
Travis & Company, Inc.
325 Boston Post Road
Sudbury, MA 01776
Telephone: (508) 443-4000

Date of birth: May 10, 1939

Hyzen Photography & Video

EDUCATION:
Rutgers University
B.A., 1961
New York University
M.B.A., 1965

MILITARY:
Second Lieutenant, United States Army, 1961 to 1963

SPECIAL INTERESTS AND HOBBIES:
Tennis, travel, hiking

EMPLOYMENT HISTORY:
1978 to present: Travis & Company, Inc.
1972 to 1978: Director, Selection and Management Development, The
Kendall Company
1965 to 1972: Personnel Director, Leeming Pacquin Division, Pfizer, Inc.
1961 to 1965: Commercial Cadet, Public Service Electric & Gas Company

WHAT I LOOK FOR IN GENERAL IN A CANDIDATE:

- Communications skills
- Record of accomplishment, including regular upward movement in compensation and responsibility as well as the production of identifiable results
- Reasonable stability (loyalty), considering the industry involved
- Career goals that make sense
- Ability to analyze situations and take appropriate action
- Ability to select and motivate people
- Personal chemistry that fits client needs

GEOGRAPHIC SCOPE OF RECRUITING ACTIVITIES:
Serve clients nationwide and Europe

TOTAL YEARS OF RETAINER-TYPE RECRUITING EXPERIENCE:
16 years

JANET TWEED
Cofounder
Gilbert Tweed Associates, Inc.
415 Madison Avenue
New York, NY 10017
Telephone: (212) 758-3000

Date of birth: May 7, 1941

Gilbert Tweed Associates, Inc.

EDUCATION:
Montclair College
B.S., business, 1963
Columbia University
Graduate course, business, 1965

SPECIAL INTERESTS AND HOBBIES:
Trekking, gardening, and reading

EMPLOYMENT HISTORY:
1972 to present: Gilbert Tweed Associates, Inc.
1970 to 1972: Teacher, Katherine Gibbs Secretarial School
1968 to 1970: Recruiter, Dunhill Personnel
1965 to 1968: Personnel Manager, Benrus Watch Company

WHAT I LOOK FOR IN GENERAL IN A CANDIDATE:

Candidates excel when they show creativity, resourceful enthusiasm, and bottom-line problem-solving capabilities. All candidates should fill specifications, be well credentialed, and have good, well-chosen company affiliations. I look for the exceptional candidates who don't just fill the boxes, but step ahead of the pack. I look for the "soft issues."

Past accomplishments and successes indicate future potential accomplishments and success.

Executives who analyze well, make good timely decisions, and communicate well do well on an interview.

Well-presented, physically fit executives show attention to one's whole being.

GEOGRAPHIC SCOPE OF RECRUITING ACTIVITIES:
Serve clients nationwide and internationally

TOTAL YEARS OF RETAINER-TYPE RECRUITING EXPERIENCE:
21 years

J. LARRY TYLER
President
Tyler & Company
1000 Abernathy Road, Suite 1400
Atlanta, GA 30328
Telephone: (404) 396-3939

Date of birth: May 29, 1948

Tyler & Company

EDUCATION:
> Georgia Institute of Technology
>> Bachelor of Industrial Management, 1970
> Georgia State University
>> Master of Professional Accountancy, 1973

SPECIAL INTERESTS AND HOBBIES:
> Tennis, sailing, gardening

EMPLOYMENT HISTORY:
> 1978 to present: Tyler & Company
> 1976 to 1978: Chief Financial Officer, Regency Cosmetics
> 1975 to 1976: Controller, Southern Industrial Builders
> 1973 to 1975: Accountant, Price Waterhouse
> 1970 to 1973: Director, Georgia Institute of Technology

WHAT I LOOK FOR IN GENERAL IN A CANDIDATE:

When I look for a candidate, I look first to see if the candidate fits the client specs. I view search consulting as "matchmaking" and try to match the client and candidate as closely as possible. If there is not a fit with the specs, then I move on. I don't try to force a fit.

Second, I look for a strong set of responsibilities and accomplishments on each job. I look especially for quantification of the responsibilities and accomplishments.

In the interview, I look for an acceptable appearance, a pleasing personality, intelligence, and the ability to communicate. It is especially important that the candidates have a good understanding of themselves and what they want from a job, a career, and from life. Again, I try to ascertain whether the philosophies and values are a match with the client. I especially want honest answers to my questions. There are no good reasons for lying, and I expect full disclosure, especially regarding terminations. Accordingly, the candidates should expect me to be candid about my client and the assignment.

GEOGRAPHIC SCOPE OF RECRUITING ACTIVITIES:
> Serve clients nationwide

TOTAL YEARS OF RETAINER-TYPE RECRUITING EXPERIENCE:
> 17 years

LEE van LEEUWEN
Managing Vice President
Korn/Ferry International
1800 Century Park East, Suite 900
Los Angeles, CA 90067
Telephone: (310) 552-1834

Date of Birth: November 26, 1937

Merrett in Century City

EDUCATION:
> UCLA
>> Bachelor of Arts, psychology, 1960

SPECIAL INTERESTS AND HOBBIES:
> Golf, fishing, reading

EMPLOYMENT HISTORY:
> 1975 to present: Korn/Ferry International
> 1973 to 1975: Partner, Stephens/Van Leeuwen
> 1970 to 1973: Vice President, Korn/Ferry International
> 1969 to 1970: Vice President, F.P. Droesch Associates
> 1967 to 1969: Vice President, Hergen Rather & Associates

WHAT I LOOK FOR IN GENERAL IN A CANDIDATE:

Believe it or not, I look for normal! People—people who are straightforward, calm and direct. Not prone to exaggeration and displays of ego. People who can describe themselves and their experience in an organized, factual way, even disqualify themselves if they think the position is not right for them.

I also like to see intellectual and personal balance. "Work only" ethic does not impress me. A range of interests outside of career is important. Humility and honesty are very important traits. Finally, I like to see that the person has some "self-made" characteristics in their background, i.e., paid for part (or all) of college, entered work force in a timely fashion, etc.

GEOGRAPHIC SCOPE OF RECRUITING ACTIVITIES:
> Serve clients nationwide and in Mexico, Canada and France

TOTAL YEARS OF RETAINER-TYPE RECRUITING EXPERIENCE:
> 27 years

GAIL HAMITY VERGARA
Director of Health Care Practice
SpencerStuart
401 N. Michigan Avenue, Suite 3400
Chicago, IL 60611
Telephone: (312) 822-0088

HONOREE: 1992, 1994

Date of birth: January 6, 1948

Stuart-Rodgers-Reilly Photography

EDUCATION:
Pine Manor College
A.A.S., 1968
University of Colorado
B.A., 1970
University of Illinois
Master of Social Work, 1973

SPECIAL INTERESTS AND HOBBIES:
Volunteer with shelter for homeless women, horseback riding, tennis, jogging

EMPLOYMENT HISTORY:
1991 to present: SpencerStuart
1980 to 1991: Executive Vice President, Witt Associates
1973 to 1980: Coordinator–Outpatient Psychiatry, Mercy Hospital

WHAT I LOOK FOR IN GENERAL IN A CANDIDATE:
Today's health care environment is in a constant state of flux and change. Therefore, the individuals our clients seek must be true leaders and visionaries. The ability to survive with the constant challenge in the health care industry demands raw intelligence and common sense. Individuals must have incredible energy and flexibility. I believe that the successful health care leaders of the future will be those individuals who have a good deal of self-esteem and the ability to look inward at their own strengths and weaknesses. They will be able to create an environment where people are challenged with healthy competition and also a sensitivity to others' needs. Honesty and integrity should always be at the top of any personal qualifications.

GEOGRAPHIC SCOPE OF RECRUITING ACTIVITIES:
Serve clients nationwide and occasionally internationally

TOTAL YEARS OF RETAINER-TYPE RECRUITING EXPERIENCE:
14 years

JACK H. VERNON
Managing Director
Russell Reynolds Associates, Inc.
45 School Street
Boston, MA 02108
Telephone: (617) 523-1111

HONOREE: 1992, 1994

Date of birth: February 25, 1930

Russell Reynolds Associates, Inc.

EDUCATION:
>   Amherst College
>   B.A., chemistry, 1952
>   Massachusetts Institute of Technology
>   M.S., metallurgy and industrial management, 1954

MILITARY:
>   Lieutenant, United States Navy, 1955 to 1958

SPECIAL INTERESTS AND HOBBIES:
>   Travel, music, golf, tennis

EMPLOYMENT HISTORY:
>   1981 to present: Russell Reynolds Associates, Inc.
>   1975 to 1981: Senior Vice President, Heidrick & Struggles, Inc.
>   1971 to 1975: President, Scientific Energy Systems
>   1962 to 1970: Executive Vice President, Instron Corp.
>   1958 to 1962: Associate, Arthur D. Little Inc.

WHAT I LOOK FOR IN GENERAL IN A CANDIDATE:

Integrity, proven track record, desire for input/feedback and ability to listen, ability to communicate, visible within the organization, people skills, personally secure and sense of humor, curious, flexible, impatient with bureaucracy, decisive without being autocratic, creative and willing to take prudent risks, a mind-set that couples a commitment for quality and service to customers, today and in the future, with an appropriate near- and long-term return to shareholders.

GEOGRAPHIC SCOPE OF RECRUITING ACTIVITIES:
>   Serve clients nationally and in Europe, Asia Pacific, and Australia

TOTAL YEARS OF RETAINER-TYPE RECRUITING EXPERIENCE:
>   19 years

JUDITH M. von SELDENECK
Chief Executive Officer
The Diversified Search Companies, Inc.
2005 Market Street, Suite 3300
Philadelphia, PA 19103
Telephone: (215) 732-6666

HONOREE: 1990, 1992, 1994

Date of birth: June 6, 1940

The Diversified Search Companies, Inc.

EDUCATION:
University of North Carolina
B.A., political science, 1962

SPECIAL INTERESTS AND HOBBIES:
Golf, fishing, boating, reading

EMPLOYMENT HISTORY:
1973 to present: The Diversified Search Companies, Inc.
1963 to 1972: Executive Assistant, Senator Walter F. Mondale

WHAT I LOOK FOR IN GENERAL IN A CANDIDATE:

- Down-to-earth, unpretentious, straightforward, bright, smart, good communication skills
- Career-oriented and committed to succeeding
- Appropriate blend of self-confidence and humility
- Clearly evident personal qualities in terms of trust, integrity, and honesty
- Consistent track record of success
- Wisdom and perception
- Sense of humor

GEOGRAPHIC SCOPE OF RECRUITING ACTIVITIES:
Serve clients nationwide

TOTAL YEARS OF RETAINER-TYPE RECRUITING EXPERIENCE:
13 years

FREDERICK W. WACKERLE
Partner
McFeely Wackerle Shulman
20 N. Wacker Drive, Suite 3110
Chicago, IL 60606
Telephone: (312) 641-2977

HONOREE: 1990, 1992, 1994

Date of birth: June 25, 1939

John Reilly Photography

EDUCATION:
Monmouth College, Monmouth, Illinois
B.A., English; chemistry minor, 1961

MILITARY:
A3C-Reserves, United States Air Force, 1956 to 1960

SPECIAL INTERESTS AND HOBBIES:
Board of directors: Monmouth College and Rehabilitation Institute of
Chicago; columnist: *Crains' Chicago Business;* golf, tuba, modern art, busi-
ness writing

EMPLOYMENT HISTORY:
1970 to present: McFeely Wackerle Shulman
1968 to 1970: Vice President, R.M. Schmitz
1966 to 1968: Partner, Berry Henderson & Aberlin
1964 to 1966: Associate, A.T. Kearney Search
1962 to 1964: Assistant Personnel Director, Stewart Warner Corp.
1961 to 1962: Operations Manager, Ball Brothers Co.

WHAT I LOOK FOR IN GENERAL IN A CANDIDATE:

Unquestioned integrity
High work ethic
Ability to handle failure
Leadership/motivational skill
High personal values
Appropriate balance between business and family
Ability to separate and prioritize
High self-confidence
Earnest and truthful
Willingness to make a tough, or unpopular, decision

GEOGRAPHIC SCOPE OF RECRUITING ACTIVITIES:
Serve clients nationwide

TOTAL YEARS OF RETAINER-TYPE RECRUITING EXPERIENCE:
30 years

J. ALVIN WAKEFIELD
Managing Director
Wakefield Talabisco International
P.O. Box 1248
Pittsford, VT 05763
Telephone: (802) 483-9356

HONOREE: 1990, 1992, 1994

Date of birth: July 25, 1938

Wakefield Talabisco International

EDUCATION:
New York University
B.A., English literature, 1960

MILITARY:
Captain, United States Air Force, 1961 to 1966

SPECIAL INTERESTS AND HOBBIES:
Snowboarding, tennis, basketball, skiing, flute, classical music, modern jazz

EMPLOYMENT HISTORY:
1993 to present: Wakefield Talabisco International
1986 to 1993: Managing Director, Gilbert Tweed Associates, Inc.
1984 to 1986: President, Wakefield Enterprises, Inc.
1981 to 1983: Vice President, Korn/Ferry International
1973 to 1981: Vice President Personnel Worldwide, Avon Products, Inc.
1970 to 1972: Manager–Recruiting, Singer Company
1968 to 1970: Supervisor–Employee Relations, Celanese Corporation
1966 to 1968: Employee Relations Assistant, Mobil Oil Corporation

WHAT I LOOK FOR IN GENERAL IN A CANDIDATE:

I look for what my client is looking for. My client is my partner.

In the critical process of searching for and recruiting the most appropriate slate of candidates, I become the client. I am its eyes, its ears, its nose, its judgment. I even have temporary control over a portion of its pocketbook. As always, but even more so now, clients are demanding the best candidates to meet their specific needs. Sometimes these needs are long-term; frequently—oddly enough—they are short-term. More often than in previous times, needs change in the middle of the search. I respond to those changes.

My responsibility is to fully understand my client's needs, and if I undertake the search, to accept them and bring the most appropriate candidates—and only the most appropriate candidates—to the client—in the fastest time possible.

Each search is different; I strive to recognize its unique requirements and work tirelessly to identify and recruit what my client is looking for. I am the client.

GEOGRAPHIC SCOPE OF RECRUITING ACTIVITIES:
Serve clients nationwide in Europe, South America, and Pacific Rim

TOTAL YEARS OF RETAINER-TYPE RECRUITING EXPERIENCE:
11 years

ANTHONY C. (TONY) WARD
President
Ward Liebelt Associates Inc.
50 Riverside Avenue
Westport, CT 06880
Telephone: (203) 454-0414

Date of birth: August 22, 1939

Ward Liebelt Associates, Inc.

EDUCATION:
> Fairfield University, Fairfield, CT
> > B.A., philosophy, history, 1961

SPECIAL INTERESTS AND HOBBIES:
> All sports, stock market, landscaping

EMPLOYMENT HISTORY:
> 1971 to present: Ward Liebelt Associates Inc.
> 1968 to 1971: Executive Vice President, Partner, Ward Clancy Associates, NY
> 1964 to 1968: Department Manager–Marketing, Gilbert Lane, NY
> 1961 to 1964: Employee Relations Management Trainee, Allstate Insurance
> > Co., NY

WHAT I LOOK FOR IN GENERAL IN A CANDIDATE:

As specialists in marketing, sales management, and general management with consumer products and services, we look for tangible and intangible skills in assessing candidates.

In the process of evaluating technical skills and accomplishments, style becomes very important. We are asked to assess leadership, judgment, maturity, confidence, creative ability, and potential. Gut instincts and intuition become very important. Those instincts evolve from twenty-five years of evaluating personnel from corporations known for recruiting, training, and developing the brightest and the best.

Finally, matching background and style to corporate culture or the ability to change or influence cultural change without major disruption is the chemistry we are asked to achieve in making searches long-term successes.

GEOGRAPHIC SCOPE OF RECRUITING ACTIVITIES:
> Serve clients nationwide and in Mexico, Latin America, Europe, and parts of
> > Asia

TOTAL YEARS OF RETAINER-TYPE RECRUITING EXPERIENCE:
> 23 years

PUTNEY WESTERFIELD
Managing Director
Boyden International
275 Battery Street
San Francisco, CA 94111
Telephone: (415) 981-7900

HONOREE: 1990, 1992, 1994

Date of birth: February 9, 1930

EDUCATION:
Yale University
B.A., 1951

SPECIAL INTERESTS AND HOBBIES:
Reading, international affairs, tennis,
nature, piano

Triad Photography Group

EMPLOYMENT HISTORY:
1976 to present: Boyden International
1973 to 1975: President, Chase World Information Corp., Chase-Manhattan
1957 to 1973: Time Inc.
 1968 to 1973: Publisher, *Fortune*
 1966 to 1967: Assistant Publisher, *Life*
 1965 to 1967: Assistant Publisher, *Time*
 1957 to 1965: Circulation Director
1953 to 1957: Political Officer, Department of State
1951 to 1952: Manager–Southeast Asia, Swen Publications, Inc.

WHAT I LOOK FOR IN GENERAL IN A CANDIDATE:
I make judgments about candidates in these five key areas:
Problem solving
 Problem analysis—grasps the nature of a problem
 Judgment—reaches appropriate conclusions
Communication
 Dialogue skills—effectiveness of discussion and expression
 Listening skills—attends to what others are saying
 Presentation skills—expresses ideas effectively
 Writing skills
Motivation
 Initiative—self-starting behavior; readiness to be the first to start
 Drive—sustained energy in accomplishing objectives
 Reaction to pressure—effective under stress
 Commitment to excellence—sees that tasks will be done well
Interpersonal
 Leadership—directs behavior of others toward achievement of common
  goals by charisma, insights, or assertion of will
 Sensitivity—considers the needs and feeling of others
 Impact—creates positive impression of self-assurance
Administrative
 Planning and organization—anticipates situations and problems
 Delegation—assigns work and responsibility effectively

GEOGRAPHIC SCOPE OF RECRUITING ACTIVITIES:
Serve clients nationally

TOTAL YEARS OF RETAINER-TYPE RECRUITING EXPERIENCE:
17 years

MARY T. WHEELER
Partner
Lamalie Amrop International
489 Fifth Avenue
New York, NY 10017-6105
Telephone: (212) 953-7900

Date of birth: June 25, 1939

Jannick Grossman/Arista Photo Services

EDUCATION:
Smith College
B.A., French, 1961

SPECIAL INTERESTS AND HOBBIES:
Choral singing, tennis, hiking, travel, opera (as spectator)

EMPLOYMENT HISTORY:
1991 to present: Lamalie Amrop International
1980 to 1991: Partner, Boyden International
1977 to 1979: Phoenix House Foundation
1975 to 1977: Manager, Special Gifts, Planned Parenthood Federation of
America

WHAT I LOOK FOR IN GENERAL IN A CANDIDATE:

The easiest aspects of recruiting the ideal candidate are to meet the experiential and industry needs which the position requires.

What is difficult is trying to figure out the chemistry that will work between candidate and client. That is why it is so important to spend as much up-front time with the client as possible to develop a position description which reflects the client's personal as well as professional wish list. This is made all the more complicated when search committees are involved and there are multiple points of view.

In general, with the client's particular wish list always in mind, I look for the following characteristics in candidates: a stable career progression, a high energy level, intelligence (not necessarily intellectual capacity), enthusiasm, a sense of humor, specificity in answering questions, open communications, and a balanced lifestyle. Some red flags are people who describe themselves as workaholics; as having superior interpersonal skills (have you ever heard anyone say that they have poor ones?); and as leaders—it's up to the recruiter, references, and the hiring manager to assess leadership.

GEOGRAPHIC SCOPE OF RECRUITING ACTIVITIES:
Serve clients nationally and internationally

TOTAL YEARS OF RETAINER-TYPE RECRUITING EXPERIENCE:
14 years

DANIEL C. WIER
President/Chief Executive Officer
Daniel Wier & Associates
333 S. Grand Avenue, Suite 2980
Los Angeles, CA 90071
Telephone: (213) 628-2580

Date of birth: March 24, 1941

Daniel Wier & Associates

EDUCATION:
　　University of Southern California
　　　　B.A., international relations, 1964
　　　　M.A., international relations, 1965

SPECIAL INTERESTS AND HOBBIES:
　　Vintage sports car racing, tennis, golf, college athletics

EMPLOYMENT HISTORY:
　　1991 to present: Daniel Wier & Associates
　　1989 to 1991: Managing Director, Heidrick & Struggles, Inc.
　　1983 to 1989: Managing Director–Western Region, SpencerStuart
　　1977 to 1983: Managing Director–Western Region, William H. Clark
　　1973 to 1977: Manager–Executive Search Practice, Deloitte & Touche
　　1972 to 1973: Executive Search Manager, Darling & Alsobrook
　　1968 to 1972: Director of Human Resources, Litton Industries
　　1965 to 1968: Associate Director, Alumni Affairs, University of Southern California

WHAT I LOOK FOR IN GENERAL IN A CANDIDATE:

　　The first task is, of course, to find a candidate with successful, applicable experience. Having established that intelligence, technical, and experiential parameters have been met, I believe the single most important factor in a candidate is integrity. From this flows honesty, responsibility, and loyalty. In looking for someone to manage/lead a function or an organization, I believe flexibility and caring are two essential traits. The flexibility to adapt to new markets, new technologies, and changing resources and management methodologies is increasingly important in this era of rapid and unprecedented change.

　　I think that a leader who cares about the dignity and well-being of his coworkers will tend to share ownership and power in the establishment and pursuit of an organization's goals and objectives. This inevitably leads to lower turnover and higher productivity.

GEOGRAPHIC SCOPE OF RECRUITING ACTIVITIES:
　　Serve clients nationwide

TOTAL YEARS OF RETAINER-TYPE RECRUITING EXPERIENCE:
　　22 years

WILLIAM R. WILKINSON
Partner
Wilkinson & Ives
One Bush Street, Suite 550
San Francisco, CA 94104
Telephone: (415) 433-2155

HONOREE: 1990, 1992, 1994

Date of birth: February 5, 1932

EDUCATION:
    St. Lawrence University, New York
        B.A., sociology, 1953

Gabriel Moulin Studios

MILITARY:
    Sergeant, United States Army, 1953 to 1955

SPECIAL INTERESTS AND HOBBIES:
    Tennis, walking, bicycling, skiing, reading, family, four directorships with
        client companies; author, *Executive Musical Chairs*

EMPLOYMENT HISTORY:
    1984 to present: Wilkinson & Ives
    1971 to 1984: President, William R. Wilkinson & Company, Inc.
    1961 to 1971: Founder and CEO, Wilkinson, Sedwick & Yelverton, Inc.
    1956: to 1961: Vice President, McMurry, Hamstra & Company

WHAT I LOOK FOR IN GENERAL IN A CANDIDATE:

My interview style is to be relaxed and informal so as to encourage spontaneous and open response, and to be thorough enough to gain an understanding
of the ingrained behavioral patterns that govern the candidate's personal and
career performance. People don't change much throughout their lives, and careful probing and attentive listening will reveal their behavioral patterns readily.

In assessing a candidate's qualifications, I seek to learn of appropriate experience and accomplishment, leadership and management styles and skills, and
other performance characteristics that are required for effective functioning in
the position for which the candidate is being considered. At almost any level, it is
critical that the candidate's thought processes be crisp, clear, and uncluttered.
The same might be said for the candidate's management style, vision of the possibilities, and conceptual capacities.

There must also be the health, energy, depth of intellect, and motivation to perform at a consistently high level. Verbal and written communications need to be
acute. In these concerned times, ethical and behavioral values need to be above
reproach, and judgment and decisiveness cannot be cluttered by hidden agendas. As
a manager, and, often, as a leader, the candidate must have proven his worth in creating work cultures that are people-oriented and encourage and reward team play.

High character and personal integrity are always obligatory. A balanced lifestyle is
desirable, and a history of personal, avocational, and career successes is compelling.

GEOGRAPHIC SCOPE OF RECRUITING ACTIVITIES:
    Serve clients nationwide and in Canada and Europe

TOTAL YEARS OF RETAINER-TYPE RECRUITING EXPERIENCE:
    37 years

WILLIAM H. WILLIS, JR.
President and Managing Director
William Willis Worldwide, Inc.
164 Mason Street
Greenwich, CT 06830
Telephone: (203) 661-4500

HONOREE: 1990, 1992, 1994

Date of birth: December 19, 1927

William Willis Worldwide, Inc.

EDUCATION:
> Yale University
>> B.A., sociology, 1949

MILITARY:
> Sergeant First Class, United States Army, 1950 to 1952

SPECIAL INTERESTS AND HOBBIES:
> Sailing, tennis, squash, travel

EMPLOYMENT HISTORY:
> 1970 to present: William Willis Worldwide, Inc.
> 1965 to 1970: Partner, Devine, Baldwin & Willis
> 1962 to 1965: Manager, Food Processing Equipment Business, AMF
> 1956 to 1962: Marketing Manager, Owens-Corning Fiberglas Corporation
> 1953 to 1956: Assistant to Executive Vice President, Heidelberg Eastern, Inc.
> 1952 to 1953: Expedition Leader, American Museum of Natural History
> 1949 to 1950: Registered Representative, Gordon Graves & Co., Inc.

WHAT I LOOK FOR IN GENERAL IN A CANDIDATE:

In assessing a candidate, the number one requirement I seek is integrity. Then the critical judgment has to be "does this candidate's qualifications match the requirements of the position?" and "will they fit in the corporate culture?" Key elements I look for include:

- Management and leadership skills (a "leader," not a "follower").
- A record of significant and relevant accomplishments.
- Appropriate education.
- Effective communication skills.
- Technical qualifications and industry knowledge.
- Sufficient drive.
- A personal chemistry match with the hiring manager.
- A sense of humor.

I see executive search consultants as true matchmakers.

GEOGRAPHIC SCOPE OF RECRUITING ACTIVITIES:
> Serve clients nationally and in the Americas, Europe, Middle East, Africa,
> Asia Pacific, including the People's Republic of China

TOTAL YEARS OF RETAINER-TYPE RECRUITING EXPERIENCE:
> 27 years

PATRICIA L. WILSON
Partner
Leon A. Farley Associates
468 Jackson Street
San Francisco, CA 94111
Telephone: (415) 989-0989

Date of birth: July 5, 1955

Jock McDonald

EDUCATION:
Stanford University
B.A., philosophy, 1977
Hastings College of the Law
J.D., 1982

SPECIAL INTERESTS AND HOBBIES:
Tennis, music, theater, travel

EMPLOYMENT HISTORY:
1989 to present: Leon A. Farley Associates
1989 to 1990: Vice President and General Counsel, Matrix Leasing International
1988 to 1989: Associate General Counsel, PLM International, Inc.
1985 to 1987: Senior Corporate Counsel, CIS Corporation
1984 to 1985: Corporate Counsel, Itel Rail Corporation
1982 to 1984: Attorney, Murphy, Weir & Butler

WHAT I LOOK FOR IN GENERAL IN A CANDIDATE:

Critical to the success of an executive search is a thorough understanding of the corporate client's needs—both spoken and unspoken. Only after fully understanding the client's business and culture can I know what to look for in a candidate.

Most accomplished senior executives are particularly good presenters. My task is to pierce those well-honed facades and identify the personal characteristics, motivations, values, and management style that would be most effective in addressing my client's needs.

During the course of an assignment, I thoroughly examine the professional qualifications and personal attributes of dozens of executives. Determining functional competence, intelligence, and leadership abilities is only the beginning.

I am a true believer that the most accurate predictor of future performance is past behavior. By probing a candidate's path since early childhood, I uncover why certain choices were made, understand the influences that shape decisions, and evaluate core motivations.

GEOGRAPHIC SCOPE OF RECRUITING ACTIVITIES:
Serve clients nationwide and occasionally internationally

TOTAL YEARS OF RETAINER-TYPE RECRUITING EXPERIENCE:
5 years

DALE WINSTON
President
Battalia Winston International, Inc.
300 Park Avenue
New York, NY 10022
Telephone: (212) 308-8080

Date of birth: August 15, 1948

Battalia Winston International, Inc.

EDUCATION:
Finch College
B.A., psychology, 1970

SPECIAL INTERESTS AND HOBBIES:
Travel, golf

EMPLOYMENT HISTORY:
1983 to present: Battalia Winston International, Inc.
1978 to 1983: Vice President, Gilbert Tweed Associates, Inc.

WHAT I LOOK FOR IN GENERAL IN A CANDIDATE:
I believe that there is both an art and a science to evaluating a candidate. The following are things that I look for:

- I look for people who possess intuitive skills because they are able to see things that others cannot. The result is that they are often visionaries. In addition, the intuitive skill enables a person to be particularly sensitive to others and to pick up nonverbal communications.
- I look for candidates who share the same value systems as my clients. This is one of the key components that enables individuals to be successful in new environments.
- I spend a lot of time verifying my own intuitive skills. I speak with people known to the candidate and have them verify my views.
- I believe that candidate evaluation is 80 percent gut once you've qualified the candidate's technical skills.
- Finally, I make sure that the job is the right career move for the candidate, because you cannot find the right candidate for the job unless it is the right job for the candidate.

GEOGRAPHIC SCOPE OF RECRUITING ACTIVITIES:
Serve clients nationwide and through Euram offices in the United Kingdom, France, Sweden, Germany, Denmark, and Canada

TOTAL YEARS OF RETAINER-TYPE RECRUITING EXPERIENCE:
15 years

DAVID L. WITTE
Managing Director
Ward Howell International, Inc.
1000 Louisiana Street, Suite 3150
Houston, TX 77002
Telephone: (713) 655-7155

Date of birth: January 29, 1942

David Nance

EDUCATION:
Michigan State University
B.S., 1964

SPECIAL INTERESTS AND HOBBIES:
Global business development, sailing

EMPLOYMENT HISTORY:
1987 to present: Ward Howell International, Inc.
1983 to 1987: Owner, David Witte, Inc.
1976 to 1983: Executive Director/Consulting Services, Tenneco, Inc.
1972 to 1976: Co-Owner, Alexander & Sterling Consulting Services
1964 to 1972: Pharmaceutical Division Manager, Johnson & Johnson

WHAT I LOOK FOR IN GENERAL IN A CANDIDATE:

Leadership, insight, profitable results, global experience, intuitive business instincts, strong relationship-building skills, balanced family life, strong communication skills, demonstrating high moral and ethical character.

GEOGRAPHIC SCOPE OF RECRUITING ACTIVITIES:
Serve clients globally—in Moscow, Singapore, Tokyo, Seoul, United Kingdom, Central and Eastern Europe, Latin America

TOTAL YEARS OF RETAINER-TYPE RECRUITING EXPERIENCE:
14 years

THOMAS C. ZAY
Chairman
Boyden/Zay & Company
Two Midtown Plaza, Suite 1740
1360 Peachtree Street, NE
Atlanta, GA 30309
Telephone: (404) 876-9986

Zay & Company/Boyden

HONOREE: 1992, 1994

Date of birth: December 2, 1932

EDUCATION:
Northwestern University
    B.S., business administration/finance,
    1954

MILITARY:
Captain/Naval Aviator, United States Marine Corps, 1954 to 1957

EMPLOYMENT HISTORY:
1982 to present: Boyden/Zay & Company
1968 to 1982: Executive Vice President, Paul R. Ray & Company, Inc.
1966 to 1968: Senior Vice President, Howard W. Voss, Associates
1962 to 1966: Associate, Booz, Allen & Hamilton
1960 to 1962: Manager–Sales Development, Wisconsin Gas Company
1957 to 1960: Territory Sales Manager, Shell Oil Company

WHAT I LOOK FOR IN GENERAL IN A CANDIDATE:
There are several qualities that distinguish exceptional executives within their universe, but in my experience there are two attributes which have proven to be consistent indicators of unusually competent managerial capacity. A well-orchestrated interview process will reveal the extent to which these qualities are part of the makeup of an individual candidate.

Integrity and Intellectual Honesty
The individual who sets and maintains high ethical and moral standards will succeed in even the most alien and adversarial environments—both those encountered within an organization or outside in the marketplace. Consistent adherence to one's principles in all matters and a record of honoring commitments made, even when costly, sends a powerful message of dependability and leadership to all levels of a constituency. It is a rigorous test of an individual's character to convey accurate and truthful reports of bad news, reflecting a willingness to experience the heat of the moment to avoid the future dishonor of revealed duplicity.

Courage
The personal fortitude to confront highly unpleasant situations and resolve them honestly, even at the risk of dire consequences, is a rare quality. An individual who is willing to challenge authority with valid alternatives, whether on business judgments or human issues, is an extremely valuable ingredient in an organization. To remain resolute in the pursuit of credible and responsible goals, which are unpopular because they represent change to the majority, requires uncommon determination.

GEOGRAPHIC SCOPE OF RECRUITING ACTIVITIES:
Serve clients nationwide and all of Latin America

TOTAL YEARS OF RETAINER-TYPE RECRUITING EXPERIENCE:
32 years

JANIS M. ZIVIC
President
The Zivic Group, Inc.
611 Washington Street, Suite 2505
San Francisco, CA 94111
Telephone: (415) 421-2325

HONOREE: 1990, 1992, 1994

Date of birth: July 17, 1942

EDUCATION:
California State College
    B.S., 1964
University of Pittsburgh
    M.A., 1967

Triad Photography Group

SPECIAL INTERESTS AND HOBBIES:
Community activist and nonprofit board participation

EMPLOYMENT HISTORY:
1983 to present: The Zivic Group, Inc.
1982 to 1983: Vice President and Managing Director, William H. Clark Associates
1978 to 1982: Vice President and Partner, Heidrick & Struggles, Inc.
1974 to 1978: Manager–Professional Recruitment, Castle & Cooke, Inc.
1973 to 1974: Management Recruiter, Crown Zellerbach
1967 to 1972: Educator in Pennsylvania and Ohio

WHAT I LOOK FOR IN GENERAL IN A CANDIDATE:

We have finally convinced the public that we are not "headhunters"; we're matchmakers. We identify and recruit candidates whose leadership style, management expertise, and technical competency meet the needs of the client and the culture of the client organization.

At a minimum, we are expected to penetrate the interviewing skills of the practiced candidate to assess this "match." I am convinced that the individual's behavior and communication during the interview directly predicts the way s/he will work, manage, and lead.

Not as "superficial" as many believe, the interview is as critical to the process of candidate selection as is reference checking. In fact, the references should serve to validate what the search consultant has already perceived to be true.

Executives who will succeed in the 90s are those who articulate intelligently, listen thoughtfully, have both a personal and a professional vision which they communicate clearly, and demonstrate these characteristics in their daily lives before and after the interview.

GEOGRAPHIC SCOPE OF RECRUITING ACTIVITIES:
Serve clients nationwide and internationally

TOTAL YEARS OF RETAINER-TYPE RECRUITING EXPERIENCE:
16 years

5

AREAS OF RECRUITER SPECIALIZATION

This chapter categorizes and ranks recruiters qualifying for this book according to their individual *functional* competencies and areas of *organizational or industry* specialization. A recruiter's standing in each category is a function of the number of nominating points from both clients and peers, as well as his or her own individual ranking of organizational and functional skills.

FUNCTIONAL SPECIALIZATION

Categories

General management	Manufacturing/production/operations
Administration	Marketing/sales–consumer
Advertising/promotion	Marketing/sales–industrial
Direct marketing	Merchandising
Director recruitment	MIS/computer operations
Editorial	Planning
Engineering	Public relations/government affairs
Finance and accounting	Purchasing/materials
Human resources/personnel	Research and development
International	Women, handicapped, minorities
Legal	

Those recruiters who work essentially only in specific organizational or industry specializations are identified by the following symbols:

    (HC)   Health care
    (HO)   Hospitality
    (LE)   Legal
    (ED)   Education and related fields

GENERAL MANAGEMENT

1. **Gerard R. Roche,** Heidrick & Struggles, Inc., New York
2. **Thomas J. Neff,** SpencerStuart, New York
3. **Leon A. Farley,** Leon A. Farley Associates, San Francisco
4. **Frederick W. Wackerle,** McFeely Wackerle Shulman, Chicago
5. **William E. Gould,** Gould & McCoy, New York
6. **Robert W. Dingman,** Robert W. Dingman Co., Inc., Westlake Village, CA
7. **Roger M. Kenny,** Kenny, Kindler, Hunt & Howe, New York
8. **John F. Johnson,** Lamalie Amrop International, Cleveland
9. **E. Pendleton James,** Pendleton James & Associates, Inc., New York
10. **Windle B. Priem,** Korn/Ferry International, New York
11. **James M. Montgomery,** Houze, Shourds & Montgomery, Inc., Long Beach, CA
12. **John Lucht,** The John Lucht Consultancy Inc., New York
13. **Paul R. Ray, Jr.,** Paul Ray Berndtson, Fort Worth
14. **Ralph Dieckmann,** Dieckmann & Associates, Ltd., Chicago
15. **John R. Clarey,** Clarey & Andrews, Inc., Northbrook, IL
16. **Putney Westerfield,** Boyden, San Francisco
17. **Daniel M. Shepherd,** Shepherd Bueschel & Provus, Inc., Chicago
18. **Millington F. McCoy,** Gould & McCoy, Inc., New York
19. **Theodore B. Martin, Jr.,** Nordeman Grimm, Inc., Chicago
20. **Jonathan E. McBride,** McBride Associates, Inc., Washington, DC
21. **Mary Shourds,** Houze, Shourds & Montgomery, Inc., Long Beach, CA
22. **Robert L. Smith,** Smith & Sawyer, Inc., New York
23. **Skott B. Burkland,** Skott/Edwards Consultants, Rutherford, NJ
24. **Joseph E. Onstott,** The Onstott Group, Inc., Wellesley, MA
25. **Jay Gaines,** Jay Gaines & Company, Inc., New York

J.R. Akin, J.R. Akin & Company, Fairfield, CT
Donald Allerton, Allerton Heneghan & O'Neill, Chicago
Jerry H. Baker, Schuyler, Frye & Baker, Inc., Atlanta
Bruce M. Bastoky, January Management Group, Inc., Columbus, OH
Martin H. Bauman, Martin H. Bauman Associates, New York
Lynn Tendler Bignell, Gilbert Tweed Associates, New York
Susan K. Bishop, Bishop Partners, Ltd., New York
William J. Bowen, Heidrick & Struggles, Inc., Chicago
Michael D. Boxberger, Korn/Ferry International, Chicago
Gerald J. Bump, D.E. Foster & Partners, Atlanta
John H. Callen, Jr., Ward Howell International, New York
Donald B. Clark, Paul Ray Berndtson, Chicago
Peter D. Crist, Russell Reynolds Associates, Inc., Chicago
Richard J. Cronin, Hodge-Cronin & Associates, Inc., Rosemont, IL
Steven M. Darter, People Management Northeast, Inc., Avon, CT
David M. deWilde, Chartwell Partners International, San Francisco
James J. Drury III, SpencerStuart, Chicago
John R. Ferneborg, Ferneborg & Associates, Inc., Redwood City, CA
Richard Ferry, Korn/Ferry International, Los Angeles
John W. Franklin, Jr., Russell Reynolds Associates, Inc., Washington, DC

John T. Gardner, Heidrick & Struggles, Inc., Chicago
Ronald G. Goerss, Ronald Goerss & Associates, San Francisco
Peter G. Grimm, Nordeman Grimm, Inc., New York
Jordan M. Hadelman, Witt/Kieffer, Ford, Hadelman & Lloyd, Oak Brook, IL (HC)
Robert L. Heidrick, The Heidrick Partners, Chicago
Richard L. Hertan, Executive Manning Corporation, Ft. Lauderdale, FL
William A. Hertan, Executive Manning Corporation, Ft. Lauderdale, FL
James Heuerman, Korn/Ferry International, San Francisco (HC)
David Hoffmann, DHR International, Chicago
Jonathan S. Holman, The Holman Group, Inc., San Francisco
James E. Hunt, Kenny, Kindler, Hunt & Howe, New York, NY
W. Jerry Hyde, Hyde Danforth & Company, Dallas
Richard K. Ives, Wilkinson & Ives, San Francisco
Carol S. Jeffers, John Sibbald Associates, Inc., Chicago (HO)
Stanley C. Johnson, Johnson & Company, Wilton, CT
Charles W. Kepler, Russell Reynolds Associates, Inc., Chicago
Richard Kinser, Richard Kinser & Associates, New York
Helga Long, H.M. Long International, Ltd., New York
Theodore E. Lusk, Nadzam, Lusk & Associates, Inc., Santa Clara, CA
William H. Marumoto, The Interface Group, Ltd./Boyden, Washington, DC
Neal L. Maslan, Ward Howell International, Inc., Encino, CA
Lawrence R. Masse, Ward Howell International, Inc., Barrington, IL
Horacio McCoy, Korn/Ferry International, Mexico City
Clarence E. McFeely, McFeely Wackerle Shulman, Chicago
Charles M. Meng, Meng, Finseth & Associates, Torrance, CA
John T. Mestepey, A.T. Kearney Executive Search, Miami
Herbert Mines, Herbert Mines Associates, Inc., New York
P. John Mirtz, Mirtz Morice, Inc., Stamford, CT
Norman F. Mitchell, A.T. Kearney, Inc., Atlanta
Richard J. Nadzam, Nadzam, Lusk & Associates, Inc., Santa Clara, CA
Jacques C. Nordeman, Nordeman Grimm, Inc., New York
Dayton Ogden, SpencerStuart, Stamford, CT
Charles A. Polachi, Jr., Fenwick Partners, Lexington, MA
David L. Powell, David Powell, Inc., Woodside, CA
P. Anthony Price, Russell Reynolds Associates, Inc., San Francisco
Conrad E. Prusak, Ethos Consulting Inc., San Francisco
Charles C. Ratigan, Heidrick & Struggles, Inc., Chicago
John H. Robison, Robison & McAulay, Charlotte, NC
Nancy R. Roblin, Paul-Tittle Associates, McLean, VA
Robert S. Rollo, R. Rollo Associates, Los Angeles
Patricia L. Sawyer, Smith & Sawyer, Inc., New York
Peter R. Schmidt, Boyden, Morristown, NJ
Lee J. Schweichler, Schweichler Associates, Inc., Corte Madera, CA
Mel Shulman, McFeely Wackerle Shulman, San Francisco
Richard C. Slayton, Slayton International, Inc., Chicago
Robert D. Spriggs, Spriggs & Company, Inc., Glenview, IL
William K. Sur, Canny, Bowen Inc., New York

Charles W. Sweet, A.T. Kearney Executive Search, Chicago
Michael A. Tappan, Ward Howell International, Inc., New York
William E. Tholke, Canny, Bowen Inc., New York
Gail Hamity Vergara, SpencerStuart, Chicago (HC)
J. Alvin Wakefield, Wakefield Talabisco International, Pittsford, VT
William R. Wilkinson, Wilkinson & Ives, San Francisco
Thomas C. Zay, Sr., Boyden/Zay & Company, Atlanta
Janis M. Zivic, The Zivic Group, Inc., San Francisco

ADMINISTRATION

1. **Robert W. Dingman,** Robert W. Dingman Co., Inc., Westlake Village, CA
2. **John R. Clarey,** Clarey & Andrews, Inc., Northbrook, IL
3. **Windle B. Priem,** Korn/Ferry International, New York
4. **Jordan M. Hadelman,** Witt/Kieffer, Ford, Hadelman & Lloyd, Oak Brook, IL (HC)
5. **John S. Lloyd,** Witt/Kieffer, Ford, Hadelman & Lloyd, Oak Brook, IL (HC)
6. **William E. Gould,** Gould & McCoy, New York
7. **Herbert Mines,** Herbert Mines Associates, New York
8. **Jerry H. Baker,** Schuyler, Frye & Baker, Inc., Atlanta
9. **Daniel M. Shepherd,** Shepherd Bueschel & Provus, Inc., Chicago
10. **Jonathan E. McBride,** McBride Associates, Inc., Washington, DC

W. Michael Danforth, Hyde Danforth & Company, Dallas
Steven M. Darter, People Management Northeast, Inc., Avon, CT
Claire W. Gargalli, The Diversified Search Companies, Philadelphia
Peter G. Grimm, Nordeman Grimm, Inc., New York
David O. Harbert, Sweeney Harbert & Mummert, Inc., Tampa, FL
Richard L. Hertan, Executive Manning Corporation, Ft. Lauderdale, FL
James E. Hunt, Kenny, Kindler, Hunt & Howe, New York
W. Jerry Hyde, Hyde Danforth & Company, Dallas
John Isaacson, Isaacson, Miller, Boston
Harold E. Johnson, Norman Broadbent International, New York
Roger M. Kenny, Kenny, Kindler, Hunt & Howe, New York
Ira W. Krinsky, Korn/Ferry International, Los Angeles (ED)
Helga Long, H.M. Long International, Ltd., New York
William H. Marumoto, The Interface Group, Ltd./Boyden, Washington, DC
Charles M. Meng, Meng, Finseth & Associates, Torrance, CA
Norman C. Roberts, Norman Roberts & Associates, Inc., Los Angeles
John H. Robison, Robison & McAulay, Charlotte, NC
Steven A. Seiden, Seiden Associates, Inc., New York
Judith M. von Seldeneck, The Diversified Search Companies, Inc., Philadelphia
Mary T. Wheeler, Lamalie Amrop International, New York

ADVERTISING/PROMOTION

1. **Susan K. Bishop,** Bishop Partners, Ltd., New York
2. **Putney Westerfield,** Boyden, San Francisco

3. **Nancy R. Roblin,** Paul-Tittle Associates, McLean, VA
4. **James H. Cornehlsen,** Heidrick & Struggles, Inc., New York
5. **Gilbert R. Stenholm, Jr.,** SpencerStuart, Chicago
6. **Joseph J. Carideo,** Thorndike Deland Associates, New York
7. **Charles M. Meng,** Meng, Finseth & Associates, Torrance, CA
8. **James J. Drury III,** SpencerStuart, Chicago
9. **William M. Humphreys,** Robison Humphreys & Associates, Inc., Etobicoke, Ontario
10. **D. John Ingram,** Ingram & Aydelotte, Inc., New York

Gary R. Barton, Barton Raben, Inc., Houston
Robert E. Beaudine, Eastman & Beaudine, Inc., Dallas
Peter Dromeshauser, Dromeshauser Associates, Wellesley, MA
Sidney Humphreys, Korn/Ferry International, Toronto
Stanley C. Johnson, Johnson & Company, Wilton, CT
David S. Joys, Heidrick & Struggles, Inc., New York
David R. Lauderback, A.T. Kearney Executive Search, Cleveland
Richard E. Linde, The Ogdon Partnership, New York
Millington F. McCoy, Gould & McCoy, New York
Thomas H. Ogdon, The Ogdon Partnership, New York
Rene Plessner, Rene Plessner Associates, New York
John Plummer, Plummer & Associates, Inc., Stamford, CT
Roland L. Poirier, Poirier, Hoevel & Co., Los Angeles
Mary T. Wheeler, Lamalie Amrop International, New York

DIRECT MARKETING

1. **Herbert Mines,** Herbert Mines Associates, Inc., New York
2. **Paul R. Ray, Jr.,** Paul Ray Berndtson, Fort Worth
3. **Susan K. Bishop,** Bishop Partners, Ltd., New York
4. **John H. Robison,** Robison & McAulay, Charlotte, NC
5. **Putney Westerfield,** Boyden, San Francisco
6. **J. Alvin Wakefield,** Wakefield Talabisco International, Pittsford, VT
7. **David A. Bueschel,** Shepherd Bueschel & Provus, Inc., Chicago
8. **Stanley C. Johnson,** Johnson & Co., Wilton, CT
9. **Martin H. Bauman,** Martin H. Bauman Associates, New York
10. **Anthony B. Cashen,** Lamalie Amrop International, New York

Jerry H. Baker, Schuyler, Frye & Baker, Inc., Atlanta
Joseph J. Carideo, Thorndike Deland Associates, New York
David E. Chambers, David Chambers & Associates, Inc., Greenwich, CT
James H. Cornehlsen, Heidrick & Struggles, Inc., New York
Peter Dromeshauser, Dromeshauser Associates, Wellesley, MA
James J. Drury III, SpencerStuart, Chicago
Claire W. Gargalli, The Diversified Search Companies, Philadelphia
Sidney Humphreys, Korn/Ferry International, Toronto
Durant A. Hunter, Pendleton James and Associates, Inc., Boston
Thomas H. Ogdon, The Ogdon Partnership, New York
Steven G. Pezim, The Bedford Consulting Group, Inc., Toronto
John Plummer, Plummer & Associates, Inc., Stamford, CT

Charles C. Ratigan, Heidrick & Struggles, Inc., Chicago
Fred Siegel, CONEX, Inc., New York
Charles Splaine, Splaine & Associates, Los Gatos, CA
William K. Sur, Canny, Bowen Inc., New York
Anthony C. Ward, Ward Liebelt Associates, Westport, CT
William R. Wilkinson, Wilkinson & Ives, San Francisco

DIRECTOR RECRUITMENT

1. **Gerard R. Roche,** Heidrick & Struggles, Inc., New York
2. **Thomas J. Neff,** SpencerStuart, New York
3. **Frederick W. Wackerle,** McFeely Wackerle Shulman, Chicago
4. **Roger M. Kenny,** Kenny, Kindler, Hunt & Howe, New York
5. **John F. Johnson,** Lamalie Amrop International, Cleveland
6. **Millington F. McCoy,** Gould & McCoy, New York
7. **John Lucht,** The John Lucht Consultancy, New York
8. **Putney Westerfield,** Boyden, San Francisco
9. **Richard M. Ferry,** Korn/Ferry International, Los Angeles
10. **Joseph E. Onstott,** The Onstott Group, Inc., Wellesley, MA

   Martin H. Bauman, Martin H. Bauman Associates, New York
   William J. Bowen, Heidrick & Struggles, Inc., Chicago
   Gerald J. Bump, D.E. Foster & Partners, Atlanta
   W. Hoyt Colton, The Colton Partnership, Inc., New York
   Peter D. Crist, Russell Reynolds Associates, Inc., Chicago
   David deWilde, Chartwell Partners International, San Francisco
   Leon A. Farley, Leon A. Farley Associates, San Francisco
   John T. Gardner, Heidrick & Struggles, Inc., Chicago
   John Hawkins, Russell Reynolds Associates, Inc., Washington, DC
   Gardner W. Heidrick, The Heidrick Partners, Chicago
   Robert L. Heidrick, The Heidrick Partners, Chicago
   John Isaacson, Isaacson, Miller, Boston
   Herbert Mines, Herbert Mines Associates, New York
   Caroline W. Nahas, Korn/Ferry International, Los Angeles
   Dayton Ogden, SpencerStuart, Stamford, CT
   Mel Shulman, McFeely Wackerle Shulman, San Francisco
   J. Gerald Simmons, Handy HRM Corporation, New York
   John T. Thompson, Heidrick & Struggles, Inc., Menlo Park, CA
   William R. Wilkinson, Wilkinson & Ives, San Francisco
   Thomas C. Zay, Sr., Boyden/Zay & Company, Atlanta

EDITORIAL

1. **John Lucht,** The John Lucht Consultancy, New York
2. **Susan K. Bishop,** Bishop Partners, Ltd., New York
3. **Richard E. Linde,** The Ogdon Partnership, New York
4. **Richard J. Cronin,** Hodge-Cronin & Associates, Inc., Rosemont, IL
5. **Thomas H. Ogdon,** The Ogdon Partnership, New York
6. **Trina D. Gordon,** Boyden, Chicago
7. **Richard F. Larsen,** Larsen, Zilliacus & Associates, Inc., Los Angeles

ENGINEERING

1. **Leon A. Farley,** Leon A. Farley Associates, San Francisco
2. **Richard K. Ives,** Wilkinson & Ives, San Francisco
3. **James M. Montgomery,** Houze, Shourds & Montgomery, Inc., Long Beach, CA
4. **R. Paul Kors,** Kors Montgomery International, Houston
5. **Peter R. Schmidt,** Boyden, Morristown, NJ
6. **Richard C. Slayton,** Slayton International Inc., Chicago
7. **Norman F. Mitchell,** A.T. Kearney, Inc., Atlanta
8. **Lee J. Schweichler,** Schweichler Associates, Inc., Corte Madera, CA
9. **Richard J. Nadzam,** Nadzam, Lusk & Associates, Inc., Santa Clara, CA
10. **William H. Marumoto,** The Interface Group, Ltd./Boyden, Washington, DC

Donald Allerton, Allerton Heneghan & O'Neill, Chicago
Jerry H. Baker, Schuyler, Frye & Baker, Inc., Atlanta
Otis H. Bowden II, Bowden & Company, Inc., Cleveland
Skott B. Burkland, Skott/Edwards Consultants, Rutherford, NJ
Richard J. Cronin, Hodge-Cronin & Associates, Inc., Rosemont, IL
W. Michael Danforth, Hyde Danforth & Company, Dallas
Paul M. DiMarchi, DiMarchi Partners, Denver
Peter Dromeshauser, Dromeshauser Associates, Wellesley, MA
Theodore E. Lusk, Nadzam, Lusk & Associates, Inc., Santa Clara, CA
James P. Masciarelli, Fenwick Partners, Lexington, MA
Charles A. Polachi, Jr., Fenwick Partners, Lexington, MA
David L. Powell, David Powell Inc., Woodside, CA
Charles C. Ratigan, Heidrick & Struggles, Inc., Chicago
Norman C. Roberts, Norman Roberts & Associates, Inc., Los Angeles
John H. Robison, Robison & McAulay, Charlotte, NC
Mel Shulman, McFeely Wackerle Shulman, San Francisco
Charles Splaine, Splaine & Associates, Los Gatos, CA
Robert D. Spriggs, Spriggs & Company, Inc., Glenview, IL
Charles W. Sweet, A.T. Kearney Executive Search, Chicago
William E. Tholke, Canny, Bowen Inc., New York

FINANCE AND ACCOUNTING

1. **Thomas J. Neff,** SpencerStuart, New York
2. **Leon A. Farley,** Leon A. Farley Associates, San Francisco
3. **Frederick W. Wackerle,** McFeely Wackerle Shulman, Chicago
4. **Robert W. Dingman,** Robert W. Dingman Co., Inc., Westlake Village, CA
5. **Windle B. Priem,** Korn/Ferry International, New York
6. **E. Pendleton James,** Pendleton James & Associates, Inc., New York
7. **John F. Johnson,** Lamalie Amrop International, Cleveland
8. **William E. Gould,** Gould & McCoy, New York
9. **Ralph Dieckmann,** Dieckmann & Associates, Ltd., Chicago
10. **John R. Clarey,** Clarey & Andrews, Northbrook, IL

Susan K. Bishop, Bishop Partners, Ltd., New York
Skott B. Burkland, Skott/Edwards Consultants, Rutherford, NJ
Donald B. Clark, Paul Ray Berndtson, Inc., Chicago
John R. Ferneborg, Ferneborg & Associates, Inc., Redwood City, CA
Jay Gaines, Jay Gaines & Company, Inc., New York
Peter G. Grimm, Nordeman Grimm, Inc., New York
Hugh Illsley, Ward Howell Illsley & Partners, Toronto
Roger M. Kenny, Kenny, Kindler, Hunt & Howe, New York
Theodore B. Martin, Jr., Nordeman Grimm, Inc., Chicago
Jonathan E. McBride, McBride Associates, Inc., Washington, DC
Millington F. McCoy, Gould & McCoy, New York
James M. Montgomery, Houze, Shourds & Montgomery, Inc., Long Beach, CA
Caroline W. Nahas, Korn/Ferry International, Los Angeles
Jacques C. Nordeman, Nordeman Grimm, Inc., New York
Joseph E. Onstott, The Onstott Group, Inc., Wellesley, MA
David W. Palmlund, Lamalie Amrop International, Dallas
Lee J. Schweichler, Schweichler Associates, Inc., Corte Madera, CA
Daniel M. Shepherd, Shepherd Bueschel & Provus, Inc., Chicago
Mary E. Shourds, Houze, Shourds & Montgomery, Inc., Long Beach, CA
Robert D. Spriggs, Spriggs & Company, Inc., Glenview, IL

HUMAN RESOURCES/PERSONNEL

1. **John F. Johnson,** Lamalie Amrop International, Cleveland
2. **Mary E. Shourds,** Houze, Shourds & Montgomery, Inc., Long Beach, CA
3. **Windle B. Priem,** Korn/Ferry International, New York
4. **William E. Gould,** Gould & McCoy, New York
5. **Robert W. Dingman,** Robert W. Dingman Co., Inc., Westlake Village, CA
6. **John R. Clarey,** Clarey & Andrews, Inc., Northbrook, IL
7. **Millington F. McCoy,** Gould & McCoy, New York
8. **Barbara L. Provus,** Shepherd, Bueschel & Provus, Inc., Chicago
9. **Paul R. Ray, Jr.,** Paul Ray Berndtson, Fort Worth
10. **Peter G. Grimm,** Nordeman Grimm, Inc., New York

Donald Allerton, Allerton Heneghan & O'Neill, Chicago
David M. deWilde, Chartwell Partners International, San Francisco
Ralph Dieckmann, Dieckmann & Associates, Ltd., Chicago
Leon A. Farley, Leon A. Farley Associates, San Francisco
John R. Ferneborg, Ferneborg & Associates, Inc., Redwood City, CA
Ronald G. Goerss, Ronald Goerss & Associates, San Francisco
William A. Hertan, Executive Manning Corporation, Ft. Lauderdale, FL
David Hoffmann, DHR International, Chicago
E. Pendleton James, Pendleton James & Associates, Inc., New York
Harold E. Johnson, Norman Broadbent International, Inc., New York
John Lucht, The John Lucht Consultancy, New York
Jonathan E. McBride, McBride Associates, Inc., Washington, DC
P. John Mirtz, Mirtz Morice, Inc., Stamford, CT

James M. Montgomery, Houze, Shourds & Montgomery, Inc., Long Beach, CA
Jacques C. Nordeman, Nordeman Grimm, Inc., New York
Charles C. Ratigan, Heidrick & Struggles, Inc., Chicago
Richard D. Sbarbaro, Lauer, Sbarbaro Associates, Inc., Chicago
Robert L. Smith, Smith & Sawyer, Inc., New York
William E. Tholke, Canny, Bowen Inc., New York
Thomas C. Zay, Boyden/Zay & Company, Atlanta

INTERNATIONAL

1. **Gerard R. Roche,** Heidrick & Struggles, Inc., New York
2. **Thomas J. Neff,** SpencerStuart, New York
3. **William E. Gould,** Gould & McCoy, New York
4. **Leon A. Farley,** Leon A. Farley Associates, San Francisco
5. **Roger M. Kenny,** Kenny, Kindler, Hunt & Howe, New York
6. **Paul R. Ray, Jr.,** Paul Ray Berndtson, Fort Worth
7. **Linda Bialecki,** Bialecki Inc., New York
8. **Helga Long,** H.M. Long International, Ltd., New York
9. **Windle B. Priem,** Korn/Ferry International, New York
10. **Peter R. Schmidt,** Boyden, Morristown, NJ

John H. Callen, Jr., Ward Howell International, Inc., New York
David Hoffmann, DHR International, Chicago
Durant A. Hunter, Pendleton James & Associates, Inc., Boston
Richard K. Ives, Wilkinson & Ives, San Francisco
Harold E. Johnson, Norman Broadbent International, Inc., New York
R. Paul Kors, Kors Montgomery International, Houston
Theodore B. Martin, Jr., Nordeman Grimm, Inc., Chicago
Lawrence R. Masse, Ward Howell International, Inc., Barrington, IL
John T. Mestepey, A.T. Kearney Executive Search, Miami
James M. Montgomery, Houze, Shourds & Montgomery, Inc., Long Beach, CA
Dayton Ogden, SpencerStuart, Stamford, CT
Nancy R. Roblin, Paul-Tittle Associates, McLean, VA
Robert L. Smith, Smith & Sawyer, Inc., New York
Charles W. Sweet, A.T. Kearney Executive Search, Chicago
Michael A. Tappan, Ward Howell International, Inc., New York
A. Robert Taylor, A.T. Kearney Executive Search, Miami
Putney Westerfield, Boyden, San Francisco
Mary T. Wheeler, Lamalie Amrop International, New York
William H. Willis, Jr., William Willis Worldwide Inc., Greenwich, CT
Thomas C. Zay, Boyden/Zay & Company, Atlanta

LEGAL

1. **Leon A. Farley,** Leon A. Farley Associates, San Francisco
2. **E. Pendleton James,** Pendleton James & Associates, Inc., New York
3. **Robert W. Dingman,** Robert W. Dingman Co., Inc., Westlake Village, CA

4. **John R. Clarey,** Clarey & Andrews, Inc., Northbrook, IL
5. **Jonathan E. McBride,** McBride Associates, Inc., Washington, DC
6. **W. Michael Danforth,** Hyde Danforth & Company, Dallas
7. **David M. deWilde,** Chartwell Partners International, San Francisco
8. **Bert H. Early,** Bert Early Associates, Chicago ⓁⒺ
9. **Jerry H. Baker,** Schuyler, Frye & Baker, Inc., Atlanta
10. **W. Jerry Hyde,** Hyde Danforth & Company, Dallas

Otis H. Bowden II, Bowden & Company, Inc., Cleveland
David A. Bueschel, Shepherd Bueschel & Provus, Inc., Chicago
Paul M. DiMarchi, DiMarchi Partners, Denver
Ronald G. Goerss, Ronald Goerss & Associates, San Francisco
William E. Gould, Gould & McCoy, New York
James Heuerman, Korn/Ferry International, San Francisco ⒽⒸ
James E. Hunt, Kenny, Kindler, Hunt & Howe, New York
Richard Kinser, Richard Kinser & Associates, New York
Richard E. Linde, The Ogdon Partnership, New York
Mark Lorenzetti, Roberts Ryan and Bentley, Inc., Baltimore, MD
William H. Marumoto, The Interface Group, Ltd./Boyden, Washington, DC
Horacio McCoy, Korn/Ferry International, Mexico City
Thomas H. Ogdon, The Ogdon Partnership, New York
David R. Peasback, Canny, Bowen Inc., New York
Barbara L. Provus, Shepherd Bueschel & Provus, Inc., Chicago
Ken Rich, Paul Ray Berndtson, Inc., New York
John H. Robison, Robison & McAulay, Charlotte, NC
Lambert Schuyler, Jr., Schuyler, Frye & Baker, Inc., Atlanta
Mary E. Shourds, Houze, Shourds & Montgomery, Inc., Long Beach, CA
Patricia L. Wilson, Leon A. Farley Associates, San Francisco

MANUFACTURING/PRODUCTION/OPERATIONS

1. **Leon A. Farley,** Leon A. Farley Associates, San Francisco
2. **Robert W. Dingman,** Robert W. Dingman Co., Inc., Westlake Village, CA
3. **James M. Montgomery,** Houze, Shourds & Montgomery, Inc., Long Beach, CA
4. **Ralph Dieckmann,** Dieckmann & Associates, Ltd., Chicago
5. **John R. Clarey,** Clarey & Andrews, Inc., Northbrook, IL
6. **William E. Gould,** Gould & McCoy, New York
7. **Theodore B. Martin, Jr.,** Nordeman Grimm, Inc., Chicago
8. **Norman F. Mitchell,** A.T. Kearney, Inc., Atlanta
9. **Richard C. Slayton,** Slayton International, Inc., Chicago
10. **William E. Tholke,** Canny, Bowen Inc., New York

Lynn Tendler Bignell, Gilbert Tweed Associates, Inc., New York
John H. Callen, Jr., Ward Howell International, Inc., New York
Richard J. Cronin, Hodge-Cronin Associates, Inc., Rosemont, IL
W. Michael Danforth, Hyde Danforth & Company, Dallas
David O. Harbert, Sweeney Harbert & Mummert, Inc., Tampa, FL
Donald A. Heneghan, Allerton Heneghan & O'Neill, Chicago

William A. Hertan, Executive Manning Corporation, Ft. Lauderdale, FL
David Hoffmann, DHR International, Chicago
Charles W. Kepler, Russell Reynolds Associates, Inc., Chicago
Richard Kinser, Richard Kinser & Associates, New York
Helga Long, H.M. Long International, Ltd., New York
Lawrence R. Masse, Ward Howell International, Inc., Barrington, IL
Joseph E. Onstott, The Onstott Group, Inc., Wellesley, MA
Charles C. Ratigan, Heidrick & Struggles, Inc., Chicago
Peter R. Schmidt, Boyden, Morristown, NJ
Lee J. Schweichler, Schweichler Associates, Inc., Corte Madera, CA
Daniel M. Shepherd, Shepherd Bueschel & Provus, Inc., Chicago
Mary E. Shourds, Houze, Shourds & Montgomery, Inc., Long Beach, CA
Robert D. Spriggs, Spriggs & Company, Inc., Glenview, IL
William R. Wilkinson, Wilkinson & Ives, San Francisco

MARKETING/SALES–CONSUMER

1. **Thomas J. Neff,** SpencerStuart, New York
2. **William E. Gould,** Gould & McCoy, New York
3. **Roger M. Kenny,** Kenny, Kindler, Hunt & Howe, New York
4. **James M. Montgomery,** Houze, Shourds & Montgomery, Inc., Long Beach, CA
5. **Theodore B. Martin, Jr.,** Nordeman Grimm, Inc., Chicago
6. **John Lucht,** The John Lucht Consultancy, New York
7. **Paul R. Ray, Jr.,** Paul Ray Berndtson, Fort Worth
8. **Susan K. Bishop,** Bishop Partners, Ltd., New York
9. **Robert W. Dingman,** Robert W. Dingman Co., Inc., Westlake Village, CA
10. **Leon A. Farley,** Leon A. Farley Associates, San Francisco

David A. Bueschel, Shepherd Bueschel & Provus, Inc., Chicago
John R. Ferneborg, Ferneborg & Associates, Inc., Redwood City, CA
Ronald G. Goerss, Ronald Goerss & Associates, San Francisco
David Hoffmann, DHR International, Chicago
Richard Kinser, Richard Kinser & Associates, Chicago
Helga Long, H.M. Long International, Ltd., New York
Theodore E. Lusk, Nadzam, Lusk & Associates, Santa Clara, CA
Millington F. McCoy, Gould & McCoy, New York
Herbert Mines, Herbert Mines Associates, Inc., New York
Richard J. Nadzam, Nadzam, Lusk & Associates, Inc., Santa Clara, CA
Jacques C. Nordeman, Nordeman Grimm, Inc., New York
Joseph E. Onstott, The Onstott Group, Inc., Wellesley, MA
Windle B. Priem, Korn/Ferry International, New York
Barbara L. Provus, Shepherd Bueschel & Provus, Inc., Chicago
Charles C. Ratigan, Heidrick & Struggles, Inc., Chicago
Daniel M. Shepherd, Shepherd Bueschel & Provus, Inc., Chicago
Mary E. Shourds, Houze, Shourds & Montgomery, Inc., Long Beach, CA
Robert L. Smith, Smith & Sawyer, Inc., New York
William E. Tholke, Canny, Bowen Inc., New York
Putney Westerfield, Boyden, San Francisco

MARKETING/SALES–INDUSTRIAL

1. **Leon A. Farley,** Leon A. Farley Associates, San Francisco
2. **William E. Gould,** Gould & McCoy, New York
3. **Thomas J. Neff,** SpencerStuart, New York
4. **James M. Montgomery,** Houze, Shourds & Montgomery, Inc., Long Beach, CA
5. **Roger M. Kenny,** Kenny, Kindler, Hunt & Howe, New York
6. **Theodore B. Martin, Jr.,** Nordeman Grimm, Inc., Chicago
7. **Robert W. Dingman,** Robert W. Dingman Co., Inc., Westlake Village, CA
8. **Linda Bialecki,** Bialecki, Inc., New York
9. **Jonathan E. McBride,** McBride Associates, Inc., Washington, DC
10. **John T. Thompson,** Heidrick & Struggles, Inc., Menlo Park, CA

David A. Bueschel, Shepherd Bueschel & Provus, Inc., Chicago
Skott B. Burkland, Skott/Edwards Consultants, Rutherford, NJ
Ralph Dieckmann, Dieckmann & Associates, Ltd., Chicago
Jay Gaines, Jay Gaines & Company, Inc., New York
Ronald G. Goerss, Ronald Goerss & Associates, San Francisco
Richard K. Ives, Wilkinson & Ives, San Francisco
Richard Kinser, Richard Kinser & Associates, New York
Theodore E. Lusk, Nadzam, Lusk & Associates, Inc., Santa Clara, CA
Millington F. McCoy, Gould & McCoy, New York
Richard J. Nadzam, Nadzam, Lusk & Associates, Inc., Santa Clara, CA
Joseph E. Onstott, The Onstott Group, Inc., Wellesley, MA
Barbara L. Provus, Shepherd Bueschel & Provus, Inc., Chicago
Charles C. Ratigan, Heidrick & Struggles, Inc., Chicago
Paul R. Ray, Jr., Paul Ray Berndtson, Fort Worth
Lee J. Schweichler, Schweichler Associates, Inc., Corte Madera, CA
Mel Shulman, McFeely Wackerle Shulman, San Francisco
Robert L. Smith, Smith & Sawyer, Inc., New York
Charles Splaine, Splaine & Associates, Los Gatos, CA
William E. Tholke, Canny, Bowen Inc., New York
Putney Westerfield, Boyden, San Francisco

MERCHANDISING

1. **Herbert Mines,** Herbert Mines Associates, Inc., New York
2. **Joseph J. Carideo,** Thorndike Deland Associates, New York
3. **Bruce M. Bastoky,** January Management Group, Inc., Columbus, OH
4. **Roger M. Kenny,** Kenny, Kindler, Hunt & Howe, New York
5. **Rene Plessner,** Rene Plessner Associates, New York
6. **Barbara L. Provus,** Shepherd Bueschel & Provus, Inc., Chicago
7. **Robert Nesbit,** Korn/Ferry International, New York
8. **David W. Palmlund,** Lamalie Amrop International, Dallas, TX
9. **John H. Callen, Jr.,** Ward Howell International, Inc., New York
10. **Stanley C. Johnson,** Johnson & Company, Wilton, CT

Robert E. Beaudine, Eastman & Beaudine, Inc., Dallas
James J. Drury III, SpencerStuart, Chicago

John R. Ferneborg, Ferneborg & Associates, Inc., Redwood City, CA
Peter G. Grimm, Nordeman Grimm, Inc., New York
John Lucht, The John Lucht Consultancy, New York
George W. Ott, Ott & Hansen, Inc., Pasadena, CA
Steven G. Pezim, The Bedford Consulting Group, Inc., Toronto
Richard D. Sbarbaro, Lauer, Sbarbaro Associates, Inc., Chicago
Robert H. Staub, Staub, Warmbold & Associates, New York
J. Alvin Wakefield, Wakefield Talabisco International, Pittsford, VT
Putney Westerfield, Boyden, San Francisco

MIS/COMPUTER OPERATIONS

1. **Mary E. Shourds,** Houze, Shourds & Montgomery, Inc., Long Beach, CA
2. **David A. Bueschel,** Shepherd Bueschel & Provus, Inc., Chicago
3. **Jay Gaines,** Jay Gaines & Company, Inc., New York
4. **Theodore B. Martin, Jr.,** Nordeman Grimm, Inc., Chicago
5. **Patricia L. Sawyer,** Smith & Sawyer, Inc., New York
6. **Norman D. Sanders,** Norm Sanders Associates, Hazlet, NJ
7. **David W. Palmlund,** Lamalie Amrop International, Dallas
8. **Peter R. Schmidt,** Boyden, Morristown, NJ
9. **Jack L. Groban,** A.T. Kearney Executive Search, Los Angeles
10. **David O. Harbert,** Sweeney Harbert & Mummert, Inc., Tampa, FL

John H. Callen, Jr., Ward Howell International, Inc., New York
Steven M. Darter, People Management Northeast, Inc., Avon, CT
Peter Dromeshauser, Dromeshauser Associates, Wellesley, MA
John R. Ferneborg, Ferneborg & Associates, Inc., Redwood City, CA
Ronald G. Goerss, Ronald Goerss & Associates, San Francisco
Donald A. Heneghan, Allerton Heneghan & O'Neill, Chicago
David Hoffmann, DHR International, Chicago
James E. Hunt, Kenny, Kindler, Hunt & Howe, New York
R. Paul Kors, Kors Montgomery International, Houston
Beverly A. Lieberman, Halbrecht Lieberman Associates, Stamford, CT
John Lucht, The John Lucht Consultancy, New York
Millington F. McCoy, Gould & McCoy, New York
Jacques C. Nordeman, Nordeman Grimm, Inc., New York
Roland L. Poirier, Poirier, Hoevel & Co., Los Angeles
Charles A. Polachi, Jr., Fenwick Partners, Lexington, MA
Conrad E. Prusak, Ethos Consulting Inc., San Francisco
Lambert Schuyler, Jr., Schuyler, Frye & Baker, Inc., Atlanta
J. Gerald Simmons, Handy HRM Corporation, New York
John T. Thompson, Heidrick & Struggles, Inc., Menlo Park, CA
Patricia L. Wilson, Leon A. Farley Associates, San Francisco

PLANNING

1. **William E. Gould,** Gould & McCoy, New York
2. **E. Pendleton James,** Pendleton James & Associates, Inc., New York
3. **Windle B. Priem,** Korn/Ferry International, New York

4. **David A. Bueschel,** Shepherd Bueschel & Provus, Inc., Chicago
5. **John S. Lloyd,** Witt/Kieffer, Ford, Hadelman & Lloyd, Oak Brook, IL (HC)
6. **David W. Palmlund,** Lamalie Amrop International, Dallas
7. **Patricia L. Sawyer,** Smith & Sawyer, Inc., New York
8. **Robert L. Smith,** Smith & Sawyer, Inc., New York
9. **Jay Gaines,** Jay Gaines & Company, Inc., New York
10. **Peter G. Grimm,** Nordeman Grimm, Inc., New York

O. William Battalia, Battalia Winston International, New York
Skott B. Burkland, Skott/Edwards Consultants, Rutherford, NJ
William B. Clemens, Jr., Norman Broadbent International, New York
David M. deWilde, Chartwell Partner International, San Francisco
Ralph Dieckmann, Dieckmann & Associates, Ltd., Chicago
James J. Drury III, SpencerStuart, Chicago
Jordan M. Hadelman, Witt/Kieffer, Ford, Hadelman & Lloyd, Oak Brook, IL HC
David O. Harbert, Sweeney Harbert & Mummert, Inc., Tampa, FL
James Heuerman, Korn/Ferry International, San Francisco (HC)
James E. Hunt, Kenny, Kindler, Hunt & Howe, New York
John Isaacson, Isaacson, Miller, Boston
Richard K. Ives, Wilkinson & Ives, San Francisco
Theodore B. Martin, Jr., Nordeman Grimm, Inc., Chicago
Millington F. McCoy, Gould & McCoy, New York
Jacques C. Nordeman, Nordeman Grimm, Inc., New York
David L. Powell, David Powell, Inc., Woodside, CA
Conrad E. Prusak, Ethos Consulting, Inc., San Francisco
Paul R. Ray, Jr., Paul Ray Berndtson, Fort Worth
Gilbert R. Stenholm, Jr., SpencerStuart, Chicago
Gail H. Vergara, SpencerStuart, Chicago (HC)

PUBLIC RELATIONS/GOVERNMENT AFFAIRS

1. **E. Pendleton James,** Pendleton James & Associates, Inc., New York
2. **Jonathan E. McBride,** McBride Associates, Inc., Washington, DC
3. **Richard Kinser,** Richard Kinser & Associates, New York
4. **Barbara L. Provus,** Shepherd Bueschel & Provus, Inc., Chicago
5. **Joseph E. Onstott,** The Onstott Group, Inc., Wellesley, MA
6. **Charles M. Meng,** Meng, Finseth & Associates, Torrance, CA
7. **Jordan M. Hadelman,** Witt/Kieffer, Ford, Hadelman & Lloyd, Oak Brook, IL (HC)
8. **Susan K. Bishop,** Bishop Partners, Ltd., New York
9. **Carl W. Menk,** Canny, Bowen Inc., New York
10. **Judith M. von Seldeneck,** The Diversified Search Companies, Inc., Philadelphia

Jerry H. Baker, Schuyler, Frye & Baker, Inc., Atlanta
Joy Reed Belt, Joy Reed Belt & Associates, Inc., Oklahoma City
James H. Cornehlsen, Heidrick & Struggles, Inc., New York
Trina D. Gordon, Boyden, Chicago
W. Jerry Hyde, Hyde Danforth & Company, Dallas

John Isaacson, Isaacson, Miller, Boston
John Lucht, The John Lucht Consultancy, New York
William H. Marumoto, The Interface Group, Ltd./Boyden, Washington, DC
Lawrence R. Masse, Ward Howell International, Inc., Barrington, IL
James M. Montgomery, Houze, Shourds & Montgomery, Inc., Long Beach, CA
David R. Peasback, Canny, Bowen Inc., New York
John H. Robison, Robison & McAulay, Charlotte, NC
George A. Rossi, Heidrick & Struggles, Inc., Boston
Steven A. Seiden, Seiden Associates, Inc., New York
J. Gerald Simmons, Handy HRM Corporation, New York
Robert D. Spriggs, Spriggs & Company, Inc., Glenview, IL
William E. Tholke, Canny, Bowen Inc., New York
J. Alvin Wakefield, Wakefield Talabisco International, Pittsford, VT
Mary T. Wheeler, Lamalie Amrop International, New York
Patricia L. Wilson, Leon A. Farley Associates, San Francisco

PURCHASING

1. **Theodore B. Martin, Jr.,** Nordeman Grimm, Inc., Chicago
2. **J. R. Akin,** J.R. Akin & Company, Fairfield, CT
3. **James M. Montgomery,** Houze, Shourds & Montgomery, Inc., Long Beach, CA
4. **Ronald Dukes,** Heidrick & Struggles, Inc., Chicago
5. **Manual Papayanopulos,** Korn/Ferry International, Mexico City
6. **Robert M. Callan,** Callan Associates, Ltd., Oak Brook, IL
7. **John T. Mestepey,** A.T. Kearney Executive Search, Miami
8. **Richard C. Slayton,** Slayton International, Inc., Chicago
9. **Daniel M. Shepherd,** Shepherd Bueschel & Provus, Inc., Chicago
10. **David W. Palmlund,** Lamalie Amrop International, Dallas

Jacques P. Andre, Paul Ray Berndtson, New York
O. William Battalia, Battalia Winston International, New York
Martin H. Bauman, Martin H. Bauman Associates, New York
David G. Hansen, Ott & Hansen, Inc., Pasadena, CA
William A. Hertan, Executive Manning Corporation, Ft. Lauderdale, FL
Michael J. Hoevel, Poirier, Hoevel & Company, Los Angeles
William T. Mangum, Thomas Mangum Company, Pasadena, CA
Barbara Nelson, Herman Smith Executive Initiatives, Toronto
David R. Peasback, Canny, Bowen Inc., New York
Roland L. Poirier, Poirier, Hoevel & Co., Los Angeles
Charles C. Ratigan, Heidrick & Struggles, Inc., Chicago
Norman C. Roberts, Norman Roberts & Associates, Inc., Los Angeles

RESEARCH AND DEVELOPMENT

1. **Linda Bialecki,** Bialecki Inc., New York
2. **Skott B. Burkland,** Skott/Edwards Consultants, Rutherford, NJ
3. **Helga Long,** H.M. Long International, Ltd., New York

4. **Richard K. Ives,** Wilkinson & Ives, San Francisco
5. **Richard J. Nadzam,** Nadzam, Lusk & Associates, Inc., Santa Clara, CA
6. **Donald Allerton,** Allerton Heneghan & O'Neill, Chicago
7. **Theodore E. Lusk,** Nadzam, Lusk & Associates, Inc., Santa Clara, CA
8. **Norman F. Mitchell,** A.T. Kearney, Inc., Atlanta
9. **Charles Splaine,** Splaine & Associates, Los Gatos, CA
10. **David H. Charlson,** Chestnut Hill Partners, Ltd., Deerfield, IL

Jerry H. Baker, Schuyler, Frye & Baker, Inc., Atlanta
Lynn Tendler Bignell, Gilbert Tweed Associates, Inc., New York
Peter D. Crist, Russell Reynolds Associates, Inc., Chicago
Richard J. Cronin, Hodge-Cronin Associates, Inc., Rosemont, IL
Robert L. Heidrick, The Heidrick Partners, Chicago
William A. Hertan, Executive Manning Corporation, Ft. Lauderdale, FL
Charles W. Kepler, Russell Reynolds Associates, Inc., Chicago
R. Paul Kors, Kors Montgomery International, Houston
William H. Marumoto, The Interface Group, Ltd./Boyden, Washington, DC
James P. Masciarelli, Fenwick Partners, Lexington, MA
Jonathan E. McBride, McBride Associates, Inc., Washington, DC
Joseph E. Onstott, The Onstott Group, Inc., Wellesley, MA
David L. Powell, David Powell, Inc., Woodside, CA
P. Anthony Price, Russell Reynolds Associates, Inc., San Francisco
Peter R. Schmidt, Boyden, Morristown, NJ
Lee J. Schweichler, Schweichler Associates, Inc., Corte Madera, CA
Andrew Sherwood, The Goodrich & Sherwood Company, New York
William K. Sur, Canny, Bowen Inc., New York
John A. Travis, Travis & Company, Inc., Sudbury, MA
David L. Witte, Ward Howell International, Inc., Houston

WOMEN, HANDICAPPED, MINORITIES

1. **Gerard R. Roche,** Heidrick & Struggles, Inc., New York
2. **Thomas J. Neff,** SpencerStuart, New York
3. **Mary E. Shourds,** Houze, Shourds & Montgomery, Inc., Long Beach, CA
4. **Lynn Tendler Bignell,** Gilbert Tweed Associates, Inc., New York
5. **Linda Bialecki,** Bialecki Inc., New York
6. **Ralph Dieckmann,** Dieckmann & Associates, Ltd., Chicago
7. **Gail H. Vergara,** SpencerStuart, Chicago (HC)
8. **Judith M. von Seldeneck,** The Diversified Search Companies, Inc., Philadelphia
9. **J. Alvin Wakefield,** Wakefield Talabisco International, Pittsford, VT
10. **Dulany Foster, Jr.,** Korn/Ferry International, Stamford, CT

John H. Callen, Jr., Ward Howell International, Inc., New York
David M. deWilde, Chartwell Partners International, San Francisco
Trina D. Gordon, Boyden, Chicago
Jordan M. Hadelman, Witt/Kieffer, Ford, Hadelman & Lloyd, Oak Brook, IL (HC)
Donald A. Heneghan, Allerton Heneghan & O'Neill, Chicago

William A. Hertan, Executive Manning Corporation, Fort Lauderdale, FL
William C. Houze, William C. Houze & Company, La Quinta, CA
John Isaacson, Isaacson, Miller, Boston
John Lucht, The John Lucht Consultancy, New York
Norman F. Mitchell, A.T. Kearney, Inc., Atlanta
P. John Mirtz, Mirtz Morice, Inc., Stamford, CT
David W. Palmlund, Lamalie Amrop International, Dallas
David R. Peasback, Canny, Bowen Inc., New York
Barbara L. Provus, Shepherd Bueschel & Provus, Inc., Chicago
Nancy R. Roblin, Paul-Tittle Associates, McLean, VA
Patricia L. Sawyer, Smith & Sawyer, Inc., New York
Richard D. Sbarbaro, Lauer, Sbarbaro Associates, Inc., Chicago
Mary T. Wheeler, Lamalie Amrop International, New York
William H. Willis, Jr., William Willis Worldwide Inc., Greenwich, CT

ORGANIZATIONAL OR INDUSTRY SPECIALIZATION

Categories

Aerospace
Agriculture/forestry/fishing
Associations/societies/nonprofit
Banks and S&Ls
Chemicals and allied products
Communications/telecommunications
Computer software
Construction
Eating and dining
Electrical and electronic machinery
Energy
Fabricated metal products
Food and kindred products
Government agencies/municipalities
Health services/hospitals
Holding companies
Hotels, resorts, private clubs
Insurance
Investment banking
Law, accounting, and consulting firms
Lumber and wood
Machinery, except electrical

Measuring, analyzing, controlling, and
   photographic instruments
Mining
Office machinery and computers
Packaging
Paper and allied products
Perfume, cosmetic, and toilet goods
Pharmaceutical/medical products
Primary metal industries
Publishing and printing
Radio and television broadcasting
Real estate
Retail
Rubber and plastic products
Security and commodity brokers, deal-
   ers, and exchanges
Textiles
Tobacco and liquor
Transportation by air, rail, truck, or water
Transportation equipment
Universities, colleges, schools
Venture capital
Wholesale trade

AEROSPACE

1. **Leon A. Farley,** Leon A. Farley Associates, San Francisco
2. **Frederick W. Wackerle,** McFeely Wackerle Shulman, Chicago

3. **James M. Montgomery,** Houze, Shourds & Montgomery, Inc., Long Beach, CA
4. **E. Pendleton James,** Pendleton James & Associates, Inc., New York
5. **Gerard R. Roche,** Heidrick & Struggles, Inc., New York
6. **Richard L. Hertan,** Executive Manning Corporation, Ft. Lauderdale, FL
7. **Richard J. Nadzam,** Nadzam, Lusk & Associates, Inc., Santa Clara, CA
8. **Theodore E. Lusk,** Nadzam, Lusk & Associates, Inc., Santa Clara, CA
9. **George W. Ott,** Ott & Hansen, Inc., Pasadena, CA
10. **Thomas C. Zay, Sr.,** Boyden/Zay & Company, Atlanta

Otis H. Bowden II, Bowden & Company, Inc., Cleveland
David E. Chambers, David Chambers & Associates, Inc., Greenwich, CT
David G. Hansen, Ott & Hansen, Inc., Pasadena, CA
William A. Hertan, Executive Manning Corporation, Ft. Lauderdale, FL
Michael J. Hoevel, Poirier, Hoevel & Company, Los Angeles
William C. Houze, William C. Houze & Company, La Quinta, CA
David S. Joys, Heidrick & Struggles, Inc., New York
Richard Kinser, Richard Kinser & Associates, New York
Richard F. Larsen, Larsen, Zilliacus and Associates, Inc., Los Angeles
William T. Mangum, Thomas Mangum Company, Pasadena, CA
William H. Marumoto, The Interface Group, Ltd./Boyden, Washington, DC
R. Bruce Massey, Bruce Massey & Partners, Inc., Toronto, ON
Clarence E. McFeely, McFeely Wackerle Shulman, Chicago
Charles M. Meng, Meng, Finseth & Associates, Torrance, CA
Barbara Nelson, Herman Smith Executive Initiatives, Toronto, ON
Steven Grant Pezim, The Bedford Consulting Group, Inc., Toronto, ON
Roland L. Poirier, Poirier, Hoevel & Co., Los Angles
Paul R. Ray, Sr., Paul Ray Berndtson, Fort Worth
Nancy R. Roblin, Paul-Tittle Associates, McLean, VA
Richard C. Slayton, Slayton International, Inc., Chicago

AGRICULTURE/FORESTRY/FISHING

1. **William R. Wilkinson,** Wilkinson & Ives, San Francisco
2. **Norman F. Mitchell,** A.T. Kearney, Inc., Atlanta
3. **Peter D. Crist,** Russell Reynolds Associates, Inc., Chicago
4. **Charles W. Sweet,** A.T. Kearney Executive Search, Chicago
5. **Robert W. Dingman,** Robert W. Dingman Company, Inc., Westlake Village, CA
6. **Michael D. Boxberger,** Korn/Ferry International, Chicago
7. **Richard F. Larsen,** Larsen, Zilliacus and Associates, Inc., Los Angeles
8. **Charles C. Ratigan,** Heidrick & Struggles, Inc., Chicago

ASSOCIATIONS/SOCIETIES/NONPROFIT ORGANIZATIONS

1. **Robert W. Dingman,** Robert W. Dingman, Co., Inc., Westlake Village, CA
2. **Paul R. Ray, Jr.,** Paul Ray Berndtson, Fort Worth
3. **E. Pendleton James,** Pendleton James & Associates, Inc., New York
4. **David A. Bueschel,** Shepherd Bueschel & Provus, Inc., Chicago

5. **Jonathan E. McBride,** McBride Associates, Inc., Washington, DC
6. **Jerry H. Baker,** Schuyler, Frye & Baker, Inc., Atlanta
7. **William J. Bowen,** Heidrick & Struggles, Inc., Chicago
8. **John S. Lloyd,** Witt/Kieffer, Ford, Hadelman & Lloyd, Oak Brook, IL
9. **Jordan M. Hadelman,** Witt/Kieffer, Ford, Hadelman & Lloyd, Oak Brook, IL
10. **J. Alvin Wakefield,** Wakefield Talabisco International, Pittsford, VT

Joy Reed Belt, Joy Reed Belt & Associates, Inc., Oklahoma City, OK
John H. Callen, Jr., Ward Howell International, Inc., New York
James H. Cornehlsen, Heidrick & Struggles, Inc., New York
Ralph Dieckmann, Dieckmann & Associates, Ltd., Chicago
Ronald Dukes, Heidrick & Struggles, Inc., Chicago
Anne M. Fawcett, The Caldwell Partners Amrop International, Toronto, ON
Richard M. Ferry, Korn/Ferry International, Los Angeles
Dulany Foster, Jr., Korn/Ferry International, Stamford, CT
Claire W. Gargalli, The Diversified Search Companies, Philadelphia
Trina D. Gordon, Boyden, Chicago
David G. Hansen, Ott & Hansen, Inc., Pasadena, CA
David O. Harbert, Sweeney Harbert & Mummert, Inc., Tampa, FL
James Heuerman, Korn/Ferry International, San Francisco
John Isaacson, Isaacson, Miller, Boston
Ira W. Krinsky, Korn/Ferry International, Los Angeles
William H. Marumoto, The Interface Group, Ltd./Boyden, Washington, DC
Laurence Raymond Masse, Ward Howell International, Inc., Barrington, IL
Richard M. McFarland, Brissenden, McFarland, Fuccella and Reynolds, Inc., Bridgewater, NJ
Charles M. Meng, Meng, Finseth & Associates, Torrance, CA
Jacques C. Nordeman, Nordeman Grimm, Inc., New York
Gail H. Vergara, SpencerStuart, Chicago

BANKS AND S&LS

1. **Thomas J. Neff,** SpencerStuart, New York
2. **Leon A. Farley,** Leon A. Farley Associates, San Francisco
3. **Windle B. Priem,** Korn/Ferry International, New York
4. **Gerard R. Roche,** Heidrick & Struggles, Inc., New York
5. **Millington F. McCoy,** Gould & McCoy, Inc., New York
6. **Jay Gaines,** Jay Gaines & Company, New York
7. **Jacques C. Nordeman,** Nordeman Grimm, Inc., New York
8. **Theodore B. Martin, Jr.,** Nordeman Grimm, Inc., Chicago
9. **Peter G. Grimm,** Nordeman Grimm, Inc., New York
10. **Richard M. Ferry,** Korn/Ferry International, Los Angeles

William J. Bowen, Heidrick & Struggles, Inc., Chicago
Gerald J. Bump, D.E. Foster & Partners, Atlanta

Skott B. Burkland, Skott/Edwards Consultants, Rutherford, NJ
Donald B. Clark, Paul Ray Berndtson, Inc., Chicago
Peter D. Crist, Russell Reynolds Associates, Inc., Chicago
David M. deWilde, Chartwell Partners International, San Francisco
Ralph Dieckmann, Dieckmann & Associates, Ltd., Chicago
Robert M. Flanagan, Robert M. Flanagan & Associates, North Salem, NY
Richard Kinser, Richard Kinser & Associates, New York
Gary Knisely, Johnson Smith & Knisely Accord, New York
Helga Long, H.M. Long International, Ltd., New York
Jonathan E. McBride, McBride Associates, Inc., Washington, DC
John T. Mestepey, A.T. Kearney Executive Search, Miami
James M. Montgomery, Houze, Shourds & Montgomery, Inc., Long Beach, CA
Dayton Ogden, SpencerStuart, Stamford, CT
Robert S. Rollo, R. Rollo Associates, Los Angeles
Norman D. Sanders, Norm Sanders Associates, Hazlet, NJ
Mary Shourds, Houze, Shourds & Montgomery, Inc., Long Beach, CA
Robert L. Smith, Smith & Sawyer, Inc., New York
Michael A. Tappen, Ward Howell International, Inc., New York

CHEMICALS AND ALLIED PRODUCTS

1. **William E. Gould,** Gould & McCoy, Inc., New York
2. **Frederick W. Wackerle,** McFeely Wackerle Shulman, Chicago
3. **Gerard R. Roche,** Heidrick & Struggles, Inc., New York
4. **Daniel M. Shepherd,** Shepherd Bueschel & Provus, Inc., Chicago
5. **Peter R. Schmidt,** Boyden, Morristown, NJ
6. **Mel Shulman,** McFeely Wackerle Shulman, San Francisco
7. **Robert D. Spriggs,** Spriggs & Company, Inc., Glenview, IL
8. **David Hoffmann,** DHR International, Chicago
9. **R. Paul Kors,** Kors Montgomery International, Houston
10. **Helga Long,** H.M. Long International, Ltd., New York

Donald Allerton, Allerton Heneghan & O'Neill, Chicago
O. William Battalia, Battalia Winston International, New York
Linda Bialecki, Bialecki Inc., New York
Michael D. Boxberger, Korn/Ferry International, Chicago
Richard M. Ferry, Korn/Ferry International, Los Angeles
John T. Gardner, Heidrick & Struggles, Inc., Chicago
Claire W. Gargalli, The Diversified Search Companies, Philadelphia
David G. Hansen, Ott & Hansen, Inc., Pasadena, CA
William A. Hertan, Executive Manning Corporation, Ft. Lauderdale, FL
Clarence E. McFeely, McFeely Wackerle Shulman, Chicago
P. John Mirtz, Mirtz Morice, Inc., Stamford, CT
James L. Morice, Mirtz Morice, Inc., Stamford, CT
Lawrence F. Nein, Lamalie Amrop International, Chicago
David W. Palmlund, Lamalie Amrop International, Dallas
Nick J. Pierce, Paul Ray Berndtson, Chicago
Charles C. Ratigan, Heidrick & Struggles, Inc., Chicago

John E. Smith, Jr., Smith Search, S.C., Mexico City
William K. Sur, Canny, Bowen Inc., New York
J. Alvin Wakefield, Wakefield Talabisco International, Pittsford, VT
David L. Witte, Ward Howell International, Inc., Houston

COMMUNICATIONS/TELECOMMUNICATIONS

1. **Leon A. Farley,** Leon A. Farley Associates, San Francisco
2. **Gerard R. Roche,** Heidrick & Struggles, Inc. New York
3. **Roger M. Kenny,** Kenny, Kindler, Hunt & Howe/Boardroom Consultants, NY
4. **Mary Shourds,** Houze, Shourds & Montgomery, Inc., Long Beach, CA
5. **James M. Montgomery,** Houze, Shourds & Montgomery, Inc., Long Beach, CA
6. **E. Pendleton James,** Pendleton James & Associates, Inc., New York
7. **Millington F. McCoy,** Gould & McCoy, Inc., New York
8. **John Lucht,** The John Lucht Consultancy Inc., New York
9. **Putney Westerfield,** Boyden, San Francisco
10. **Jonathan E. McBride,** McBride Associates, Inc., Washington, DC

Susan K. Bishop, Bishop Partners, Ltd., New York
Jeff E. Christian, Christian & Timbers, Cleveland
John R. Ferneborg, Ferneborg & Associates, Inc., Redwood, City, CA
David P. Francis, Heidrick & Struggles, Inc., New York
Donald A. Heneghan, Allerton Heneghan & O'Neill, Chicago
David Hoffmann, DHR International, Chicago
Jonathan S. Holman, The Holman Group, Inc., San Francisco
Richard K. Ives, Wilkinson & Ives, San Francisco
Richard Kinser, Richard Kinser & Associates, New York
Theodore E. Lusk, Nadzam, Lusk & Associates, Inc., Santa Clara, CA
Richard J. Nadzam, Nadzam, Lusk & Associates, Inc., Santa Clara, CA
Jacques C. Nordeman, Nordeman Grimm, Inc., New York
Barbara L. Provus, Shepherd Bueschel & Provus, Inc., Chicago
Conrad E. Prusak, Ethos Consulting Inc., San Francisco
Patricia L. Sawyer, Smith & Sawyer, Inc., New York
Lee J. Schweichler, Schweichler Associates, Inc., Corte Madera, CA
John T. Thompson, Heidrick & Struggles, Inc., Menlo Park, CA
Thomas C. Zay, Sr., Boyden, Atlanta

COMPUTER SOFTWARE

1. **Robert W. Dingman,** Robert W. Dingman Company, Inc., Westlake Village, CA
2. **Mary Shourds,** Houze, Shourds & Montgomery, Inc., Long Beach, CA
3. **Joseph E. Onstott,** The Onstott Group, Inc., Wellesley, MA
4. **John T. Thompson,** Heidrick & Struggles, Inc., Menlo Park, CA
5. **Lee J. Schweichler,** Schweichler Associates, Inc., Corte Madera, CA
6. **Robert L. Smith,** Smith & Sawyer, Inc., New York

7. **Jonathan E. McBride,** McBride Associates, Inc., Washington, DC
8. **Jonathan S. Holman,** The Holman Group, Inc., San Francisco
9. **Patricia L. Sawyer,** Smith & Sawyer, Inc., New York
10. **Richard K. Ives,** Wilkinson & Ives, San Francisco

Skott B. Burkland, Skott/Edwards Consultants, Rutherford, NJ
John H. Callen, Jr., Ward Howell International, New York
Jeff E. Christian, Christian & Timbers, Cleveland
Peter Dromeshauser, Dromeshauser Associates, Wellesley, MA
Michael S. Dunford, Korn/Ferry International, Chicago
John R. Ferneborg, Ferneborg & Associates, Inc., Redwood, City, CA
Jay Gaines, Jay Gaines & Company, Inc., New York
Debra S. Germaine, Gilbert Tweed Associates, Newton, MA
Peter G. Grimm, Nordeman Grimm, Inc., New York
Howard L. Karr, Howard Karr & Associates, Inc., San Mateo, CA
Richard Kinser, Richard Kinser & Associates, New York
R. Paul Kors, Kors Montgomery International, Houston
Theodore E. Lusk, Nadzam, Lusk & Associates, Inc., Santa Clara, CA
Richard J. Nadzam, Nadzam, Lusk & Associates, Inc., Santa Clara, CA
Barbara Nelson, Herman Smith Executive Initiatives, Toronto, ON
David L. Powell, Sr., David Powell, Inc., Woodside, CA
Nancy R. Roblin, Paul-Tittle Associates, McLean, VA
George A. Rossi, Heidrick & Struggles, Inc., Boston
Peter R. Schmidt, Boyden, Morristown, NJ
Mel Shulman, McFeely Wackerle Shulman, San Francisco

CONSTRUCTION

1. **Leon A. Farley,** Leon A. Farley Associates, San Francisco
2. **Thomas C. Zay, Sr.,** Boyden, Atlanta
3. **Putney Westerfield,** Boyden, San Francisco
4. **John H. Robison,** Robison & McAulay, Charlotte, NC
5. **J. R. Akin,** J.R. Akin & Company, Fairfield, CT
6. **Michael D. Boxberger,** Korn/Ferry International, Chicago
7. **Ronald G. Goerss,** Ronald Goerss & Associates, San Francisco
8. **Charles M. Meng,** Meng, Finseth & Associates, Torrance, CA
9. **George W. Ott,** Ott & Hansen, Inc., Pasadena, CA
10. **Gerald J. Bump,** D.E. Foster & Partners, Atlanta

O. William Battalia, Battalia Winston International, New York
David E. Chambers, David Chambers & Associates, Inc., Greenwich, CT
Richard M. Ferry, Korn/Ferry International, Los Angeles
Theodore E. Lusk, Nadzam, Lusk & Associates, Inc., Santa Clara, CA
Richard J. Nadzam, Nadzam, Lusk & Associates, Inc., Santa Clara, CA
David R. Peasback, Canny, Bowen Inc., New York
Lee Van Leeuwen, Korn/Ferry International, Los Angeles

EATING AND DINING PLACES

1. **David W. Palmlund,** Lamalie Amrop International, Dallas
2. **John T. Mestepey,** A.T. Kearney Executive Search, Miami
3. **Robert D. Spriggs,** Spriggs & Company, Inc., Glenview, IL
4. **William H. Willis, Jr.,** William Willis Worldwide Inc., Greenwich, CT
5. **Carol S. Jeffers,** John Sibbald Associates, Inc., Chicago
6. **Herbert L. Regehly,** IMC Group of Companies, New York
7. **Gilbert R. Stenholm, Jr.,** SpencerStuart, Inc., Chicago
8. **David G. Hansen,** Ott & Hansen, Inc., Pasadena, CA
9. **David B. Mazza,** Mazza & Riley, Inc., Wellesley Hills, MA
10. **Robert H. Staub,** Staub, Warmbold & Associates, New York

ELECTRICAL AND ELECTRONIC MACHINERY

1. **Gerard R. Roche,** Heidrick & Struggles, Inc., New York
2. **Leon A. Farley,** Leon A. Farley Associates, San Francisco
3. **Mary Shourds,** Houze, Shourds & Montgomery, Inc., Long Beach, CA
4. **James M. Montgomery,** Houze, Shourds & Montgomery, Inc., Long Beach, CA
5. **E. Pendleton James,** Pendleton James & Associates, Inc., New York
6. **William E. Gould,** Gould & McCoy, Inc., New York
7. **Robert W. Dingman,** Robert W. Dingman Company, Inc., Westlake Village, CA
8. **Richard J. Nadzam,** Nadzam, Lusk & Associates, Inc., Santa Clara, CA
9. **Jonathan E. McBride,** McBride Associates, Inc., Washington, DC
10. **Ralph Dieckmann,** Dieckmann & Associates, Ltd., Chicago

Donald Allerton, Allerton Heneghan & O'Neill, Chicago
John H. Callen, Jr., Ward Howell International, Inc., New York
W. Michael Danforth, Hyde Danforth & Company, Dallas
John R. Ferneborg, Ferneborg & Associates, Inc., Redwood, City, CA
John T. Gardner, Heidrick & Struggles, Inc., Chicago
Robert L. Heidrick, The Heidrick Partners, Inc., Chicago
William A. Hertan, Executive Manning Corporation, Ft. Lauderdale, FL
Jonathan S. Holman, The Holman Group, Inc., San Francisco
Richard K. Ives, Wilkinson & Ives, San Francisco
Charles W. Kepler, Russell Reynolds Associates, Inc., Chicago
Theodore E. Lusk, Nadzam, Lusk & Associates, Inc., Santa Clara, CA
Charles A. Polachi, Jr., Fenwick Partners, Lexington, MA
P. Anthony Price, Russell Reynolds Associates, Inc., San Francisco
Nancy R. Roblin, Paul-Tittle Associates, McLean, VA
Peter R. Schmidt, Boyden, Morristown, NJ
Lee J. Schweichler, Schweichler Associates, Inc., Corte Madera, CA
Mel Shulman, McFeely Wackerle Shulman, San Francisco
Herman M. Smith, Herman Smith Executive Initiatives Inc., Toronto
Charles Splaine, Splaine & Associates, Los Gatos, CA
Jack H. Vernon, Russell Reynolds Associates, Inc., Boston

ENERGY

1. **E. Pendleton James,** Pendleton James & Associates, Inc., New York
2. **Leon A. Farley,** Leon A. Farley Associates, San Francisco
3. **William E. Tholke,** Canny, Bowen Inc., New York
4. **R. Paul Kors,** Kors Montgomery International, Houston
5. **William H. Marumoto,** The Interface Group, Ltd./Boyden, Washington, DC
6. **John T. Mestepey,** A.T. Kearney Executive Search, Miami
7. **Michael D. Boxberger,** Korn/Ferry International, Chicago
8. **John H. Robison,** Robison & McAulay, Charlotte, NC
9. **Arthur Newman,** Lamalie Amrop International, Houston
10. **W. Jerry Hyde,** Hyde Danforth & Company, Dallas

Joy Reed Belt, Joy Reed Belt & Associates, Inc., Oklahoma City, OK
Lynn Tendler Bignell, Gilbert Tweed Associates, Inc., New York
William J. Bowen, Heidrick & Struggles, Inc., Chicago
Richard Cronin, Hodge-Cronin & Associates, Inc., Rosemont, IL
Richard M. Ferry, Korn/Ferry International, Los Angeles
Amanda C. Fox, Paul Ray Berndtson, Chicago
Henry G. Higdon, Higdon Associates, Inc., New York
Richard M. McFarland, Brissenden, McFarland, et al, Bridgewater, NJ
Charles M. Meng, Meng, Finseth & Associates, Torrance, CA
Norman F. Mitchell, A.T. Kearney, Inc., Atlanta
David R. Peasback, Canny, Bowen Inc., New York
David L. Powell, Sr., David Powell, Inc., Woodside, CA
Steve A. Raben, Barton Raben, Inc., Houston
Norman C. Roberts, Norman Roberts & Associates, Inc., Los Angeles
Charles Splaine, Splaine & Associates, Los Gatos, CA
Judith M. von Seldeneck, The Diversified Search Companies, Inc., Philadelphia
Daniel C. Wier, Daniel Wier & Associates, Los Angeles
Patricia L. Wilson, Leon A. Farley Associates, San Francisco
David L. Witte, Ward Howell International, Inc., Houston

FABRICATED METAL PRODUCTS

1. **Robert W. Dingman,** Robert W. Dingman Company, Inc., Westlake Village, CA
2. **Frederick W. Wackerle,** McFeely Wackerle Shulman, Chicago
3. **Ralph Dieckmann,** Dieckmann & Associates, Ltd., Chicago
4. **William E. Gould,** Gould & McCoy, Inc., New York
5. **Theodore B. Martin, Jr.,** Nordeman Grimm, Inc., Chicago
6. **Peter R. Schmidt,** Boyden, Morristown, NJ
7. **Norman F. Mitchell,** A.T. Kearney, Inc., Atlanta
8. **Charles W. Kepler,** Russell Reynolds Associates, Inc., Chicago
9. **Charles W. Sweet,** A.T. Kearney Executive Search, Chicago
10. **Richard L. Hertan,** Executive Manning Corporation, Ft. Lauderdale, FL

J. R. Akin, J.R. Akin & Company, Fairfield, CT
Donald Allerton, Allerton, Heneghan & O'Neill, Chicago
Bruce M. Bastoky, January Management Group, Inc., Columbus, OH
Peter D. Crist, Russell Reynolds Associates, Inc., Chicago
Richard Cronin, Hodge-Cronin & Associates, Inc., Rosemont, IL
John T. Gardner, Heidrick & Struggles, Inc., Chicago
William A. Hertan, Executive Manning Corporation, Ft. Lauderdale, FL
Richard Kinser, Richard Kinser & Associates, New York
Theodore E. Lusk, Nadzam, Lusk & Associates, Inc., Santa Clara, CA
Laurence Raymond Masse, Ward Howell International, Inc., Barring-
    ton, IL
P. John Mirtz, Mirtz Morice, Inc., Stamford, CT
James L. Morice, Mirtz Morice, Inc., Stamford, CT
Richard J. Nadzam, Nadzam, Lusk & Associates, Inc., Santa Clara, CA
George W. Ott, Ott & Hansen, Inc., Pasadena, CA
Charles C. Ratigan, Heidrick & Struggles, Inc., Chicago
Steven A. Seiden, Seiden Associates, Inc., New York
Richard C. Slayton, Slayton International, Inc., Chicago
John E. Smith, Jr., Smith Search, S.C., Mexico City, MX
Robert H. Staub, Staub, Warmbold & Associates, New York
Jack H. Vernon, Russell Reynolds Associates, Inc., Boston

FOOD AND KINDRED PRODUCTS

1. **Gerard R. Roche,** Heidrick & Struggles, Inc., New York
2. **Thomas J. Neff,** SpencerStuart, New York
3. **William E. Gould,** Gould & McCoy, Inc., New York
4. **Robert W. Dingman,** Robert W. Dingman Company, Inc., Westlake Vil-
    lage, CA
5. **Theodore B. Martin, Jr.,** Nordeman Grimm, Inc., Chicago
6. **Paul R. Ray, Jr.,** Paul Ray Berndtson, Fort Worth
7. **Roger M. Kenny,** Kenny, Kindler, Hunt & Howe/Boardroom Consul-
    tants, New York
8. **Daniel M. Shepherd,** Shepherd Bueschel & Provus, Inc., Chicago
9. **John R. Clarey,** Clarey & Andrews, Inc., Northbrook, IL
10. **Robert D. Spriggs,** Spriggs & Company, Inc., Glenview, IL

Richard Cronin, Hodge-Cronin & Associates, Inc., Rosemont, IL
James J. Drury III, SpencerStuart, Chicago
Richard M. Ferry, Korn/Ferry International, Los Angeles
Ronald G. Goerss, Ronald Goerss & Associates, San Francisco
Peter G. Grimm, Nordeman Grimm, Inc., New York
Robert L. Heidrick, The Heidrick Partners, Inc., Chicago
David Hoffmann, DHR International, Chicago
Stanley C. Johnson, Johnson & Company, Wilton, CT
Richard Kinser, Richard Kinser & Associates, New York
Helga Long, H.M. Long International, Ltd., New York

William H. Marumoto, The Interface Group, Ltd./Boyden, Washington, DC
Carl W. Menk, Canny, Bowen Inc., New York
P. John Mirtz, Mirtz Morice, Inc., Stamford, CT
Caroline W. Nahas, Korn/Ferry International, Los Angeles
David W. Palmlund, Lamalie Amrop International, Dallas
Barbara L. Provus, Shepherd Bueschel & Provus, Inc., Chicago
Charles W. Sweet, A.T. Kearney Executive Search, Chicago
Putney Westerfield, Boyden, San Francisco
William R. Wilkinson, Wilkinson & Ives, San Francisco
Thomas C. Zay, Sr., Boyden, Atlanta

GOVERNMENT AGENCIES/MUNICIPALITIES

1. **Norman C. Roberts,** Norman Roberts & Associates, Inc., Los Angeles
2. **Jordan M. Hadelman,** Witt/Kieffer, Ford, Hadelman & Lloyd, Oak Brook, IL
3. **Mary T. Wheeler,** Lamalie Amrop International, New York
4. **J. Alvin Wakefield,** Wakefield Talabisco International, Pittsford, VT
5. **John Isaacson,** Isaacson, Miller, Boston
6. **Ira W. Krinsky,** Korn/Ferry International, Los Angeles
7. **Charles M. Meng,** Meng, Finseth & Associates, Torrance, CA
8. **Janis M. Zivic,** The Zivic Group, Inc., San Francisco
9. **Joseph J. Carideo,** Thorndike Deland Associates, New York
10. **Barbara Nelson,** Herman Smith Executive Initiatives, Toronto, ON

HEALTH SERVICES/HOSPITALS

1. **John S. Lloyd,** Witt/Kieffer, Ford, Hadelman & Lloyd, Oak Brook, IL
2. **Gail H. Vergara,** SpencerStuart, Chicago
3. **Michael C. Kieffer,** Witt/Kieffer, Ford, Hadelman & Lloyd, Oak Brook, IL
4. **Jordan M. Hadelman,** Witt/Kieffer, Ford, Hadelman & Lloyd, Oak Brook, IL
5. **Robert W. Dingman,** Robert W. Dingman Company, Inc., Westlake Village, CA
6. **Roger M. Kenny,** Kenny, Kindler, Hunt & Howe/Boardroom Consultants, New York
7. **William E. Tholke,** Canny, Bowen Inc., New York
8. **Janis M. Zivic,** The Zivic Group, Inc., San Francisco
9. **J. Robert Clarke,** The Furst Group/MPI, Rockford, IL
10. **James Heuerman,** Korn/Ferry International, San Francisco

Jerry H. Baker, Schuyler, Frye & Baker, Inc., Atlanta
Joy Reed Belt, Joy Reed Belt & Associates, Inc., Oklahoma City, OK
Michael D. Caver, Heidrick & Struggles, Inc., Chicago
Steven M. Darter, People Management Northeast, Inc., Avon, CT
J. Daniel Ford, Witt/Kieffer, Ford, Hadelman & Lloyd, Oak Brook, IL
Amanda C. Fox, Paul Ray Berndtson, Chicago

Trina D. Gordon, Boyden, Chicago
James E. Hunt, Kenny, Kindler, Hunt & Howe, New York
Mark Lorenzetti, Roberts Ryan and Bentley, Inc., Inc., Baltimore
William T. Mangum, Thomas Mangum Company, Pasadena, CA
Neal L. Maslan, Ward Howell International, Inc., Encino, CA
Charles M. Meng, Meng, Finseth & Associates, Torrance, CA
Norman F. Mitchell, A.T. Kearney, Inc., Atlanta
Joseph E. Onstott, The Onstott Group, Inc., Wellesley, MA
Michael S. Reeder, Lamalie Amrop International, Atlanta
Richard D. Sbarbaro, Lauer, Sbarbaro Associates, Inc., Chicago
Janet Tweed, Gilbert Tweed Associates, Inc., New York
J. Larry Tyler, Tyler & Company, Atlanta
Judith M. von Seldeneck, The Diversified Search Companies, Inc., Philadelphia
Mary T. Wheeler, Lamalie Amrop International, New York

HOLDING COMPANIES

1. **Frederick W. Wackerle,** McFeely Wackerle Shulman, Chicago
2. **Ralph Dieckmann,** Dieckmann & Associates, Ltd., Chicago
3. **John R. Clarey,** Clarey & Andrews, Inc., Northbrook, IL
4. **Paul R. Ray, Jr.,** Paul Ray Berndtson, Fort Worth
5. **Peter G. Grimm,** Nordeman Grimm, Inc., New York
6. **David Hoffmann,** DHR International, Chicago
7. **Jacques C. Nordeman,** Nordeman Grimm, Inc., New York
8. **Clarence E. McFeely,** McFeely Wackerle Shulman, Chicago
9. **John T. Mestepey,** A.T. Kearney Executive Search, Miami
10. **Charles M. Meng,** Meng, Finseth & Associates, Torrance, CA

Martin H. Bauman, Martin H. Bauman Associates, New York
C. Douglas Caldwell, The Caldwell Partners Amrop International, Toronto, ON
David E. Chambers, David Chambers & Associates, Inc., Greenwich, CT
Donald B. Clark, Paul Ray Berndtson, Chicago
Steven M. Darter, People Management Northeast, Inc., Avon, CT
Anne M. Fawcett, The Caldwell Partners Amrop International, Toronto, ON
Dulany Foster, Jr., Korn/Ferry International, Stamford, CT
Michael J. Hoevel, Poirier, Hoevel & Company, Los Angeles
James E. Hunt, Kenny, Kindler, Hunt & Howe, New York
Harold E. Johnson, Norman Broadbent International, Inc., New York
Theodore B. Martin, Jr., Nordeman Grimm, Inc., Chicago
Richard A. McCallister, Boyden, Chicago
P. John Mirtz, Mirtz Morice, Inc., Stamford, CT
Ken Rich, Paul Ray Berndtson, Inc., New York
Robert S. Rollo, R. Rollo Associates, Los Angeles
Norman D. Sanders, Norm Sanders Associates, Hazlet, NJ
Steven A. Seiden, Seiden Associates, Inc., New York
Charles W. Sweet, A.T. Kearney Executive Search, Chicago

J. Robert Swidler, Egon Zehnder International, Inc., Montreal
William R. Wilkinson, Wilkinson & Ives, San Francisco

HOTELS, RESORTS, PRIVATE CLUBS

1. **Carol S. Jeffers,** John Sibbald Associates, Inc., Chicago
2. **Janis M. Zivic,** The Zivic Group, Inc., San Francisco
3. **Donald A. Heneghan,** Allerton Heneghan & O'Neill, Chicago
4. **W. Michael Danforth,** Hyde Danforth & Company, Dallas
5. **Herbert L. Regehly,** IMC Group of Companies, New York
6. **Robert S. Rollo,** R. Rollo Associates, Los Angeles
7. **John R. Ferneborg,** Ferneborg & Associates, Inc., Redwood City, CA
8. **Roger M. Kenny,** Kenny, Kindler, Hunt & Howe/Boardroom Consultants, New York
9. **Joseph J. Carideo,** Thorndike Deland Associates, New York
10. **Steven A. Seiden,** Seiden Associates, Inc., New York

John R. Berry II, Nordeman Grimm, Inc., Chicago
Sidney Humphreys, Korn/Ferry International, Toronto, ON
Stanley C. Johnson, Johnson & Company, Wilton, CT
R. Bruce Massey, Bruce Massey & Partners, Inc., Toronto, ON
Barbara Nelson, Herman Smith Executive Initiatives, Toronto, ON
Thomas H. Ogdon, The Ogdon Partnership, New York
John Plummer, Plummer & Associates, Inc., Stamford, CT
Fred Siegel, CONEX Incorporated, New York
Lee Van Leeuwen, Korn/Ferry International, Los Angeles
Judith M. von Seldeneck, The Diversified Search Companies, Inc., Philadelphia

INSURANCE

1. **Ralph Dieckmann,** Dieckmann & Associates, Ltd., Chicago
2. **Thomas J. Neff,** SpencerStuart, New York
3. **Windle B. Priem,** Korn/Ferry International, New York
4. **John Lucht,** The John Lucht Consultancy Inc., New York
5. **Millington F. McCoy,** Gould & McCoy, Inc., New York
6. **William E. Tholke,** Canny, Bowen Inc., New York
7. **Skott B. Burkland,** Skott/Edwards Consultants, Rutherford, NJ
8. **Gail H. Vergara,** SpencerStuart, Chicago
9. **Richard K. Ives,** Wilkinson & Ives, San Francisco
10. **Steven M. Darter,** People Management Northeast, Inc., Avon, CT

J. R. Akin, J.R. Akin & Company, Fairfield, CT
Gerald J. Bump, D.E. Foster & Partners, Atlanta
J. Robert Clarke, The Furst Group/MPI, Rockford, IL
William B. Clemens, Jr., Norman Broadbent International, New York
Richard M. Ferry, Korn/Ferry International, Los Angeles
James Heuerman, Korn/Ferry International, San Francisco
Lawrence J. Holmes, Consulting Associates, Inc., Baltimore, MD

James E. Hunt, Kenny, Kindler, Hunt & Howe, New York
Roger M. Kenny, Kenny, Kindler, Hunt & Howe/Boardroom Consultants, New York
John S. Lloyd, Witt/Kieffer, Ford, Hadelman & Lloyd, Oak Brook, IL
Neal L. Maslan, Ward Howell International, Inc., Encino, CA
James L. Morice, Mirtz Morice, Inc., Stamford, CT
Dayton Ogden, SpencerStuart, Stamford, CT
Ken Rich, Paul Ray Berndtson, Inc., New York
John H. Robison, Robison & McAulay, Charlotte, NC
Robert S. Rollo, R. Rollo Associates, Los Angeles
Norman D. Sanders, Norm Sanders Associates, Hazlet, NJ
Lambert Schuyler, Jr., Schuyler, Frye & Baker, Inc., Atlanta
Michael A. Tappan, Ward Howell International, Inc., New York
Thomas C. Zay, Sr., Boyden, Atlanta

INVESTMENT BANKING

1. **Thomas J. Neff,** SpencerStuart, New York
2. **Roger M. Kenny,** Kenny, Kindler, Hunt & Howe/Boardroom Consultants, New York
3. **Windle B. Priem,** Korn/Ferry International, New York
4. **Theodore B. Martin, Jr.,** Nordeman Grimm, Inc., Chicago
5. **Linda Bialecki,** Bialecki Inc., New York
6. **Jay Gaines,** Jay Gaines & Company, Inc., New York
7. **Norman D. Sanders,** Norm Sanders Associates, Hazlet, NJ
8. **Michael A. Tappan,** Ward Howell International, Inc., New York
9. **David M. deWilde,** Chartwell Partners International, San Francisco
10. **Donald B. Clark,** Paul Ray Berndtson, Inc., Chicago

Jacques P. Andre, Paul Ray Berndtson, Inc., New York
Martin H. Bauman, Martin H. Bauman Associates, New York
Jeffrey G. Bell, Norman Broadbent International, Inc., New York
Anthony B. Cashen, Lamalie Amrop International, New York
W. Hoyt Colton, The Colton Partnership, Inc., New York
Peter D. Crist, Russell Reynolds Associates, Inc., Chicago
Peter Drummond-Hay, Russell Reynolds Associates, Inc., New York
Henry G. Higdon, Higdon Associates, Inc., New York
Michael J. Hoevel, Poirier, Hoevel & Company, Los Angeles
Durant A. Hunter, Pendleton James and Associates, Inc., Boston
David S. Joys, Heidrick & Struggles, Inc., New York
James F. Keresey, James Keresey Associates, Inc., New York
Horacio J. McCoy, Korn/Ferry International, Mexico City, MX
Dayton Ogden, SpencerStuart, Stamford, CT
Joseph E. Onstott, The Onstott Group, Inc., Wellesley, MA
Ken Rich, Paul Ray Berndtson, Inc., New York
George A. Rossi, Heidrick & Struggles, Inc., Boston
Patricia L. Sawyer, Smith & Sawyer, Inc., New York
Brian M. Sullivan, Sullivan & Company, New York
William H. Willis, Jr., William Willis Worldwide Inc., Greenwich, CT

LAW, ACCOUNTING, AND CONSULTING FIRMS

1. **Leon A. Farley,** Leon A. Farley Associates, San Francisco
2. **Ralph Dieckmann,** Dieckmann & Associates, Ltd., Chicago
3. **Robert L. Smith,** Smith & Sawyer, Inc., New York
4. **Joseph E. Onstott,** The Onstott Group, Inc., Wellesley, MA
5. **Paul R. Ray, Jr.,** Paul Ray Brendtson, Ft. Worth, TX
6. **Jay Gaines,** Jay Gaines & Company, Inc., New York
7. **Patricia L. Sawyer,** Smith & Sawyer, Inc., New York
8. **Ronald G. Goerss,** Ronald Goerss & Associates, San Francisco
9. **Patricia L. Wilson,** Leon A. Farley Associates, San Francisco
10. **W. Michael Danforth,** Hyde Danforth & Company, Dallas

Donald B. Clark, Paul Ray Berndtson, Inc., Chicago
David M. deWilde, Chartwell Partners International, San Francisco
Paul M. DiMarchi, DiMarchi Partners, Denver
Michael J. Hoevel, Poirier, Hoevel & Company, Los Angeles
W. Jerry Hyde, Hyde Danforth & Company, Dallas
Richard Kinser, Richard Kinser & Associates, New York
William H. Marumoto, The Interface Group, Ltd./Boyden, Washington, DC
Neal L. Maslan, Ward Howell International, Inc., Encino, CA
Jonathan E. McBride, McBride Associates, Inc., Washington, DC
Norman F. Mitchell, A.T. Kearney, Inc., Atlanta
Edwin S. Mruk, Mruk & Partners, New York
Jacques C. Nordeman, Nordeman Grimm, Inc., New York
Thomas H. Ogdon, The Ogdon Partnership, New York
Conrad E. Prusak, Ethos Consulting Inc., San Francisco
John H. Robison, Robison & McAulay, Charlotte, NC
Brenda L. Ruello, Heidrick & Struggles, Inc., New York
Lambert Schuyler, Jr., Schuyler, Frye & Baker, Inc., Atlanta
Fred Siegel, CONEX Incorporated, New York
Judith M. von Seldeneck, The Diversified Search Companies, Inc., Philadelphia
Janis M. Zivic, The Zivic Group, Inc., San Francisco

LUMBER AND WOOD PRODUCTS

1. **Daniel M. Shepherd,** Shepherd Bueschel & Provus, Inc., Chicago
2. **John R. Clarey,** Clarey & Andrews, Inc., Northbrook, IL
3. **Norman F. Mitchell,** A.T. Kearney, Inc., Atlanta
4. **Richard L. Hertan,** Executive Manning Corporation, Ft. Lauderdale, FL
5. **William H. Marumoto,** The Interface Group, Ltd./Boyden, Washington, DC
6. **Bruce M. Bastoky,** January Management Group, Inc., Columbus, OH
7. **Steven A. Seiden,** Seiden Associates, Inc., New York
8. **William A. Hertan,** Executive Manning Corporation, Ft. Lauderdale, FL
9. **Paul R. Ray, Sr.,** Paul Ray Berndtson, Fort Worth
10. **William R. Wilkinson,** Wilkinson & Ives, San Francisco

MACHINERY, EXCEPT ELECTRICAL

1. **Frederick W. Wackerle,** McFeely Wackerle Shulman, Chicago
2. **John R. Clarey,** Clarey & Andrews, Inc., Northbrook, IL
3. **William E. Gould,** Gould & McCoy, Inc., New York
4. **Charles C. Ratigan,** Heidrick & Struggles, Inc., Chicago
5. **Robert D. Spriggs,** Spriggs & Company, Inc., Glenview, IL
6. **Theodore B. Martin, Jr.,** Nordeman Grimm, Inc., Chicago
7. **Norman F. Mitchell,** A.T. Kearney, Inc., Atlanta
8. **Richard C. Slayton,** Slayton International, Inc., Chicago
9. **Charles W. Kepler,** Russell Reynolds Associates, Inc., Chicago
10. **Charles W. Sweet,** A.T. Kearney Executive Search, Chicago

J. R. Akin, J.R. Akin & Company, Fairfield, CT
Donald Allerton, Allerton, Heneghan & O'Neill, Chicago
Lynn Tendler Bignell, Gilbert Tweed Associates, Inc., New York
Gerald J. Bump, D.E. Foster & Partners, Atlanta
John H. Callen, Jr., Ward Howell International, Inc., New York
Peter D. Crist, Russell Reynolds Associates, Inc., Chicago
John T. Gardner, Heidrick & Struggles, Inc., Chicago
Ronald G. Goerss, Ronald Goerss & Associates, San Francisco
Trina D. Gordon, Boyden, Chicago
Richard L. Hertan, Executive Manning Corporation, Ft. Lauderdale, FL
William A. Hertan, Executive Manning Corporation, Ft. Lauderdale, FL
Laurence Raymond Masse, Ward Howell International, Inc., Barrington, IL
Clarence E. McFeely, McFeely Wackerle Shulman, Chicago
James L. Morice, Mirtz Morice, Inc., Stamford, CT
Fred Siegel, CONEX Incorporated, New York
Charles Splaine, Splaine & Associates, Los Gatos, CA
Jack H. Vernon, Russell Reynolds Associates, Inc., Boston

MEASURING, ANALYZING, CONTROLLING, AND PHOTOGRAPHIC INSTRUMENTS

1. **James M. Montgomery,** Houze, Shourds & Montgomery, Inc., Long Beach, CA
2. **Mary Shourds,** Houze, Shourds & Montgomery, Inc., Long Beach, CA
3. **Richard J. Nadzam,** Nadzam, Lusk & Associates, Inc., Santa Clara, CA
4. **Theodore E. Lusk,** Nadzam, Lusk & Associates, Inc., Santa Clara, CA
5. **George W. Henn, Jr.,** G.W. Henn & Company, Columbus, Ohio
6. **Richard C. Slayton,** Slayton International, Inc., Chicago
7. **Jack H. Vernon,** Russell Reynolds Associates, Inc., Boston
8. **Helga Long,** H.M. Long International, Ltd., New York
9. **Lynn Tendler Bignell,** Gilbert Tweed Associates, Inc., New York
10. **Peter Dromeshauser,** Dromeshauser Associates, Wellesley, MA

Robert M. Callan, Callan Associates, Ltd., Oak Brook, IL
William C. Houze, William C. Houze & Company, La Quinta, CA

William M. Humphreys, Robison Humphreys & Associates, Inc., Etobicoke, ON
James L. Morice, Mirtz Morice, Inc., Stamford, CT
George W. Ott, Ott & Hansen, Inc., Pasadena, CA
Nick J. Pierce, Paul Ray Berndtson, Inc., Chicago
Daniel M. Shepherd, Shepherd Bueschel & Provus, Inc., Chicago
Robert H. Staub, Staub, Warmbold & Associates, New York
Michael A. Tappan, Ward Howell International, Inc., New York
John A. Travis, Travis & Company, Inc., Sudbury, MA
Dale Winston, Battalia Winston International, New York

MINING

1. **David L. Powell, Sr.,** David Powell, Inc., Woodside, CA
2. **John T. Gardner,** Heidrick & Struggles, Inc., Chicago
3. **Gerald J. Bump,** D.E. Foster & Partners, Atlanta
4. **Robert D. Spriggs,** Spriggs & Company, Inc., Glenview, IL
5. **O. William Battalia,** Battalia Winston International, New York
6. **Sidney Humphreys,** Korn/Ferry International, Toronto, ON

OFFICE MACHINERY AND COMPUTERS

1. **Gerard R. Roche,** Heidrick & Struggles, Inc., New York
2. **Leon A. Farley,** Leon A. Farley Associates, San Francisco
3. **Thomas J. Neff,** SpencerStuart, New York
4. **James M. Montgomery,** Houze, Shourds & Montgomery, Inc., Long Beach, CA
5. **Robert L. Smith,** Smith & Sawyer, Inc., New York
6. **Jonathan E. McBride,** McBride Associates, Inc., Washington, DC
7. **Richard K. Ives,** Wilkinson & Ives, San Francisco
8. **Richard Kinser,** Richard Kinser & Associates, New York
9. **John T. Thompson,** Heidrick & Struggles, Inc., Menlo Park, CA
10. **Robert W. Dingman,** Robert W. Dingman Company, Inc., Westlake Village, CA

Bruce M. Bastoky, January Management Group, Inc., Columbus, OH
David A. Bueschel, Shepherd Bueschel & Provus, Inc., Chicago
Jeff E. Christian, Christian & Timbers, Cleveland
O. D. Cruse, SpencerStuart, Dallas
Paul M. DiMarchi, DiMarchi Partners, Denver
John R. Ferneborg, Ferneborg & Associates, Inc., Redwood City, CA
Jonathan S. Holman, The Holman Group, Inc., San Francisco
Charles W. Kepler, Russell Reynolds Associates, Inc., Chicago
R. Paul Kors, Kors Montgomery International, Houston
Theodore E. Lusk, Nadzam, Lusk & Associates, Inc., Santa Clara, CA
James P. Masciarelli, Fenwick Partners, Lexington, MA
Richard J. Nadzam, Nadzam, Lusk & Associates, Inc., Santa Clara, CA
Charles A. Polachi, Jr., Fenwick Partners, Lexington, MA
P. Anthony Price, Russell Reynolds Associates, Inc., San Francisco

Barbara L. Provus, Shepherd Bueschel & Provus, Inc., Chicago
Patricia L. Sawyer, Smith & Sawyer, Inc., New York
Peter R. Schmidt, Boyden, Morristown, NJ
Mel Shulman, McFeely Wackerle Shulman, San Francisco
J. Gerald Simmons, Handy HRM Corporation, New York
Charles Splaine, Splaine & Associates, Los Gatos, CA
Stephen R. Strain, SpencerStuart, Menlo Park, CA

PACKAGING

1. **Michael D. Boxberger,** Korn/Ferry International, Chicago
2. **Carl W. Menk,** Canny, Bowen Inc., New York
3. **Richard Cronin,** Hodge-Cronin & Associates, Inc., Rosemont, IL
4. **David Hoffmann,** DHR International, Chicago
5. **Harold E. Johnson,** Norman Broadbent International, Inc., New York
6. **Robert M. Callan,** Callan Associates, Ltd., Oak Brook, IL
7. **George A. Rossi,** Heidrick & Struggles, Inc., Boston
8. **Henry G. Higdon,** Higdon Associates, Inc., New York
9. **P. John Mirtz,** Mirtz Morice, Inc., Stamford, CT
10. **David R. Peasback,** Canny, Bowen Inc., New York

Donald Allerton, Allerton Heneghan & O'Neill, Chicago
Ronald Dukes, Heidrick & Struggles, Inc., Chicago
Kai Lindholst, Egon Zehnder International, Inc., Chicago
William T. Mangum, Thomas Mangum Company, Pasadena, CA
Rene Plessner, Rene Plessner Associates, New York
Steven A. Seiden, Seiden Associates, Inc., New York
Andrew Sherwood, The Goodrich & Sherwood Company, New York
William K. Sur, Canny, Bowen Inc., New York
William R. Wilkinson, Wilkinson & Ives, San Francisco

PAPER AND ALLIED PRODUCTS

1. **John F. Johnson,** Lamalie Amrop International, Cleveland
2. **Putney Westerfield,** Boyden, San Francisco
3. **Helga Long,** H.M. Long International, Ltd., New York
4. **Thomas C. Zay, Sr.,** Boyden/Zay & Company, Atlanta
5. **Robert D. Spriggs,** Spriggs & Company, Inc., Glenview, IL
6. **Thomas J. Neff,** SpencerStuart, New York
7. **Stanley C. Johnson,** Johnson & Company, Wilton, CT
8. **William K. Sur,** Canny, Bowen Inc., New York
9. **Donald Allerton,** Allerton Heneghan & O'Neill, Chicago
10. **Richard L. Hertan,** Executive Manning Corporation, Ft. Lauderdale, FL

Gary R. Barton, Barton Raben, Inc., Houston
O. William Battalia, Battalia Winston International, New York
Otis H. Bowden II, Bowden & Company, Inc., Cleveland
Gerald J. Bump, D.E. Foster & Partners, Atlanta
James H. Cornehlsen, Heidrick & Struggles, Inc., New York

Michael S. Dunford, Korn/Ferry International, Chicago
Richard M. Ferry, Korn/Ferry International, Los Angeles
Peter G. Grimm, Nordeman Grimm, Inc., New York
David O. Harbert, Sweeney Harbert & Mummert, Inc., Tampa, FL
George Henn, Jr., G.W. Henn & Company, Columbus, OH
William R. Hertan, Executive Manning Corp., Fort Lauderdale
Edward R. Howe, Jr., Howe, Lawlor & Associates, Radnor, PA
Charles W. Kepler, Russell Reynolds Associates, Inc., Chicago
Richard M. McFarland, Brissenden, McFarland, Wagoner & Fuccella, Inc., Stamford, CT
P. John Mirtz, Mirtz Morice, Inc., Stamford, CT
David R. Peasback, Canny, Bowen Inc., New York
Steven Grant Pezim, The Bedford Consulting Group, Inc., Toronto, ON
Charles C. Ratigan, Heidrick & Struggles, Inc., Chicago
Paul R. Ray, Sr., Paul Ray Berndtson, Fort Worth
Steven A. Seiden, Seiden Associates, Inc., New York

PERFUME, COSMETICS, AND TOILET GOODS

1. **William E. Gould,** Gould & McCoy, Inc., New York
2. **Helga Long,** H.M. Long International, Ltd., New York
3. **Skott B. Burkland,** Skott/Edwards Consultants, Rutherford, NJ
4. **J. Alvin Wakefield,** Wakefield Talabisco International, Pittsford, VT
5. **P. John Mirtz,** Mirtz Morice, Inc., Stamford, CT
6. **Stanley C. Johnson,** Johnson & Company, Wilton, CT
7. **William K. Sur,** Canny, Bowen Inc., New York
8. **James J. Drury III,** SpencerStuart, Chicago
9. **William H. Willis, Jr.,** William Willis Worldwide Inc., Greenwich, CT
10. **Harold E. Johnson,** Norman Broadbent International, Inc., New York

Jacques P. Andre, Paul Ray Berndtson, Inc., New York
Martin H. Bauman, Martin H. Bauman Associates, New York
W. Michael Danforth, Hyde Danforth & Company, Dallas
David G. Hansen, Ott & Hansen, Inc., Pasadena, CA
Theodore N. Jadick, Heidrick & Struggles, Inc., New York
Richard E. Linde, The Ogdon Partnership, New York
Kai Lindholst, Egon Zehnder International, Inc., Chicago
Horacio J. McCoy, Korn/Ferry International, Mexico City, MX
Thomas H. Ogdon, The Ogdon Partnership, New York
Manuel Papayanopulos, Korn/Ferry International, Mexico City, MX
Rene Plessner, Rene Plessner Associates, New York
John Plummer, Plummer & Associates, Inc., Stamford, CT
Paul R. Ray, Jr., Paul Ray Berndtson, Fort Worth
Andrew Sherwood, The Goodrich & Sherwood Company, New York
J. Gerald Simmons, Handy HRM Corporation, New York
Robert H. Staub, Staub, Warmbold & Associates, New York
Gilbert R. Stenholm, Jr., SpencerStuart, Chicago
John A. Travis, Travis & Company, Inc., Sudbury, MA

PHARMACEUTICAL/MEDICAL PRODUCTS

1. **Thomas J. Neff,** SpencerStuart, New York
2. **Frederick W. Wackerle,** McFeely Wackerle Shulman, Chicago
3. **William E. Gould,** Gould & McCoy, Inc., New York
4. **Roger M. Kenny,** Kenny, Kindler, Hunt & Howe/Boardroom Consultants, New York
5. **Robert W. Dingman,** Robert W. Dingman Company, Inc., Westlake Village, CA
6. **E. Pendleton James,** Pendleton James & Associates, Inc., New York
7. **Jonathan E. McBride,** McBride Associates, Inc., Washington, DC
8. **Paul R. Ray, Jr.,** Paul Ray Berndtson, Fort Worth,
9. **Skott B. Burkland,** Skott/Edwards Consultants, Rutherford, NJ
10. **Putney Westerfield,** Boyden, San Francisco

Donald Allerton, Allerton Heneghan & O'Neill, Chicago
Lynn Tendler Bignell, Gilbert Tweed Associates, Inc., New York
David A. Bueschel, Shepherd Bueschel & Provus, Inc., Chicago
David H. Charlson, Chestnut Hill Partners, Ltd., Deerfield, IL
Ronald G. Goerss, Ronald Goerss & Associates, San Francisco
Peter G. Grimm, Nordeman Grimm, Inc., New York
John Hawkins, Russell Reynolds Associates, Inc., Washington, DC
Helga Long, H.M. Long International, Ltd., New York
Neal L. Maslan, Ward Howell International, Inc., Encino, CA
Clarence E. McFeely, McFeely Wackerle Shulman, Chicago
P. John Mirtz, Mirtz Morice, Inc., Stamford, CT
Frank Palma, Goodrich & Sherwood, Parsippany, NJ
P. Anthony Price, Russell Reynolds Associates, Inc., San Francisco
Barbara L. Provus, Shepherd Bueschel & Provus, Inc., Chicago
Conrad E. Prusak, Ethos Consulting Inc., San Francisco
William K. Sur, Canny, Bowen Inc., New York
A. Robert Taylor, A.T. Kearney Executive Search, Miami
John A. Travis, Travis & Company, Inc., Sudbury, MA
Gail H. Vergara, SpencerStuart, Chicago
Judith M. von Seldeneck, The Diversified Search Companies, Inc., Philadelphia

PRIMARY METAL INDUSTRIES

1. **John F. Johnson,** Lamalie Amrop International, Cleveland
2. **Richard C. Slayton,** Slayton International, Inc., Chicago
3. **Michael D. Boxberger,** Korn/Ferry International, Chicago
4. **David O. Harbert,** Sweeney Harbert & Mummert, Inc., Tampa, FL
5. **Trina D. Gordon,** Boyden, Chicago
6. **William R. Wilkinson,** Wilkinson & Ives, San Francisco
7. **Dale Winston,** Battalia Winston International, New York
8. **Norman F. Mitchell,** A.T. Kearney, Inc., Atlanta
9. **Ronald Dukes,** Heidrick & Struggles, Inc., Chicago
10. **Richard A. McCallister,** Boyden, Chicago

O. D. Cruse, SpencerStuart, Dallas
Michael S. Dunford, Korn/Ferry International, Chicago
George Henn, Jr., G.W. Henn & Company, Columbus, OH
William A. Hertan, Executive Manning Corp., Fort Lauderdale
David L. Witte, Ward Howell International, Inc., Houston

PUBLISHING AND PRINTING

1. **John Lucht,** The John Lucht Consultancy Inc., New York
2. **Putney Westerfield,** Boyden, San Francisco
3. **Daniel M. Shepherd,** Shepherd Bueschel & Provus, Inc., Chicago
4. **Roger M. Kenny,** Kenny, Kindler, Hunt & Howe/Boardroom Consultants, New York
5. **Jay Gaines,** Jay Gaines & Company, Inc., New York
6. **Robert L. Heidrick,** The Heidrick Partners, Inc., Chicago
7. **Ralph Dieckmann,** Dieckmann & Associates, Ltd., Chicago
8. **Joseph E. Onstott,** The Onstott Group, Inc., Wellesley, MA
9. **Thomas C. Zay, Sr.,** Boyden/Zay & Company, Atlanta
10. **Robert D. Spriggs,** Spriggs & Company, Inc., Glenview, IL

John R. Berry II, Nordeman Grimm, Inc., Chicago
Michael D. Boxberger, Korn/Ferry International, Chicago
David E. Chambers, David Chambers & Associates, Inc., Greenwich, CT
James H. Cornehlsen, Heidrick & Struggles, Inc., New York
Richard Cronin, Hodge-Cronin & Associates, Inc., Rosemont, IL
Peter Dromeshauser, Dromeshauser Associates, Wellesley, MA
George Enns, George Enns Partners Inc., Toronto, ON
Michael J. Hoevel, Poirier, Hoevel & Company, Los Angeles
William M. Humphreys, Robison Humphreys & Associates, Inc., Etobicoke, ON
Harold E. Johnson, Norman Broadbent International, Inc., New York
Richard E. Linde, The Ogdon Partnership, New York
Richard A. McCallister, Boyden, Chicago
Barbara Nelson, Herman Smith Executive Initiatives, Toronto, ON
Thomas H. Ogdon, The Ogdon Partnership, New York
David R. Peasback, Canny, Bowen Inc., New York
Steven Grant Pezim, The Bedford Consulting Group, Inc., Toronto, ON
Nick J. Pierce, Paul Ray Berndtson, Inc., Chicago
Rene Plessner, Rene Plessner Associates, New York
Charles C. Ratigan, Heidrick & Struggles, Inc., Chicago
Mary T. Wheeler, Lamalie Amrop International, New York

RADIO AND TELEVISION BROADCASTING

1. **Gerard R. Roche,** Heidrick & Struggles, Inc., New York
2. **John Lucht,** The John Lucht Consultancy Inc., New York
3. **Susan K. Bishop,** Bishop Partners, Ltd., New York
4. **Nancy R. Roblin,** Paul-Tittle Associates, McLean, VA

   5. **Gary Knisely,** Johnson Smith & Knisely Accord, New York
   6. **William R. Wilkinson,** Wilkinson & Ives, San Francisco
   7. **James H. Cornehlsen,** Heidrick & Struggles, Inc., New York
   8. **Robert E. Beaudine,** Eastman & Beaudine, Inc., Dallas
   9. **Thomas H. Ogdon,** The Ogdon Partnership, New York
  10. **Roland L. Poirier,** Poirier, Hoevel & Co., Los Angeles

   John R. Berry II, Nordeman Grimm, Inc., Chicago
   Carl W. Menk, Canny, Bowen Inc., New York
   Ken Rich, Paul Ray Berndtson, Inc., New York
   Carlton W. Thompson, SpencerStuart, Stamford, CT
   Frederick W. Wackerle, McFeely Wackerle Shulman, Chicago
   William H. Willis, Jr., William Willis Worldwide Inc., Greenwich, CT

REAL ESTATE

   1. **William E. Gould,** Gould & McCoy, Inc., New York
   2. **Windle B. Priem,** Korn/Ferry International, New York
   3. **David M. deWilde,** Chartwell Partners International, San Francisco
   4. **Jacques C. Nordeman,** Nordeman Grimm, Inc., New York
   5. **Dayton Ogden,** SpencerStuart, Stamford, CT
   6. **Leon A. Farley,** Leon A. Farley Associates, San Francisco
   7. **Richard M. Ferry,** Korn/Ferry International, Los Angeles
   8. **W. Jerry Hyde,** Hyde Danforth & Company, Dallas
   9. **David W. Palmlund,** Lamalie Amrop International, Dallas
  10. **Donald B. Clark,** Paul Ray Berndtson, Inc., Chicago

   Robert E. Beaudine, Eastman & Beaudine, Inc., Dallas
   Anthony B. Cashen, Lamalie Amrop International, New York
   W. Michael Danforth, Hyde Danforth & Company, Dallas
   John R. Ferneborg, Ferneborg & Associates, Inc., Redwood City, CA
   Sanford I. Gadient, Huntress Real Estate Executive Search, Kansas City, MO
   Donald A. Heneghan, Allerton Heneghan & O'Neill, Chicago
   Sidney Humphreys, Korn/Ferry International, Toronto, ON
   John Isaacson, Isaacson, Miller, Boston
   Richard F. Larsen, Larsen, Zilliacus and Associates, Inc., Los Angeles
   David R. Lauderback, A.T. Kearney Executive Search, Cleveland
   Charles M. Meng, Meng, Finseth & Associates, Torrance, CA
   Edwin S. Mruk, Mruk & Partners, New York
   George W. Ott, Ott & Hansen, Inc., Pasadena, CA
   Ken Rich, Paul Ray Berndtson, Inc., New York
   John H. Robison, Robison & McAulay, Charlotte, NC
   George A. Rossi, Heidrick & Struggles, Inc., Boston
   J. Robert Swidler, Egon Zehnder International, Inc., Montreal
   Lee Van Leeuwen, Korn/Ferry International, Los Angeles

RETAIL

1. **Herbert Mines,** Herbert Mines Associates, Inc., New York
2. **David A. Bueschel,** Shepherd Bueschel & Provus, Inc., Chicago
3. **Barbara L. Provus,** Shepherd Bueschel & Provus, Inc., Chicago
4. **Ronald G. Goerss,** Ronald Goerss & Associates, San Francisco
5. **Richard M. Ferry,** Korn/Ferry International, Los Angeles
6. **David W. Palmlund,** Lamalie Amrop International, Dallas
7. **Peter G. Grimm,** Nordeman Grimm, Inc., New York
8. **Robert L. Smith,** Smith & Sawyer, Inc., New York
9. **E. Pendleton James,** Pendleton James & Associates, Inc., New York
10. **Conrad E. Prusak,** Ethos Consulting Inc., San Francisco

Bruce M. Bastoky, January Management Group, Inc., Columbus, OH
Joseph J. Carideo, Thorndike Deland Associates, New York
Paul M. DiMarchi, DiMarchi Partners, Denver
John R. Ferneborg, Ferneborg & Associates, Inc., Redwood City, CA
Joseph E. Griesedieck, SpencerStuart, San Francisco
David O. Harbert, Sweeney Harbert & Mummert, Inc., Tampa, FL
A. D. Hart, Jr., Russell Reynolds Associates, Inc., New York
Stanley C. Johnson, Johnson & Company, Wilton, CT
Laurence Raymond Masse, Ward Howell International, Inc., Barrington, IL
David B. Mazza, Mazza & Riley, Inc., Wellesley Hills, MA
Richard A. McCallister, Boyden, Chicago
John T. Mestepey, A.T. Kearney Executive Search, Miami
Robert Nesbit, Korn/Ferry International, New York
John Plummer, Plummer & Associates, Inc., Stamford, CT
George A. Rossi, Heidrick & Struggles, Boston
Patricia L. Sawyer, Smith & Sawyer, Inc., New York
Daniel M. Shepherd, Shepherd Bueschel & Provus, Inc., Chicago
Mel Shulman, McFeely Wackerle Shulman, San Francisco
Gilbert R. Stenholm, Jr., SpencerStuart, Chicago
J. Robert Swidler, Egon Zehnder International, Inc., Montreal

RUBBER AND PLASTIC PRODUCTS

1. **John F. Johnson,** Lamalie Amrop International, Cleveland
2. **Richard C. Slayton,** Slayton International, Inc., Chicago
3. **William A. Hertan,** Executive Manning Corporation, Fort Lauderdale
4. **Jerry H. Baker,** Schuyler, Frye & Baker, Inc., Atlanta
5. **Peter R. Schmidt,** Boyden, Morristown, NJ
6. **Richard J. Cronin,** Hodge-Cronin & Associates, Inc., Rosemont, IL
7. **David L. Witte,** Ward Howell International, Inc., Houston
8. **Richard L. Hertan,** Executive Manning Corporation, Fort Lauderdale
9. **Otis H. Bowden II,** Bowden & Company, Inc., Cleveland
10. **Robert M. Callan,** Callan Associates, Ltd., Oak Brook, IL

David E. Chambers, David Chambers & Associates, Inc., Greenwich, CT
Ronald Dukes, Heidrick & Struggles, Inc., Chicago

David G. Hansen, Ott & Hansen, Inc., Pasadena, CA
George Henn, Jr., G.W. Henn & Company, Columbus, OH
Mike Jacobs, Thorne, Brieger Associates, Inc., New York
David R. Lauderback, A.T. Kearney Executive Search, Cleveland
Richard M. McFarland, Brissenden, McFarland, et al, Bridgewater, NJ
George W. Ott, Ott & Hansen, Inc., Pasadena, CA
Steven G. Pezim, The Bedford Consulting Group, Inc., Toronto
Charles C. Ratigan, Heidrick & Struggles, Inc., Chicago
Andrew Sherwood, The Goodrich & Sherwood Company, New York
Gilbert R. Stenholm, Jr., SpencerStuart, Chicago

SECURITY AND COMMODITY BROKERS, DEALERS, AND EXCHANGES

1. **Thomas J. Neff,** SpencerStuart, Inc., New York
2. **Windle B. Priem,** Korn/Ferry International, New York
3. **Jay Gaines,** Jay Gaines & Company, Inc., New York
4. **Mary E. Shourds,** Houze, Shourds & Montgomery, Inc., Long Beach, CA
5. **Jacques C. Nordeman,** Nordeman Grimm, Inc., New York
6. **Robert L. Smith,** Smith & Sawyer, Inc., New York
7. **Roger M. Kenny,** Kenny, Kindler, Hunt & Howe, New York
8. **Michael A. Tappan,** Ward Howell International, Inc., New York
9. **Norman D. Sanders,** Norm Sanders Associates, Hazlet, NJ
10. **Robert S. Rollo,** R. Rollo Associates, Los Angeles

Jacques P. Andre, Paul Ray Berndtson, Inc., New York
Jeffrey G. Bell, Norman Broadbent International, Inc., New York
Hobson Brown, Jr., Russell Reynolds Associates, Inc., New York
Anthony B. Cashen, Lamalie Amrop International, New York
W. Hoyt Colton, The Colton Partnership, Inc., New York
Craig J. Dudley, Conrey Paul Ray International, Mexico
Henry G. Higdon, Higdon Associates, Inc., New York
Durant A. Hunter, Pendleton James & Associates, Inc., New York
Richard K. Ives, Wilkinson & Ives, San Francisco
David S. Joys, Heidrick & Struggles, Inc., New York
Richard F. Larsen, Larsen, Zilliacus & Associates, Inc., Los Angeles
Ferdinand Nadherny, Russell Reynolds Associates, Inc., New York
Roland L. Poirier, Poirier, Hoevel & Co., Los Angeles
Ken Rich, Paul Ray Berndtson, Inc., New York
Carlos A. Rojas-Magnon, Amrop International, Mexico
Richard D. Sbarbaro, Lauer, Sbarbaro Associates, Inc., Chicago
Lambert Schuyler, Jr., Schuyler, Frye & Baker, Inc., Atlanta
J. Gerald Simmons, Handy HRM Corporation, New York
Brian M. Sullivan, Sullivan & Company, New York
Patricia L. Wilson, Leon A. Farley Associates, San Francisco

TEXTILES

1. **Herbert Mines,** Herbert Mines Associates, Inc., New York
2. **John H. Callen, Jr.,** Ward Howell International, Inc., New York

3. **John H. Robison,** Robison & McAulay, Charlotte, NC
4. **Carl W. Menk,** Canny, Bowen Inc., New York
5. **Joseph J. Carideo,** Thorndike Deland Associates, New York
6. **John Plummer,** Plummer & Associates, Inc., Stamford, CT
7. **Edwin S. Mruk,** Mruk & Partners, New York
8. **William K. Sur,** Canny, Bowen Inc., New York
9. **Rene Plessner,** Rene Plessner Associates, New York
10. **Thomas C. Zay, Sr.,** Boyden/Zay & Company, Atlanta

TOBACCO AND LIQUOR

1. **Gerard R. Roche,** Heidrick & Struggles, Inc., New York
2. **Thomas J. Neff,** SpencerStuart, New York
3. **Robert L. Heidrick,** The Heidrick Partners, Chicago
4. **James J. Drury III,** SpencerStuart, Chicago
5. **William H. Marumoto,** The Interface Group, Ltd./Boyden, Washington, DC
6. **Gilbert R. Stenholm, Jr.,** SpencerStuart, Chicago
7. **Michael A. Tappan,** Ward Howell International, Inc., New York
8. **Joseph J. Carideo,** Thorndike Deland Associates, New York
9. **Paul R. Ray, Sr.,** Paul Ray Berndtson, Inc., Fort Worth
10. **George Enns,** George Enns Partners, Inc., Toronto

TRANSPORTATION BY AIR, RAIL, TRUCK, OR WATER

1. **Gerard R. Roche,** Heidrick & Struggles, Inc., New York
2. **Robert W. Dingman,** Robert W. Dingman Co., Inc., Westlake Village, CA
3. **Thomas J. Neff,** SpencerStuart, New York
4. **Leon A. Farley,** Leon A. Farley Associates, San Francisco
5. **Roger M. Kenny,** Kenny, Kindler, Hunt & Howe, New York
6. **E. Pendleton James,** Pendleton James & Associates, Inc., New York
7. **Mary E. Shourds,** Houze, Shourds & Montgomery, Inc., Long Beach, CA
8. **Charles C. Ratigan,** Heidrick & Struggles, Inc., Chicago
9. **David M. deWilde,** Chartwell Partners International, San Francisco
10. **Martin H. Bauman,** Martin H. Bauman Associates, New York

John R. Berry II, Nordeman Grimm, Inc., Chicago
Peter D. Crist, Russell Reynolds Associates, Inc., Chicago
James J. Drury III, SpencerStuart, Chicago
Ronald G. Goerss, Ronald Goerss & Associates, San Francisco
Robert L. Heidrick, The Heidrick Partners, Inc., Chicago
Henry G. Higdon, Higdon Associates, Inc., New York
John Isaacson, Isaacson, Miller, Boston
Richard K. Ives, Wilkinson & Ives, San Francisco
William T. Mangum, Thomas Mangum Company, Pasadena, CA
David W. Palmlund, Lamalie Amrop International, Dallas
David R. Peasback, Canny, Bowen Inc., New York
Roland L. Poirier, Poirier, Hoevel & Co., Los Angeles
Norman C. Roberts, Norman Roberts & Associates, Inc., Los Angeles
John H. Robison, Robison & McAulay, Charlotte, NC

Norman D. Sanders, Norm Sanders Associates, Hazlet, NJ
Mel Shulman, McFeely Wackerle Shulman, San Francisco
Robert D. Spriggs, Spriggs & Company, Inc., Glenview, IL
Judith M. von Seldeneck, The Diversified Search Companies, Inc., Philadelphia
J. Alvin Wakefield, Wakefield Talabisco International, Pittsford, VT
William R. Wilkinson, Wilkinson & Ives, San Francisco

TRANSPORTATION EQUIPMENT

1. **John F. Johnson,** Lamalie Amrop International, Cleveland
2. **Richard C. Slayton,** Slayton International, Inc., Chicago
3. **Frederick W. Wackerle,** McFeely Wackerle Shulman, Chicago
4. **John T. Gardner,** Heidrick & Struggles, Inc., Chicago
5. **Otis H. Bowden II,** Bowden & Company, Inc., Cleveland
6. **Donald A. Heneghan,** Allerton Heneghan & O'Neill, Chicago
7. **Lawrence R. Masse,** Ward Howell International, Inc., Barrington, IL
8. **Martin H. Bauman,** Martin H. Bauman Asociates, New York
9. **David G. Hansen,** Ott & Hansen, Inc., Pasadena, CA
10. **Ronald Dukes,** Heidrick & Struggles, Inc., Chicago

Robert M. Callan, Callan Associates, Ltd., Oak Brook, IL
David E. Chambers, David Chambers & Associates, Inc., Greenwich, CT
William C. Houze, William C. Houze & Company, La Quinta, CA
David S. Joys, Heidrick & Struggles, Inc., New York
Kai Lindholst, Egon Zehnder International, Inc., Chicago
James L. Morice, Mirtz Morice Inc., Stamford, CT
David L. Witte, Ward Howell International, Inc., Houston

UNIVERSITIES/COLLEGES/SCHOOLS

1. **William J. Bowen,** Heidrick & Struggles, Inc., Chicago
2. **Ira W. Krinsky,** Korn/Ferry International, Los Angeles
3. **Gary J. Posner,** Educational Management Network, Nashville
4. **Nancy A. Martin,** Educational Management Network, Nantucket, MA
5. **Jerry H. Baker,** Schuyler, Frye & Baker, Inc., Atlanta
6. **John Lucht,** The John Lucht Consultancy, New York
7. **Thomas C. Zay, Sr.,** Boyden/Zay & Company, Atlanta
8. **John S. Lloyd,** Witt/Kieffer, Ford, Hadelman & Lloyd, Oak Brook, IL
9. **Jordan M. Hadelman,** Witt/Kieffer, Ford, Hadelman & Lloyd, Oak Brook, IL
10. **John Isaacson,** Isaacson, Miller, Boston

W. Michael Danforth, Hyde Danforth & Company, Dallas
Claire W. Gargalli, The Diversified Search Companies, Inc., Philadelphia
William C. Houze, William C. Houze & Company, La Quinta, CA
Lawrence R. Masse, Ward Howell International, Inc., Barrington, IL
Charles M. Meng, Meng, Finseth & Associates, Torrance, CA

Norman C. Roberts, Norman Roberts & Associates, Inc., Los Angeles
John H. Robison, Robison & McAulay, Charlotte, NC
George A. Rossi, Heidrick & Struggles, Inc., Boston
Richard D. Sbarbaro, Lauer, Sbarbaro Associates, Inc., Chicago
J. Robert Swidler, Egon Zehnder International, Inc., Montreal
J. Alvin Wakefield, Wakefield Talabisco International, Pittsford, VT
Mary T. Wheeler, Lamalie Amrop International, New York
Daniel C. Wier, Daniel Wier & Associates, Los Angeles

VENTURE CAPITAL

1. **Theodore B. Martin, Jr.,** Nordeman Grimm, Inc., Chicago
2. **Skott B. Burkland,** Skott/Edwards Consultants, Rutherford, NJ
3. **William E. Tholke,** Canny, Bowen Inc., New York
4. **Joseph E. Onstott,** The Onstott Group, Inc., Wellesley, MA
5. **Herbert Mines,** Herbert Mines Associates, Inc., New York
6. **William R. Wilkinson,** Wilkinson & Ives, San Francisco
7. **Martin H. Bauman,** Martin H. Bauman Associates, New York
8. **Jonathan S. Holman,** The Holman Group, Inc., San Francisco
9. **Neal L. Maslan,** Ward Howell International, Inc., Encino, CA
10. **David B. Mazza,** Mazza & Riley, Inc., Wellesley Hills, MA

Joseph J. Carideo, Thorndike Deland Associates, New York
Donald B. Clark, Paul Ray Berndtson, Inc., Chicago
W. Michael Danforth, Hyde Danforth & Company, Dallas
David M. deWilde, Chartwell Partners International, San Francisco
Paul M. DiMarchi, DeMarchi Partners, Denver
James J. Drury III, SpencerStuart, Chicago
David O. Harbert, Sweeney Harbert & Mummert, Inc., Tampa, FL
John Hawkins, Russell Reynolds Associates, Inc., Washington, DC
Durant A. Hunter, Pendleton James & Associates, Inc. Boston
Richard K. Ives, Wilkinson & Ives, San Francisco
James F. Keresey, James Keresey Associates, Inc., New York
Charles A. Polachi, Jr., Fenwick Partners, Lexington, MA
David L. Powell, Sr., David Powell, Inc., Woodside, CA
Conrad E. Prusak, Ethos Consulting Inc., San Francisco
Michael S. Reeder, Lamalie Amrop International, Atlanta
Ken Rich, Paul Ray Berndtson, Inc., New York
Patricia L. Sawyer, Smith & Sawyer, Inc., New York
Robert L. Smith, Smith & Sawyer, Inc., New York
Robert D. Spriggs, Spriggs & Company, Inc., Glenview, IL
Charles W. Sweet, A.T. Kearney Executive Search, Chicago

WHOLESALE TRADE

1. **Herbert Mines,** Herbert Mines Associates, Inc., New York
2. **John R. Ferneborg,** Ferneborg & Associates, Inc., Redwood City, CA
3. **David O. Harbert,** Sweeney Harbert & Mummert, Inc., Tampa, FL
4. **Joseph J. Carideo,** Thorndike Deland Associates, New York

5. **Richard A. McAllister,** Boyden, Chicago
6. **Martin H. Bauman,** Martin H. Bauman Associates, New York
7. **John T. Mestepey,** A.T. Kearney Executive Search, Miami
8. **Stanley C. Johnson,** Johnson & Company, Wilton, CT
9. **John Plummer,** Plummer & Associates, Inc., Stamford, CT
10. **Lambert Schuyler, Jr.,** Schuyler, Frye & Baker, Inc., Atlanta

John R. Berry II, Nordeman Grimm, Inc., Chicago
Craig J. Dudley, Conrey Paul Ray International, Mexico
Michael S. Dunford, Korn/Ferry International, Chicago
Richard E. Linde, The Ogdon Partnership, New York
Steven G. Pezim, The Bedford Consulting Group, Inc., Toronto
Norman D. Sanders, Norm Sanders Associates, Hazlet, NJ

PART III

AMERICA'S "ACADEMY COMPANIES" AND THE TOP 250 FUTURE CEOS

6

AMERICA'S "ACADEMY COMPANIES"

If the recent experience of IBM is any indication of the correlation between business performance and the perception of managerial talent, the significant fall of IBM in the rankings of America's Top 50 Academy Companies would indicate that there is a strong parallel indeed. In 1992, the first year we surveyed America's top recruiters regarding the premier corporate developers of management talent, IBM stood a very healthy number 3 behind only PepsiCo and General Electric. Two years later, with no thanks to some multibillion-dollar losses along the way, Big Blue resides as a blanched number 13.

General Electric continues to stand apart as North America's finest developer of senior-management talent, but PepsiCo is putting on a rush. At least that's what the top recruiters surveyed for this book have to say. And who could argue that they are not the best possible determiners? From the very inception of the executive search business seventy years ago, recruiters have made their livings and built their reputations on the premise that they can not only assess talent when they see it but know precisely which organizations they must probe to find it. Industry by industry, function by function, year in and year out, recruiters have evolved their own empirically derived map to the pools of talent most likely to contain their perfect placements.

Of course, this doesn't mean that the recruiter is always successful in finding his or her placement in the most likely academy companies, but a recruiter who does not probe such companies is like a trout fisherman casting a line in the Everglades. That isn't to say there might not be a trout in the swamp, but if there is, there are certainly some significant questions—like how the poor creature got there in the first place, who taught it what it knows, and where is it going in the mangroves.

Through their years of searching, the best executive recruiters have discovered those companies particularly worth investigating for candidates with especially good training and experience in their specific areas of interest. Many times, too, an academy company's "alumni" are as desirable to a new employer as those still employed at the mother company. Therefore, for any professional—and every recent graduate who aspires to career progress and leadership—it is especially savvy to be currently employed by, or to have worked with in the past, an academy company. They are as much career makers as the recruiters themselves. Not only are these companies the standouts in their respective industries or functions in *developing* talent, but as a consequence they are the ones *most heavily hunted by the headhunters.*

In the pages that follow, America's academy companies are identified and ranked for the second time. (For the process by which they were selected, see pages 12–13.) The Top 50 are ranked on the basis of the total actual points they achieved from the 418 executive recruiters who offered their opinions. Following this are the rankings of the leading companies in twenty prominent industries and nine major business functions. There are ten academy companies listed in each category, except in those instances where fewer were found to be relatively far ahead of all others in that category. In the very consequential functional area of General Management, twenty companies are ranked.

Industries and functions represented in the rankings of recruiters in the previous chapter, but not included in the academy company section, have been omitted either because no single company or group of companies stood out or because the number of nominations received in that industry or function was considered statistically insignificant.

AMERICA'S TOP 50 ACADEMY COMPANIES

1994 Ranking	1992 Ranking	Company/Headquarters	Description of Business	Nomination Points
1	1	**General Electric Company** Fairfield, CT	Diversified manufacturer, high-tech products; services	739
2	3	**PepsiCo, Inc.** Purchase, NY	Consumer beverages, snacks, and restaurants	410
3	4	**The Procter & Gamble Co.** Cincinnati, OH	Consumer health, beauty aids, food, and household products	291
4	9	**Hewlett-Packard Company** Palo Alto, CA	Electronic equipment, office and factory automation; software	225
5	25	**Motorola, Inc.** Schaumburg, IL	Semiconductors, mobile radios, electronic hardware and systems	146
6	7	**Merck & Company, Inc.** Rahway, NJ	Drugs, animal health products, and specialty chemicals	145
7	8	**Kraft/General Foods** Glenview, IL	Prepared consumer food products	143
8	6	**Ford Motor Company** Dearborn, MI	Manufacturer of automobiles, trucks, and parts; services	139
9	5	**Citibank** New York, NY	Commercial banking services	122
10	15	**Johnson & Johnson** New Brunswick, NJ	Consumer health products, diagnostic and medical equipment	93
11	27	**The Goldman Sachs Group, LP** New York, NY	Investment banking and related financial services	89
12	13	**McKinsey & Co.** New York, NY	General management consulting	86
13	2	**International Business Machines** Armonk, NY	Computer hardware and software manufacturer and marketer	83
14	17	**General Mills, Inc.** Minneapolis, MN	Prepared consumer food products and specialty restaurants	82
15	19	**American Telephone & Telegraph** New York, NY	Telecommunications worldwide; computers	80
16	10	**Xerox Corporation** Stamford, CT	Copiers and duplicating equipment	78
17	43	**Minnesota Mining & Manufacturing** St. Paul, MN	Industrial, consumer, electronic imaging, and life science products	77
18	12	**Rockwell International Corp.** El Segundo, CA	Defense electronics, industrial automation, telecommunications	74

AMERICA'S TOP 50 ACADEMY COMPANIES (Cont.)

1994 Ranking	1992 Ranking	Company/Headquarters	Description of Business	Nomination Points
19	11	**Emerson Electric Co.** St. Louis, MO	Manufacturers of electrical and electronic products	72
20	14	**Bankers Trust Co.** New York, NY	Commercial banking	71
21	—	**Rubbermaid, Inc.** Wooster, OH	Manufacturer of rubber and plastic products	60
22	—	**MCI Communications Corp.** Washington, DC	Domestic and international communications services	59
23	24	**Morgan Stanley Group Inc.** New York, NY	Investment banking, securities trading worldwide	59
24	28	**Arthur Andersen & Co.** Chicago, IL	Public accounting and related business consulting services	57
25	27	**Microsoft Corporation** Redmond, WA	Developer of PC systems and application software	54
26	—	**Sara Lee Corporation** Chicago, IL	Consumer packaged goods and food service distribution	53
27	48	**Philip Morris U.S.A.** New York, NY	Tobacco products manufacturing and marketing	52
28	29	**American Express Company** New York, NY	Diversified financial services; direct marketing	51
29	—	**Quaker Oats** Chicago, IL	Consumer and pet food products	51
30	16	**Baxter International Inc.** Deerfield, IL	Manufacturer and distributor of health care products and services	49
31	28	**The Coca-Cola Company** Atlanta, GA	Consumer beverages	49
32	34	**The Dow Chemical Company** Midland, MI	Chemicals and plastics worldwide; consumer health care products	49
33	—	**Aetna Life & Casualty** Hartford, CT	Insurance and financial services	48
34	31	**The Boeing Company** Seattle, WA	Commercial and military aircraft and aerospace manufacturer	48
35	—	**Banc One Corp.** Columbus, OH	National and state trust companies, consumer financial services	46
36	26	**American Airlines, Inc.** Fort Worth, TX	Air transportation and related services	45
37	—	**Dayton Hudson** Minneapolis, MN	Department and discount stores	45

AMERICA'S TOP 50 ACADEMY COMPANIES (Cont.)

1994 Ranking	1992 Ranking	Company/Headquarters	Description of Business	Nomination Points
38	30	**E.I. du Pont de Nemours & Company** Wilmington, DE	Chemicals, fibers, coal, natural gas, diversified business products	44
39	—	**Federal Express Corp.** Memphis, TN	Letter and package delivery, private air	44
40	22	**Bristol-Myers Squibb Company** New York, NY	Drugs, household products, implants, and nutritionals	42
41	—	**Marriott Corporation** Washington, DC	Hotels, resorts, restaurants, food service	42
42	—	**Northern Telecom Ltd.** Mississauga, ON	Suppliers of telecommunications systems and information management systems	42
43	46	**The May Department Stores Co.** St. Louis, MO	Operator of conventional department stores; discount shoes	40
44	23	**Morgan Guaranty Trust Co., NY** New York, NY	Commercial banking	40
45	21	**Monsanto Company** St. Louis, MO	Industrial and agricultural chemicals, drugs, sweeteners	39
46	—	**U.S. West, Inc.** Englewood, CO	Telecommunications and other communication services, reference publications	37
47	37	**Wells Fargo Bank** San Francisco, CA	Commercial banking	37
48	50	**CIGNA Corporation** Philadelphia, PA	Property and casualty insurance and diversified financial services	35
49	—	**TRW Inc.** Cleveland, OH	Manufacturer of high-tech products and services for electronics, space, automotive, and energy markets	35
50	45	**Chubb & Son, Inc.** Warren, NJ	Property and casualty insurer	34

ACADEMY COMPANIES' INDUSTRY RANKINGS

AEROSPACE

1. **Rockwell International Corp.,** El Segundo, CA
2. **The Boeing Company,** Seattle, WA
3. **Martin Marietta Corporation,** Bethesda, MD
4. **Hughes Aircraft Company,** Los Angeles, CA

5. **General Electric Company,** Fairfield, CT
6. **TRW Inc.,** Cleveland, OH
7. **General Dynamics Corporation,** St. Louis, MO
8. **Textron, Inc.,** Providence, RI
9. **United Technologies Corporation,** Hartford, CT
10. **Bombardier Inc.,** Montreal, PQ

BANKING
1. **Citibank,** New York, NY
2. **Bankers Trust Co.,** New York, NY
3. **Morgan Guaranty Trust Co.,** New York, NY
4. **Banc One Corporation,** Columbus, OH
5. **Wells Fargo Bank,** San Francisco, CA
6. **Chase Manhattan Bank,** New York, NY
7. **Bank of America,** San Francisco, CA
8. **Nationsbank,** Charlotte, NC
9. **Chemical Bank,** New York, NY
10. **Bank of Montreal,** Montreal, PQ

CHEMICAL AND ALLIED PRODUCTS
1. **The Dow Chemical Company,** Midland, MI
2. **Monsanto Company,** St. Louis, MO
3. **E.I. du Pont de Nemours & Company,** Wilmington, DE
4. **Minnesota Mining & Manufacturing,** St. Paul, MN
5. **Hoechst-Celanese,** Somerville, NJ
6. **General Electric Plastics Group,** Pittsfield, MA
7. **Union Carbide Corporation,** Danbury, CT
8. **B.F. Goodrich Co.,** Akron, OH
9. **Eastman Chemical Products Inc.,** Kingsport, TN
10. **NALCO Chemical Co.,** Naperville, IL

COMMUNICATIONS AND TELECOMMUNICATIONS
1. **American Telephone & Telegraph,** New York, NY
2. **MCI Communications Corp.,** Washington, DC
3. **Motorola, Inc.,** Schaumburg, IL
4. **Federal Express Corporation,** Memphis, TN
5. **U.S. West, Inc.,** Englewood, CO
6. **GTE Corporation,** Stamford, CT
7. **Northern Telecom Inc.,** Nashville, TN
8. **Scientific-Atlanta Inc.,** Atlanta, GA
9. **McCaw Cellular Communications Inc.,** Kirkland, WA
10. **Bell Atlantic Mobile,** Bedminster, NJ

COMPUTER SOFTWARE
1. **Microsoft Corporation,** Redmond, WA
2. **Lotus Development Corporation,** Cambridge, MA
3. **Oracle Corporation,** Redwood Shore, CA
4. **International Business Machines,** Armonk, NY
5. **Sun Microsystems, Inc.,** Mountain View, CA
6. **Computer Sciences Corporation,** El Segundo, CA
7. **Apple Computer, Inc.,** Cupertino, CA
8. **WordPerfect Corporation,** Orem, UT

9. **Dun & Bradstreet Software,** Atlanta, GA
10. **NCR Corporation,** Dayton, OH

CONSULTING AND ACCOUNTING FIRMS
1. **McKinsey & Co.,** New York, NY
2. **Booz, Allen & Hamilton,** New York, NY
3. **Boston Consulting Group,** Boston, MA
4. **Arthur Andersen & Co.,** Chicago, IL
5. **Price Waterhouse & Co.,** New York, NY
6. **Ernst & Young,** New York, NY

ELECTRICAL AND ELECTRONIC MACHINERY
1. **General Electric Company,** Fairfield, CT
2. **Emerson Electric Co.,** St. Louis, MO
3. **Motorola, Inc.,** Schaumburg, IL
4. **Hewlett-Packard Company,** Palo Alto, CA
5. **International Business Machines,** Armonk, NY
6. **NCR Corporation,** Dayton, OH
7. **Rockwell International Corp.,** El Segundo, CA
8. **Xerox Corporation,** Stamford, CT
9. **Honeywell Inc.,** Minneapolis, MN
10. **ITT Corporation,** New York, NY

ENERGY
1. **Shell Oil Company,** Houston, TX
2. **Arco Alaska Inc.,** Anchorage, AK
3. **Enron Corp.,** Houston, TX
4. **Exxon Company, U.S.A.,** Houston, TX
5. **Mobil Oil Corporation,** Fairfax, VA
6. **Duke Power Company,** Charlotte, NC
7. **Carolina Power & Light Company,** Raleigh, NC
8. **Amoco Corporation,** Chicago, IL
9. **American Electric Power Company, Inc.,** Columbus, OH
10. **Commonwealth Edison Co.,** Chicago, IL

FOOD AND KINDRED PRODUCTS
1. **PepsiCo, Inc.,** Purchase, NY
2. **Kraft/General Foods,** Glenview, IL
3. **The Procter & Gamble Company,** Cincinnati, OH
4. **General Mills, Inc.,** Minneapolis, MN
5. **The Quaker Oats Company,** Chicago, IL
6. **The Pillsbury Company,** Minneapolis, MN
7. **Sara Lee Corporation,** Chicago, IL
8. **Kellogg Company,** Battle Creek, MI
9. **RJR Nabisco, Inc.,** New York, NY
10. **The Coca-Cola Company,** Atlanta, GA

HEALTH SERVICES/HOSPITALS
1. **Mass General Hospital,** Boston, MA
2. **Henry Ford Health Systems,** Detroit, MI
3. **Mayo Clinic,** Rochester, MN

    4. **Hospital Corporation of America,** Nashville, TN
    5. **Baxter Corporation,** Deerfield, IL
    6. **Yale–New Haven Hospital,** New Haven, CT
    7. **Blue Cross of California,** San Francisco, CA
    8. **Johns Hopkins University Hospital,** Baltimore, MD
    9. **Provenant Health Partners,** Denver, CO
  10. **Cleveland Clinic,** Cleveland, OH

HOTELS/RESORTS/CLUBS
    1. **Marriott Corporation,** Washington, DC
    2. **Four Seasons Hotels & Resorts,** Chicago, IL
    3. **Hyatt International Corporation,** Chicago, IL
    4. **Ritz-Carlton Hotel Company,** Atlanta, GA
    5. **The Walt Disney Company,** Burbank, CA
    6. **Westin Hotels & Resorts,** Seattle, WA
    7. **ITT Sheraton Corporation,** Boston, MA

INSURANCE
    1. **Aetna Life & Casualty Co.,** Hartford, CT
    2. **CIGNA Corporation,** Philadelphia, PA
    3. **Chubb & Son, Inc.,** Warren, NJ
    4. **The Prudential Insurance Co. of America,** Newark, NJ
    5. **Northwestern Mutual,** Milwaukee, WI
    6. **The Lincoln National Life Insurance Co.,** Fort Wayne, IN
    7. **United Services Automobile Association,** San Antonio, TX
    8. **The Hartford Insurance Group,** Hartford, CT
    9. **State Farm,** Bloomington, IL
  10. **Capital Holding Corp.,** Louisville, KY

INVESTMENT BANKING
    1. **The Goldman Sachs Group, LP,** New York, NY
    2. **Morgan Stanley Group, Inc.,** New York, NY
    3. **Merrill Lynch & Co., Inc.,** New York, NY
    4. **The First Boston Corporation,** New York, NY
    5. **S.G. Warburg & Co., Inc.,** New York, NY

OFFICE MACHINERY AND COMPUTERS
    1. **Hewlett-Packard Company,** Palo Alto, CA
    2. **Xerox Corporation,** Stamford, CT
    3. **International Business Machines,** Armonk, NY
    4. **Amdahl Corporation,** Sunnyvale, CA
    5. **Digital Equipment Corporation,** Maynard, MA

PAPER AND ALLIED PRODUCTS
    1. **International Paper Company,** Purchase, NY
    2. **James River Corporation,** Richmond, VA
    3. **Georgia-Pacific Corporation,** Atlanta, GA
    4. **Weyerhauser Company,** Tacoma, WA
    5. **Union Camp Corporation,** Wayne, NJ

PERFUME, COSMETICS, AND TOILET GOODS
    1. **The Procter & Gamble Company,** Cincinnati, OH
    2. **Estée Lauder Inc.,** New York, NY

3. **The Gillette Company,** Boston, MA
4. **Colgate-Palmolive Company,** New York, NY
5. **Avon Products, Inc.,** New York, NY

PHARMACEUTICAL AND MEDICAL PRODUCTS
1. **Merck & Company, Inc.,** Rahway, NJ
2. **Johnson & Johnson,** New Brunswick, NJ
3. **Abbott Laboratories,** Abbott Park, IL
4. **Pfizer, Inc.,** New York, NY
5. **Baxter International, Inc.,** Deerfield, IL
6. **Eli Lilly & Company,** Indianapolis, IN
7. **Bristol-Myers Squibb Company,** New York, NY
8. **SmithKline Beecham PLC,** Philadelphia, PA
9. **Hoffmann-LaRoche Inc.,** Nutley, NJ
10. **Ciba-Geigy Corp.,** Murray Hill, NJ

PUBLISHING AND PRINTING
1. **Time Warner Inc.,** New York, NY
2. **Simon & Schuster Inc.,** New York, NY
3. **Dow Jones & Company, Inc.,** New York, NY
4. **Knight-Ridder, Inc.,** Miami, FL
5. **R.R. Donnelly & Sons Company,** Chicago, IL

RETAIL
1. **The May Department Stores Company,** St. Louis, MO
2. **Dayton Hudson Corporation,** Minneapolis, MN
3. **Wal-Mart Stores, Inc.,** Bentonville, AR
4. **The Limited, Inc.,** Columbus, OH
5. **Federated Department Stores,** Cincinnati, OH
6. **The Gap, Inc.,** San Bruno, CA
7. **Nordstrom, Inc.,** Seattle, WA
8. **R.H. Macy & Co., Inc.,** New York, NY
9. **Office Depot Inc.,** Delray Beach, FL
10. **Toys "R" Us, Inc.,** Paramus, NJ

TRANSPORTATION
1. **American Airlines, Inc.,** Ft. Worth, TX
2. **Union Pacific Corporation,** Bethlehem, PA
3. **United Airlines,** Chicago, IL
4. **Delta Air Lines, Inc.,** Atlanta, GA
5. **Southwest Airlines Company,** Dallas, TX

ACADEMY COMPANIES' FUNCTIONAL RANKINGS

GENERAL MANAGEMENT
1. **General Electric Company,** Fairfield, CT
2. **Hewlett-Packard Company,** Palo Alto, CA
3. **PepsiCo, Inc.,** Purchase, NY
4. **Motorola, Inc.,** Schaumburg, IL
5. **Emerson Electric Co.,** St. Louis, MO
6. **Minnesota Mining and Manufacturing,** St. Paul, MN
7. **Merck & Company, Inc.,** Rahway, NJ

8. **Johnson & Johnson,** New Brunswick, NJ
9. **The Procter & Gamble Company,** Cincinnati, OH
10. **Rubbermaid Inc.,** Wooster, OH
11. **International Business Machines,** Armonk, NY
12. **Kraft/General Foods,** Glenview, IL
13. **E.I. du Pont de Nemours & Company,** Wilmington, DE
14. **Xerox Corporation,** Stamford, CT
15. **McKinsey,** New York, NY
16. **ITT Corporation,** New York, NY
17. **American Express Corporation,** New York, NY
18. **Rockwell International Corp.,** El Segundo, CA
19. **The Coca-Cola Company,** Atlanta, GA
20. **Citicorp,** New York, NY

FINANCE AND ACCOUNTING
1. **General Electric Company,** Fairfield, CT
2. **Ford Motor Company,** Dearborn, MI
3. **PepsiCo, Inc.,** Purchase, NY
4. **The Walt Disney Company,** Burbank, CA
5. **Citicorp,** New York, NY
6. **American Express Company,** New York, NY
7. **ITT Corporation,** New York, NY
8. **Xerox Corporation,** Stamford, CT
9. **Arthur Andersen & Co.,** Chicago, IL
10. **Goldman Sachs,** New York, NY

HUMAN RESOURCES/PERSONNEL
1. **PepsiCo, Inc.,** Purchase, NY
2. **General Electric Company,** Fairfield, CT
3. **Xerox Corporation,** Stamford, CT
4. **American Express Company,** New York, NY
5. **Baxter International Inc.,** Deerfield, IL
6. **Federal Express Corporation,** Memphis, TN
7. **Citicorp,** New York, NY
8. **Motorola, Inc.,** Schaumburg, IL
9. **Philip Morris Companies Inc.,** New York, NY
10. **Merck & Company Inc.,** Rahway, NJ

INTERNATIONAL
1. **PepsiCo, Inc.,** Purchase, NY
2. **The Coca-Cola Company,** Atlanta, GA
3. **International Business Machines,** Armonk, NY
4. **Philip Morris Companies, Inc.,** New York, NY
5. **The Procter & Gamble Company,** Cincinnati, OH
6. **Minnesota Mining & Manufacturing,** St. Paul, MN
7. **Ford Motor Company,** Dearborn, MI
8. **CPC International,** Englewood Cliffs, NJ
9. **Nestlé Foods Corp.,** New York, NY
10. **SmithKline Beecham, PLC,** Philadelphia, PA

MANUFACTURING/PRODUCTION/OPERATIONS
1. **General Electric Company,** Fairfield, CT
2. **Motorola, Inc.,** Schaumburg, IL

3. **Ford Motor Company,** Dearborn, MI
4. **Hewlett-Packard Company,** Palo Alto, CA
5. **Rockwell International Corp.,** El Segundo, CA
6. **Emerson Electric Co.,** St. Louis, MO
7. **The Procter & Gamble Company,** Cincinnati, OH
8. **The Black & Decker Corporation,** Towson, MD
9. **TRW Inc.,** Cleveland, OH
10. **The Boeing Company,** Seattle, WA

MARKETING/SALES–CONSUMER
1. **The Procter & Gamble Company,** Cincinnati, OH
2. **PepsiCo, Inc.,** Purchase, NY
3. **Kraft/General Foods,** Glenview, IL
4. **General Mills, Inc.,** Minneapolis, MN
5. **Philip Morris USA,** New York, NY
6. **American Express Company,** New York, NY
7. **MCI Communications Corp.,** Wilmington, DE
8. **Johnson & Johnson,** New Brunswick, NJ
9. **General Electric Company,** Fairfield, CT
10. **Baxter International Inc.,** Deerfield, IL

MARKETING/SALES–INDUSTRIAL
1. **Xerox Corporation,** Stamford, CT
2. **Hewlett-Packard Company,** Palo Alto, CA
3. **International Business Machines,** Armonk, NY
4. **General Electric Company,** Fairfield, CT
5. **Minnesota Mining & Manufacturing,** St. Paul, MN

MIS/COMPUTER OPERATIONS
1. **Arthur Andersen & Co.,** Chicago, IL
2. **Citibank,** New York, NY
3. **American Airlines, Inc.,** Ft. Worth, TX
4. **American Express Company,** New York, NY
5. **Electronic Data Systems Corp.,** Dallas, TX
6. **General Motors Corporation,** Detroit, MI
7. **Motorola, Inc.,** Schaumburg, IL
8. **Hewlett-Packard Company,** Palo Alto, CA
9. **Charles Schwab & Company, Inc.,** San Francisco, CA
10. **Federal Express Corporation,** Memphis, TN

RESEARCH AND DEVELOPMENT
1. **Merck & Company, Inc.,** Rahway, NJ
2. **International Business Machines,** Armonk, NY
3. **General Electric Company,** Fairfield, CT
4. **Eli Lilly & Co.,** Indianapolis, IN
5. **Xerox Corporation,** Stamford, CT
6. **E.I. du Pont de Nemours & Company,** Wilmington, DE
7. **American Telephone & Telegraph,** New York, NY
8. **The Procter & Gamble Company,** Cincinnati, OH
9. **Hewlett-Packard Company,** Palo Alto, CA
10. **Intel Corporation,** Santa Clara, CA

7

THE "HEIRS APPARENT"

Headhunters. What they can do to our lives and fortunes! Many of America's top companies are run today by talented executives who reached the top by being placed again and again by headhunters. Lou Gerstner, the new chairman and CEO of IBM, is just one of the more recent and most publicized. Gerry Roche gets the credit for placing him at IBM, but Tom Neff, his copartner on the IBM search, a few years earlier had placed him as CEO of RJR Nabisco.

We will see more and more of this. The Jack Welches of General Electric and Ed Artzts of Procter & Gamble, Chief Executive Officers who have risen through the ranks of one company, are a vanishing breed. Homegrown top dogs just ain't what they used to be. There are many reasons for this, but this book is not the place to explore them. Let's just accept the fact that it is happening, and it is having a profound impact on life at all levels in every kind of organization. It is most evident at the top, the organization's Chief Executive Officer position. That is also, of course, where it will ultimately have the greatest impact on the rest of the organization.

This brings us to the genesis for this chapter. Why does a book about executive recruiters and how to work with them have a chapter called "The 'Heirs Apparent'"? Why does anyone need to know who the high-potential men and women leaders of North America are? Because, incredible as it may seem, we all need to know. We need the best at the top of our government agencies, in our universities and colleges, in our hospitals, in our profit-making and non-profit organizations. And executive recruiters, the career makers this book is all about, especially need to know.

The problem we face is that it is getting harder and harder to identify who these emerging *fully capable* leaders are. Note that I say "fully" capable. Organizations are stacked up with senior people who might appear to be promotable to the Chief Executive Officer position, but are they *fully* capable, or just *apparently* capable?

Recruiter after recruiter and employer after employer are running into that most difficult question. For many of us, it was fascinating to observe how, during the very public IBM search, the press kept asking the question: Where do you look for people who can successfully run a company like IBM? Then they would speculate and offer a few candidates themselves. That search was public, and it highlighted that challenge, but the same challenge exists in every senior search today—especially at the CEO level. It is extremely difficult for anyone to identify with any degree of certainty who the future leaders of North America's major enterprises are.

This chapter is intended to make that task a bit easier. To accomplish this goal we polled the world's largest group of presumed experts, those who make their living in identifying and sleuthing out executive talent. Over six hundred of North America's most accomplished executive recruiters responded. They volunteered their personal choices of potential CEOs either for their nominees' current employers or with other organizations.

These recruiters were asked to name six top future CEO prospects in five major groups:

1. Manufacturing
2. Services (banks, brokers, venture capital, investment banking, CPA, consulting, insurance, hospitality, energy, utilities, construction, transportation, etc.)
3. Communications (telephone/telecommunications, broadcasting, systems and software, advertising/PR, publishing)
4. Health care
5. Not for profit (associations, universities, museums, etc.)

Nominees had to meet the following general criteria:

1. Preferably be fifty-two years of age or younger at the time of nomination;
2. Be currently in an officer-level position with their current employer;
3. Never been a *Chief Executive Officer* previously of a major employer.

The six hundred executive recruiters who provided nominees volunteered 1,821 future chief executive officers—hardly enough, incidentally, to fill the 2,623 CEO slots that were reportedly open in the single year of September 1992 to September 1993 (see page xiii). Fortunately for employers of all types, there remains a large pool of lesser talents—or high achievers who have not yet attained high visibility with North America's executive recruiters.

Not surprisingly, there are those who feel that revealing who these future leaders are is giving away a recruiter's stock in trade. Why should a recruiter share this information with the whole wide world, they ask. And doesn't fingering these up-and-comers put them in an embarrassing position with their current employers? Recruiters should preserve confidences, not put potential candidates at risk.

Permit me to put some perspective on this matter of the "heirs apparent." There is little evidence that recruiters themselves consider their pockets being picked by providing nominees. Of the 931 individual recruiters who received at least one nomination for inclusion in this book, 608 provided "heir apparent" names—a 65 percent participation rate. Of even greater note is that of the 250 recruiters who qualified for this edition, 211 provided "heir apparent" names—an 84 percent rate. This would seem to suggest that the better the recruiter, the less reluctant he or she is to volunteer future CEOs—their "stock in trade," as some might call them.

Then there is the empirical fact that it required at least five different recruiter nominations for an heir apparent to qualify for this first-ever compilation. *It can hardly be said that any one of these top 250 future CEOs is any individual recruiter's proprietary piece of perceived talent and potential.* Obviously, there is none amongst them who is a secret from all others. And not a few were recommended by two dozen or more recruiters.

As for putting these high achievers "at risk," quite the opposite is true. Highlighting for the first time this critically important group of future leaders—and yes, putting them in the glare of public recognition—should actually serve to accelerate their pace of advancement, if not quite yet to the CEO position, then to the next major rung up the career ladder toward that. Too many heirs apparent have been kept in the shadow of Chief Executive Officers who actually resist and resent their advancement. They need to know that there are thousands of headhunters out there just itching to help these high achievers ascend to the throne.

On a more personal front, after nearly twenty-five years of executive recruiting, and many thousands of interviews, I have yet to meet a single high achiever in any organization who didn't welcome being labeled an "heir apparent." But if there are some out there who truly feel jeopardized by the notoriety this distinction may bring them, then they have two basic courses of action: (1) They can put their career into a tailspin, or (2) accept no calls whatsoever from headhunters.

In the meantime, there they are. Exposed for the whole world to see. Gleaned from their computers, little black books, backs of envelopes, cocktail napkins, and the memories of North America's top recruiters are 250 future CEOs. How many will actually achieve that level within the next five to ten years? A very high percentage, we think, and we also believe that most will then be with employers other than the ones they're presently with. That's been the recent pattern, and it is highly likely to continue.

The "Top 250" are listed alphabetically within their appropriate group. As one might expect, there are considerably more from industry than from the academic, health care, and not-for-profit worlds. The youngest among them is thirty-six, and they average forty-seven years of age. Women number thirty-four, a welcome sight indeed. They still account for less than 14 percent of all nominees, yet it may be possible that the recognition accorded the outstanding women in this volume will help crack open the "glass ceiling" that has thwarted them for so long. But for Wayne Calloway, chairman and CEO of PepsiCo, it's clearly time to batten down the hatches. No fewer than nine of his executives are in this august group. For a change, Jack Welch of General Electric, long the preferred fishing pond for future CEOs of other companies, can rest a little easier.

North America's Top 250 Future Chief Executive Officers

MANUFACTURING

Alspach, Bruce, Vice President, Trimble Navigation Ltd., Austin, TX

Alvarado, Joseph, GM–Sales and Marketing, Inland Steel Bar Co., Munster, IN

Ambrose, Ellen, VP and GM, Nestlé Coffee Division, San Francisco, CA

Anderson, David, VP–General Counsel, Inland Steel, Chicago
Anderson, Paul M., President, Panhandle Eastern, Houston
Barad, Jill E., President and COO, Mattel, Los Angeles
Barents, Brian, President, Learjet, Wichita, KS
Barnes, Brenda, President, Pepsi-Cola South, Somers, NY
Battaglia, Anthony D., Senior VP, Chiquita Brands, Cincinnati
Bere, David, President, Breakfast Division, Quaker Oats, Chicago
Berges, James, Executive VP, Emerson Electric, St. Louis
Bowlin, John, President and COO, Miller Brewing, Milwaukee
Brady, Larry, President and COO, FMC Corp., Chicago
Burner, David L., President–Aerospace, BF Goodrich, Akron
Burnham, Daniel P., Executive VP, Allied-Signal, Morristown, NJ
Burns, Robin, President, Estée Lauder, New York
Canepa, Mark A., VP and General Manager, Advanced Systems Division, Hewlett-Packard, Chelmsford, MA
Caulk, Robert, President–North American Operations, JWA Worldwide, Racine, WI
De la Colina, Miguel, Marketing Manager, Monsanto–Mexico, Mexico City
Collins, Arthur D., Chief Operating Officer, Medtronic Inc., Minneapolis
Coughlan, Gary P., Senior VP–Finance, Abbott Labs, N. Chicago
Cowan, Rory, Senior President, R.R. Donnelley, Chicago
Cutler, Alexander M., Executive VP, Eaton Corporation, Cleveland
DiCamillo, Gary T., President–Power Tool Group, Black & Decker, Towson, MD
DeVink, Lodewijk J. R., President and COO, Warner Lambert U.S.A., Morris Plains, NJ
Egen, William, Division President, Church & Dwight, Princeton, NJ
Eichorn, Gary, VP–Workstations, Hewlett-Packard, Andover, MA
Engen, D. Travis, Executive VP, ITT Corporation, New York
Enrico, Roger, Vice Chairman, PepsiCo, Purchase, NY
Fjeldstad, Lucie, VP and GM Mulitimedia and Education, IBM Corp., Armonk, NY
Foote, William, President and COO, USG Corp., Chicago
Ford, William Clay Jr., Chairman–Finance Committee, Ford Motor Co., Deerborn, MI
Francis, Kevin, VP–Regional Manager, Xerox–Canada, North York, Ontario
Fraser, Robert J. A., Senior VP, Hercules Inc., Wilmington, DE
Galvin, Christopher, President and COO, Motorola Inc., Schaumburg, IL
Gillespie, Robert J., President, Best Foods, CPC Corp., Englewood Cliffs, NJ
Greeniaus, H. John, President, RJR Nabisco, Parsippany, NJ
Gutierrez, Carlos, Executive VP, Kellogg–USA, Battle Creek, MI
Hanrahan, Daniel, VP–Marketing, Reebok International, Stoughton, MA

Harad, George, President and COO, Boise Cascade, Boise, ID

Hassen, Fred, Group VP, American Home Products, New York

Hoye, Michael, Executive VP–North America, Colgate-Palmolive, New York

Ivester, M. Douglas, President, Coca-Cola Company, Atlanta

Jager, Durk, Executive VP, Procter & Gamble, Cincinnati

Kaplan, Beth, VP–Cosmetics & Fragrances, Procter & Gamble, Hunt Valley, MD

Kiely, W. Leo, President and COO, Coors Brewing, Golden, CO

Knight, Lester B., Executive VP, Baxter International, Deerfield, IL

Lappin, Richard C., President and COO, Farley Industries, Chicago

Leach, Brock H., VP–Brand Marketing, Frito-Lay, Inc., Dallas

Levitt, Brian M., President and COO, Imasco Ltd., Montreal

Lewent, Judy C., VP–Finance and CFO, Merck & Co., Rahway, NJ

Lustig, Paul, President, Sara Lee Bakeries, Chicago

Marineau, Philip H., President, Quaker Oats Company, Chicago

Marram, Ellen, Executive Vice President, Joseph E. Seagrams & Sons, New York

McGinnis, W. Patrick, President–Foods Group, Ralston Purina, St. Louis

McMillan, C. Steven, Executive Vice President, Sara Lee Corp., Chicago, IL

McNerney, W. James, President–Asia, General Electric, Fairfield, CT

Mejorada, Octavio Sanchez, VP–Latin America, Campbell Soup, Mexico City

Nanula, Richard C., Senior VP and CFO, Walt Disney Co., Burbank, CA

Perez, William D., President and COO–Worldwide Consumer Products, S.C. Johnson & Son, Racine, WI

Pol, Anne, President–Shipping and Weighing Systems, Pitney-Bowes, Stamford, CT

Poses, Frederic M., President–Engineered Materials, Allied-Signal, Morristown, NJ

Pratt, E. Courtney, Executive VP, Noranda, Inc., Toronto

Rand, A. Barry, Executive VP, Xerox Corp., Stamford, CT

Reinemund, Steven, Chairman, Frito-Lay, Inc., Dallas

Rogers, Gary L., President—GE Plastics, General Electric Co., Pittsfield, MA

Sanger, Stephen W., President, General Mills, Minneapolis

Sculley, David W., Senior VP, H.J. Heinz Co., Pittsburgh

Sevcik, Richard W., Group GM—Systems & Service Group, Hewlett-Packard, Palo Alto, CA

Sharer, Kevin W., President and COO, Amgen, Thousand Oaks, CA

Sinclair, Chris, President, Foods & Beverages International, PepsiCo, Somers, NY

Solso, Theodore M., Executive VP–Operations, Cummins Engine Co., Columbus, IN

Strickland, Donald, VP, Imaging & Publishing, Apple Computer, Cupertino, CA

Suwyn, Mark A., Executive VP, International Paper, Purchase, NY

Trani, John, President, GE Medical Systems, General Electric Co.,
Milwaukee

Van Cuylenburg, Peter, Executive VP, Xerox Corp., Stamford, CT

Viault, Raymond G., Chairman, Jacobs-Suchard, Philip Morris, New York

Wagoner, G. Richard, President–NAO, General Motors Corp., Detroit

Ward, Lloyd, President–Central Division, Frito-Lay, Inc., Dallas

Zyman, Sergio, Senior VP and Chief Marketing Officer, Coca-Cola, Atlanta

SERVICES

Allison, Herbert, Executive VP, Merrill Lynch, New York

Ballenbach, Steven, Executive VP, Marriott Corporation, Bethesda, MD

Barnum, Robert T., President and COO, American Savings Bank, San
Francisco

Beavers, Robert M. Jr., Senior VP and Zone Manager, McDonald's Corp., Oak
Brook, IL

Booth, Richard H., President and COO, Travelers Corp., Hartford, CT

Bouts, Larry, President–International, Toys "R" Us, Paramus, NJ

Braun, Kathryn, Executive VP, Western Digital Corp., Irvine, CA

Brooks, Nicol, Senior VP, American Express Travel Related Services, New
York

Carty, Donald J., Executive VP–Finance and CFO, AMR Corporation, Fort
Worth

Chennault, Kenneth I., President, American Express Travel Related Services,
New York

Chisholm, Jeffrey S., Vice Chairman, Bank of Montreal, Toronto

Cimet, Michael, President–Mexico, EDS, Mexico City

Coleman, Lewis W., Vice Chairman, Bank of America, San Francisco

Comper, Anthony F., President and COO, Bank of Montreal, Montreal

D'Alessandro, David F., Senior Executive VP, John Hancock Life Insurance
Co., Boston

Dilsaver, Evelyn, Senior VP and Controller, Chas. Schwab, San Francisco

Dimon, James, President and COO, The Travelers, New York

Ehrenstrom, James, Senior VP, Northwestern Mutual Life, Milwaukee

Estes, Laura, Senior VP, Aetna Life & Casualty, Hartford

Farah, Roger, Vice Chairman–Merchandising, Macy's, New York

Fernandes, Gary, Senior VP, EDS, Plano, TX

Floto, Ronald J., President–Super K-Mart Division, K-Mart Corp., Troy, MI

Floyd, William, Senior VP–Operations, KFC Inc., Irvine, CA

Glass, Dennis R., Executive VP and CFO, Jefferson-Pilot Corp.,
Greensboro, NC

Goodwin, James, Senior VP–International, United Airlines, Elk Grove, IL

Greenberg, Jack, Vice Chairman and CFO, McDonald's Corp., Oak Brook, IL

Gurwitch, Janet, Executive VP—Women's Merchandise, Neiman Marcus, Dallas

Hall, Theodore B., Director, McKinsey & Co., San Francisco

Harrison, William, Vice Chairman, Chemical Banking Corp., New York

Heitman, Scott, President, LaSalle-Talman Bank, Chicago

Hodgman, Jeffrey J., Senior VP, The Metropolitan Life Co., New York

Hondros, Paul J., President–Institutional Services, Fidelity Investments, Boston

Hora, Michael, VP, A.T. Kearney, New York

Ibrahim, S. A., Senior VP and Chief Credit Officer, Chemical Bank, New York

James, Stephen, Regional Managing Partner, Andersen Consulting, Chicago

Jaramillo, Gabriel, President, Citibank/Mexico, Mexico City

Joly, Laurent M., Senior VP, Global Private Banking, Royal Bank of Canada, Toronto

Kackley, James, Managing Partner, Arthur Andersen, Chicago

Kelly, Edmund F., President, Liberty Mutual Insurance, Boston

King, Kelly S., President, Branch Banking & Trust, Raleigh, NC

Kronick, Susan, President and COO, Rich's/Goldsmith's, Atlanta

Lewis, Kenneth D., President–General Banking, NationsBank, Charlotte, NC

Linen, Jonathan, Vice Chairman, American Express Co., New York

Lorelli, Michael, President–International, Pizza Hut, Wichita, KS

Lovejoy, David, Executive VP, Mellon Bank, Pittsburgh

McGuinn, Martin, Vice Chairman, Mellon Bank, Pittsburgh

McKeever, Michael, Managing Director, Lehman Bros. Corp. Finance, New York

Moore, Colin, Senior VP Marketing, KFC, Inc., Louisville

Mullin, Leo, President and COO, First National Bank of Chicago, Chicago

Muniz, Cesar, Principal, McKinsey & Co., Mexico City

Murray, Michael, Vice Chairman, Continental Bank, Chicago

Nakasone, Robert V., President and Vice Chairman, Toys "R" Us, Paramus, NJ

O'Neal, Edward, Vice Chairman, Bank of Boston, Boston

Paulson, Henry, Partner, Goldman Sachs, New York

Pope, John C., President, United Airlines, Elk Grove, IL

Quinnell, Bruce, Executive VP, Waldenbooks, Stamford, CT

Razzouk, William, Executive VP, Federal Express, Memphis

Roach, William, Executive VP Sales and Marketing, Quantum Corp., Milpitas, CA

Sansbury, Michael, VP–Hotel Services, Mirage Hotel & Casino, Las Vegas

Schuster, Harry F., Senior VP–Business Development, Heller International, Chicago

Servison, Roger T., President, Fidelity Investments, Boston

Shanahan, Francis P., Senior VP and CFO, Farmers Insurance, Los Angeles

Shanks, Eugene B. Jr., President and COO, Bankers Trust, New York

Sieffens, John L., Executive VP, Merrill Lynch & Co., New York
Small, Lawrence, President and COO, FNMA, Washington, DC
Steffen, Christopher, Senior Executive VP, Citicorp, New York
Strom, Terence M., President and COO, Egghead, Inc., Issaquah, WA
Thompson, Jane, Executive VP—Credit Operations, Sears, Roebuck and Co., Hoffman Estates, IL
Timbers, Stephen, President and COO, Kemper Corporation, Long Grove, IL
Tocklin, Adrian M., President, Continental Insurance, New York
Vent, Richard, President–Leisure International, ARA Services, Philadelphia
Vitale, David, Vice Chairman, First Chicago Corp. Chicago
Waite, Donald, Managing Director, McKinsey & Co., New York
Walker, Darrell, Executive VP, Wells Fargo Bank, San Francisco
Weden, Richard, Senior VP–Latin America, American Express Travel Co., Mexico City
Weiss, Michael, Vice Chairman, Limited Stores, Columbus, OH
Wert, James W., Senior EVP and CFO, Key Corp., Cleveland
Wheat, Allen, President and COO, CS First Boston, New York
Williams, Jonathan, Senior VP, Lehman Bros., New York
Young, Robert H., Executive VP, COO, CFO, Central Vermont Public Service Corp., Rutland, VT

COMMUNICATIONS

Atterbury, John, President, SBC International, Inc., San Antonio
Babbio, Lawrence, Executive Vice President and COO, Bell Atlantic Enterprises, Philadelphia
Barksdale, James, President, McCaw Cellular Communications, Kirkland, WA
Battista, Gabriel, President and COO, Cable and Wireless Communications, Vienna, VA
Beard, Eugene, Executive VP Finance/Operations, Interpublic Group, New York
Berrard, Steven, Vice Chairman, Blockbuster Entertainment, Ft. Lauderdale, FL
Bourne, Ian, Senior VP and CFO, Canada Post Corporation, Ottawa
Carpenter, Robert R., Senior VP Worldwide Customer Service, AT&T Global Information Services, Dayton, OH
Clark, Daniel L., VP, AT&T, New York
Drook, Gary, President–Enhanced Business Unit, Ameritech, Chicago
Edwardson, John A., Executive VP and CFO, Ameritech, Chicago
Evans, Jane, VP and General Manager, U.S. West, San Francisco
Faulders, Thomas, CFO, Comsat Corp., Bethesda, MD
Fitzpatrick, Michael, President—New Enterprises, Pacific Bell, San Ramon, CA
Gill, Frank, Senior VP and GM–Products Group, Intel Corp., Aloha, OR

Hamilton, Judith, President, Dataquest, San Jose, CA

Hapka, Catherine, President and COO, U.S. West, Minneapolis

House, David L., Senior VP, Intel, Corp. Santa Clara, CA

Iger, Robert A., President–ABC Television Network Group, New York

Jaffee, Barbara, President–TW Transmission Co., Time Warner, New York

Johnson, Edward, Group VP, Times Mirror Company, Los Angeles

Kavner, Robert, Senior Executive VP, Creative Artists Agency, Beverly Hills, CA

Kerr, William, President and COO, Meredith Corp., Des Moines, IA

Kofalt, James A., President and COO, Cablevision Systems Corp., Woodbury, NY

Lane, Raymond, President, W.W. Operations, Oracle Corp., Redwood Shores, CA

Mandl, Alex J., Executive VP, AT&T, Basking Ridge, NJ

Matlock, Richard, Executive VP, Hearst Corp., New York

McGraw, Harold III, President and COO, McGraw Hill, New York

McRoskey, Cecelia, VP–Information Technology, Times Mirror Co., Los Angeles

Miller, Charles C. III, VP–Strategic Planning, Bell South Enterprises, Atlanta

Rich, Norman, VP, Dun & Bradstreet, Parsippany, NJ

Seidenberg, Ivan G., President and COO, NYNEX Corp., White Plains, NY

Shaffer, David, President—Educational & Professional Publishing Group, McGraw Hill, New York

Silverstein, Robert, VP and General Manager, Northrop Grumman Corp., Great River, NY

Taylor, Gerald H., President, MCI Communications, Washington, DC

Townsend, Ronald, President, Gannett Television & Broadcasting, Arlington, VA

Tremblay, Louise, COO, Canadian Satellite Communications, Inc., Mississauga, Ontario

Wildermuth, Roger G., President, Logan Printing Co., Peoria, IL

Williams, Richard B., Senior VP, Dun Bradstreet, Westport, CT

Wilson, Phillip, Senior VP, Oracle Systems Corp., Redwood Shores, CA

HEALTH CARE

Borgstrom, Marna, Executive VP, Yale–New Haven Hospital, New Haven, CT

Bryant, James, President, Prescription Service Division, Caremark International, Northbrook, IL

Buckelew, Lawrence, President and COO, Sunrise Medical, Torrance, CA

Casey, John, President and COO, American Medical International, Dallas

Fiore, Michael, Executive VP, COO, and Director, Saluk Health Care, Los Angeles

French, Michael, COO, Inova Health Care, Springfield, VA

Goodspeed, Scott, VP and COO, Elliot Hospital, Manchester, NH

Gragnolati, Brian, VP, York Hospital, York, PA

Hanover, Kenneth, President, Bryn Mawr Hospital, Bryn Mawr, PA

Henckel, Frances, Executive VP and COO, Long Beach Memorial Hospital, CA

Hillenmeyer, John, Executive VP and COO, Orlando Regional Health Care System, FL

Johns, Michael M. E., Dean of Medicine, Johns Hopkins University School of Medicine, Baltimore, MD

McBride, William, President, Value Health, Inc., Avon, CT

Meehan, John, President, Hartford Hospital, Hartford, CT

Murray, Kathleen, Executive VP, Northwestern Memorial Hospitals, Chicago

O'Brien, Beth, Executive VP and COO, Franciscan Health System, Group West, Tacoma, WA

Ostrosky, Barry, Senior VP, St. Barnabas Medical Center, Livingston, NJ

Porth, Susan, CFO, Kaiser Foundation Health Plan of the Northwest, Portland, OR

Scott, Cheryl, Executive VP and COO, Group Health of Puget Sound, Seattle

Spears, Patrick, Managing Director–Business Development, Harris Methodist Health System, Arlington, TX

Tolosky, Mark, President, Baystate Medical Center, Springfield, MA

Whittaker, Carol, Senior VP, Jacksonville Baptist Hospital, Jacksonville, FL

Williamson, Donna, Senior VP, Caremark International, Northbrook, IL

Wolterman, Daniel, Senior VP–Operations, Sister of Charity Health Care Systems, Houston

Zenty, Thomas, Acting President, St. Joseph's Hospital & Medical Center, Phoenix, AZ

NOT FOR PROFIT

Adams, J. Michael, Dean, College of Design Arts, Drexel University, Philadelphia

Armstrong, Lloyd, Provost, University of Southern California, Los Angeles

Barrette, Lynne C., Assistant City Manager, City of Santa Monica, California

Brown, Peter, VP, School of the Art Institute, Chicago

Burke, Morgan J., Athletic Director, Purdue University, West Lafayette, IN

Curry, John, Administrative Vice Chancellor, UCLA, Los Angeles

Curvin, Robert, Program Director, Ford Foundation, New York

Davies, Bryan, Senior VP–Business & CAO, University of Toronto, Toronto, Canada

Forbes, Malcolm H., Provost, Roger Williams College, Bristol, RI

Frazier, A. D. Jr., COO, Atlanta Committee for the Olympic Games, Atlanta

Golub, Larry, Special Asst. to Sec., U.S. Dept. of Health & Human Services, Washington, DC

Gribbon, Deborah, Associate Director, J. Paul Getty Museum, Santa
Monica, CA

Hatch, Dr. Nathan, Asst. Dean, Notre Dame University, South Bend, IN

Henry, Michael, Asst. Chief Administrative Officer, Los Angeles County, CA

Husler, William, Dean, U.C. Berkeley, Haas School of Business, Berkeley, CA

Jenkins, William, Vice Chancellor–Administration, Vanderbilt University,
Nashville

Kirkpatrick, Samuel, President, University of Texas at San Antonio, San
Antonio

Mitchell, Theodore, Dean, Graduate School of Education, UCLA, Los Angeles

Munitz, Barry, Chancellor, California State University System, Long
Beach, CA

Murphy, Jerome, Dean, Harvard Graduate School of Education, Harvard
University, Cambridge, MA

Potman, Charles, Executive VP, Duke University Medical Center, Durham, NC

Rice, Condoleezza, Provost, Stanford University, Palo Alto, CA

Smith, David, Deputy County Executive, Erie County, Buffalo, New York

Sufoenberger, Robert, COO, New York Power Authority, New York

Vitale, Val, Senior VP Operations, The Conference Board, New York